PHYSICAL SYSTEMS OF THE ENVIRONMENT

Fifth Edition

Robert L. Beck

Department of Geography
IUPUI

Interior Photos and Drawings:

Photo 10-12 (p. 138) courtesy of John Brothers
Photo 14-4 (p. 187) courtesy of Gage Brogan
Photos 15-1, 15-2, 15-3, 15-5, 15-6, 15-7, 15-8, and 16-2 (pp. 190-192, 195-197, 202)
    courtesy of Rick Bein
Photos 17-5, 19-1, 19-2, 19-7, 20-7, 23-3, 23-21, 23-26, 24-28, 24-32, 28-8, 28-12, and 28-13
    (pp. 218, 234, 241, 252, 301, 311, 314, 337, 342, 401, 404-405) courtesy of Tim Brothers
Photo 22-10 (p. 285) Copyright © by Marty Nelson. Reprinted by permission.
Photo 23-14 (p. 308) courtesy of Natural Resources Conservation Service
Photo 23-24 (p. 313) courtesy of Christy Herris
Photo 23-35 (p. 319) courtesy of Kim Greeman
Drawing 23-36 (p. 319) courtesy of Kara Holmes
Photos 24-31 (p. 340) courtesy of Elmore Barce
Photos 25-17, 25-18, and 25-21 (pp. 354, 356) courtesy of Deborah Melton
Photos 28-7 and 28-9 (pp. 400, 402) courtesy of Randall L. Folker
Photos (pp. 371, 373-374) courtesy of Natural Resources Conservation Service
All other photos and drawings by Robert L. Beck or from public domain sources

Cover images © Shutterstock, Inc.

Kendall Hunt
publishing company

www.kendallhunt.com
Send all inquiries to:
4050 Westmark Drive
Dubuque, IA 52004-1840

This book is dedicated to the memory of:

Marshall Beck
Robert Berger
Shirley Fuhrman

CONTENTS

****

A YEAR IN MADISON TOWNSHIP

by Robert L. Beck

JANUARY
Falling snow and bitter cold,
blazing fires and coyotes bold.
Pink sunsets when the days are clear,
solitude at night for all to hear.
Nuthatch, downey, and titmouse abound,
if a diet of suet is left hanging around.
Barn cats stay near their source of subsistence;
howling at night is heard in the distance.

FEBRUARY
Groundhogs emerge to a midwinter's gloom,
gray skies and soon a lawn to bloom.
Tracks in the snow by animal paws,
slowly melt away as the icy ground thaws.
Sunny days expose the green-to-be grasses,
quickly inspected by starling masses.
This time of the year is a very good bet,
that our chickens will soon begin to set.
Quiet walks in woodlots near,
peaceful home of white-tailed deer.

MARCH
Blustery winds and frigid rain,
fogs envelop the soggy plain.
Crocus announce the arrival of spring,
nature promises warm weather to bring.
Peas are planted in cold garden beds;
woodpeckers mark trees with their red heads.
Bluegrass enjoys this month of the year,
mowing time will soon be here.

APRIL
Warm air returns from southern coasts,
while bluebirds seek nests in hollow posts.
Redbuds and tulips brighten the scene,
trees in woodlots reveal their green.
Dandelions flourish in the cool spring weather;
thickets diversify their varieties of feather.
Planting potatoes while daffodils yellow,
raises the spirits of the gardening fellow.

MAY
Beautiful days and mild spring nights;
mockingbirds sing from leafy heights.
Barn swallows swoop low in graceful arcs,
skimming the air over pastures and parks.
Black locust trees speckle the blue sky white,
cherry blossoms and peonies add delight.
Brown thrashers from the woods unseen,
end their calls with double-notes serene.
Turkey vultures soar above the warm fields;
farmers plant corn and hope for good yields.

JUNE
Warm weather and thunderstorms bring
summer's arrival and the end of spring.
Strawberries and pie cherries on trees,
blackbirds and catbirds devour them with ease.
Briars and bushes invade open spaces;
mosses and ferns dwell in damp, dark places.
Bats sweep the sky while starlight emerges,
fireflies emit electrical surges.

JULY
Summer flowers and wilting heat,
sunny days and barbequed meat.
Potatoes uncovered by the garden fork
are served with wax beans, sweet corn, and pork.
Watermelon and root beer refresh the mouth;
warm summer rains end the drouth.
Cattle in shadow in the heat of the day;
farmers are busy baling their hay.

AUGUST
Midsummer arrives with all its sights,
hazy days and humid nights.
Brown snakes reduce the slug population,
helping nature produce dense vegetation.
Butterflies flutter over flowers in the sod;
zinnia, ironweed, and goldenrod.
Crops nearby are still yet green,
including both corn and soybean.
Winds stir the grasses with wild motions;
hummingbirds consume their sugary potions.

SEPTEMBER
Nights turn cool and apples turn red;
vegetables linger in the garden bed.
Walnut leaves yellowing announce the fall;
ivy grows over our front brick wall.
Cats run around like little clowns;
sunflowers wear their yellow crowns.
Lime pickles are canned before summer's end,
soon there will be no garden to tend.

OCTOBER
Reds, yellows, oranges, browns;
fields of crops and leaves all around.
Faces on porches meant to astound,
are carved in pumpkins both oval and round.
The smell of corn harvest fills the air,
as farmers separate kernel from tare.
Raccoons and possums nightly forage;
seeds are collected for winter storage.

NOVEMBER
White frost and freeze now inspires,
the splitting of wood to fuel winter fires.
Barred owls hooting at sunset call,
from leafless trees mostly quite tall.
Walnuts strike earth with dull-sounding thuds;
cattails rattle in the small pond muds.
Turkey and dressing and pumpkin pie;
geese overhead fly south in the sky.
Shooting is heard across forest and field;
grain in the bins is the measure of yield.

DECEMBER
Winter arrives with a blanket of white,
earth and sky separated by a forested stripe.
Reds and greens of Christmas appear,
eggnog and chocolate give holiday cheer.
Strings of bright colors ablaze in the night,
are seen most clearly without moonlight.
Time to reflect on the beauty so near,
and now to celebrate the coming new year.

PREFACE

This textbook is not written like a textbook. The material in it is largely the same material I cover in my traditional lecture classes at IUPUI, so I have tried to write the modules in the book as I speak about them in class, using a conversational lecture format. I have been teaching the course *Physical Systems of the Environment* at IUPUI since 1982, and I have taught it more times than any other course in my teaching career.

I wanted to design the course around an inexpensive textbook, hence the black-and-white printing. One needs to use **Goode's World Atlas**, 22nd edition, to comprehend the material in some of the modules. The complete reference of the atlas is as follows:

Veregin, Howard, ed. *Goode's World Atlas*. 22nd ed. Chicago: Rand McNally & Co., 2010.

I hope you learn a lot about Earth, and physical geography in particular, after reading and studying the modules in this book. ***Do not read the modules too quickly!*** To really understand physical geography and Earth's natural systems requires a lot of thought. If you just quickly read the modules, without trying to understand how the concepts I discuss in them work in the real world, you probably will not learn much. I intend the modules to be easy to read, interesting, educational, and thought provoking.

Study the graphics associated with the modules! I have drawn many of these same graphics, by hand, for many years in my traditional lecture classes. I am a person who is a visual learner, so I try to bring a lot of visual material into my oral and written presentations. The graphics are meant to support and enhance the written words of the textbook.

I wrote the bulk of the modules from May to June 2005, and I produced most of the graphics from July to December 2005. In August and September 2007 I made some corrections, added a few words, substantially increased the bibliography, and inserted some new graphics to produce a second edition. In 2008, a few more errors were corrected, a couple of references were added to the bibliography, some new graphics were inserted, and a few words were added to produce the third edition. The fourth edition, published in 2011, incorporated many additional words and graphics; it also reflected changes made to **Goode's World Atlas** in 2010. This fifth edition, published in 2012, includes additional graphics, rescanned images, and a new module on deserts. A lot of work has been done to make this textbook available to you.

Robert L. Beck
Madison Township, Putnam County, Indiana
July 16, 2012

ACKNOWLEDGMENTS

Several people have aided me in my efforts to complete this textbook. I would like to acknowledge their contributions in helping me to publish it.

I received a Jump Start grant from the IUPUI Center for Teaching and Learning in the summer of 2005 to develop an online version of G107, *Physical Systems of the Environment*. Stacy Morrone, Rhett McDaniel, and Terri Tarr all supported my effort to secure the grant and greatly assisted me during the completion of the work it required.

Randy Newbrough was a constant source of help concerning instructional technology issues. Megan Palmer, an instructional design professional, reviewed the modules and added valuable comments. Jennifer Beasley, a professional editor, also in the IUPUI Center for Teaching and Learning, edited them. Lorie Shuck and Mark Alexander helped me prepare the final copy of the fourth edition. Lorie Shuck helped me prepare the final copy of this fifth edition.

Rick Bein and Tim Brothers, both in the IUPUI Department of Geography, gave me permission to use some of their photographs. So did Deborah Melton, a former student of mine from Embry-Riddle Aeronautical University. I commissioned Kara Holmes, an artist who lives in rural Putnam County, to produce one drawing in her delightful style. Gage Brogan, a former student of mine from DePauw University, gave me permission to use one of his photographs. So did Christy Herris and Randy Folker, also former students, but from IUPUI. John Brothers, father of Tim Brothers, assisted me by venturing into the field to photograph smudge pots.

I thank Joyce Blum, formerly of Kendall/Hunt, for contacting me about publishing my work, for working closely with me during its production, and for continuing to work with me through the second edition. Karen Slaght made many important editorial corrections in both the first and second editions. Katey Bertsch and Linda Chapman supervised the various activities in the publication of the third edition. Katie Wendler and Chelsea Beckman worked with me to produce the fourth edition. The fifth edition was supervised by Traci Vaske and copyedited by Kara McArthur. Jamie Falkovitz also contributed to the publication of the fifth edition.

My wife, Cheryl L. Beck, continues to be a great supporter of my work, so I especially thank her for that.

MODULE 1: INTRODUCTION TO GEOGRAPHY

Nature of Geography

Geography is an ancient discipline. The word *geography* is a Greek word that can be broken down into two components: *geo-* (earth) and *-graphy* (write about). The meaning of the word (to write about the earth) is, however, not very useful for constructing a modern definition of the discipline. Today many people write about the earth. Geologists, ecologists, meteorologists, chemists, and people in many other disciplines all write about the earth. What, then, distinguishes a geographer from another person who writes about the earth?

Many people have tried to define geography, but one quickly learns there is no standard definition used by all people who call themselves "geographers." Each geographer has his or her own definition of the discipline. Many of these definitions have similar wordings, but some are vastly different from one another. I personally like the loosely defined nature of geography, for it gives one a great deal of freedom and independence to pursue individual interests.

Beck's Definition of Geography

My definition of geography is the one that we will be using in this course. It is, of course, the correct one! If you take another geography course, the person who teaches it could very well have a different view of the discipline than I do. As I see it, **geography** today can be defined as the study of earth features and the processes that influence their distribution. The three key phrases in my definition are (1) earth features, (2) processes, and (3) distribution. I view this as being similar to a brick wall (Fig. 1-1).

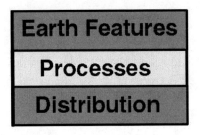

Figure 1-1. Brick Wall

The building blocks (bricks) in my wall are *earth features* and *distribution*. *Earth features* are **what** we study. Geography is not concerned with studying features on the moon or features on Mars. People who study such features might be called moonographers or Marsographers, but not geographers. The second building block is

1

distribution, for geographers are especially concerned about **where** earth features are located. The third key phrase is *processes*, the **why**, or the mortar that gives the wall strength. A brick wall constructed without mortar is not particularly strong, so people who advocate (or believe) that geography should simply involve memorizing where earth features are located weaken the discipline. Whenever you study geography, please keep in mind you should try to explain **why earth features are located where they are**. Brick walls are not constructed without mortar, so do not leave out the **why** when studying geography!

Earth Features

What do geographers study? Earth features! But geographers usually divide earth features into two major classes. Do you know what they are? Examine Figure 1-2 to see if you can find these two major features.

Figure 1-2. Nebraska Sand Hills
(Robert L. Beck photo)

Did you perceive the two major earth features are the physical features and the human features? In geography, the physical features of Earth are those that exist independent of humans, so they are sometimes known as the natural features. The human features are those that were invented or created by humans, so they are sometimes known as the cultural features of Earth. The pond, the grasses, the clouds, and the sand are all physical features. The railroad line, the windmill, the fence, and the electric pole are human features—material objects all invented by humans.

Four Spheres of the Physical World

Earth's physical features are subdivided into four major spheres. We have the sphere of air—the atmosphere; the sphere of water—the hydrosphere; the sphere of rocks and minerals—the geosphere (or lithosphere); and the sphere of plants and animals—the biosphere. You should be able to see the four spheres in the Nebraska Sand Hills photo (Fig. 1-2).

First Law of Ecology

Although it is easy to separate the four spheres in our minds, trying to do so in the natural world is difficult, for they are really interrelated. For example, small amounts of water, minerals, and plant materials are found in the atmosphere. The First Law of Ecology says that not only are these four spheres interrelated but also that a change in one sphere will affect all of the others.

Consider an Indiana forest (Fig. 1-3). Now imagine someone decides to clear a large section of the forest and believes all they have done is affect the biosphere (by cutting the trees). Is this all they have affected? No! According to the First Law of Ecology, their action in cutting the trees will also affect the atmosphere, hydrosphere,

First Law of Ecology: All of Earth's natural features are interrelated, so a change in one sphere will affect all the others.

Robert L. Beck

Figure 1-3. Indiana Forest

and geosphere. How can this be? All the person did was cut the trees! How can the atmosphere be affected? The atmosphere is likely to be a little warmer, for trees help block sunlight from reaching the earth's surface, and their leaves reflect some sunlight back to space. A lack of trees means sunlight will strike Earth's surface, causing it to become warmer, which will then cause the atmosphere to become warmer. It is with good reason that trees are sometimes known as "the air conditioners of the natural world."

How will the hydrosphere be affected? Answer is: Trees store water, so if you remove the trees the water in them will have to go somewhere . . . maybe into the atmosphere or maybe eventually into a stream or lake nearby.

How will the geosphere be affected? Answer is: The site will probably experience an increase in erosion. Rainwater will strike the earth directly and not be broken by the leaves and branches of the tree. It will probably also flow over the earth's surface at a higher rate of speed, thereby causing an increase in soil erosion.

Approaches to Geographic Study

How does a person study geography? This is both an easy and a hard question to answer. I will give you the easy answer. In general, geographers use two main approaches to study earth features—the topical approach and the regional approach.

The topical approach involves first selecting an earth feature . . . and that feature can be anything found on Earth. Could one therefore study the geography of bluebirds? Yes. How about the geography of beer? Yes. The geography of McDonald's restaurants? Yes. The geography of houses? Yes. And yes, and yes, and yes, and yes . . . . I like this freedom. In the discipline of geography one can really focus on something truly interesting to you as an individual.

One then breaks the main topic down into subtopics, subsubtopics, subsubsubtopics, and so on. How might one break down *houses* into subtopics? Well, you might look at brick houses, wooden houses, or stone houses. One then might break wooden houses down into log houses or frame houses. He or she then attempts to study the geographic distribution of such houses and provides an explanation of how this distribution came to be. The process of breaking something down into smaller units is known as ***analysis***. The topical approach, by its very nature, is analytical.

The second approach is known as the regional approach. When using this approach, one selects an area of the earth for further study. He or she then brings together the earth features found in that region. I teach a course on the Geography of Indiana. When I teach that course, I try to "bring together" the various earth features found in the state—rocks, landforms, weather, climate, vegetation, settlement, economic activities, cultural features, and political boundaries. I do not study the state by breaking it down into counties, townships, or cities. The process of bringing together many small units to form a larger whole is known as ***synthesis.*** Regional geography, by its very nature, is synthetic.

Geography Courses

The geography courses taught at American universities reflect the two approaches, so both topical geography courses and regional geography courses are offered at IUPUI. A third set of geography courses, the tools courses, are also offered at the university. The tools courses focus on the acquisition of technical skills.

Biogeography, Economic Geography, Environmental Conservation, and the Geography of Wine are four examples of topical courses. Geography of Indiana, Geography of North America, Geography of Europe, and Geography of the Caribbean are four examples of regional courses. Cartography and Graphics (mapmaking), GIS (geographic information science), Remote Sensing (using satellite data to find spatial patterns on Earth), and Spatial Statistics (using mathematical techniques in geography) are four examples of tools courses.

Is this course (G107, Physical Systems of the Environment) a topical course, a regional course, or a tools course? Answer: A topical course! The physical world is our topic. Some of the subtopics that we will be studying are Earth–sun relationships, weather, climate, vegetation, and landforms.

People who major in geography at IUPUI are required to take topical courses, regional courses, and tools courses. We want our students to be exposed to the three main divisions of the discipline. To see what courses are offered in our department, and to see what requirements we have for the major and minor, please visit our homepage online at http://www.iupui.edu/~geogdept/. If you are planning to major or minor in geography, please contact me. I will be glad to speak with you personally.

Jobs in Geography

Geographers are employed in all sorts of jobs. One of the discipline's hottest employment opportunities is the field of GIS. Government agencies and private companies hire geographers to perform various types of spatial analyses and to make computer maps. A major in geography prepares students for successful careers in fields such as education, environmental management, urban planning, conservation, public health, recreation and tourism, transportation planning, international affairs, and business. At the federal level, I have known geographers who worked for the Census Bureau, the FBI, the Department of Defense, the Department of Agriculture, and the Department of Energy. At the state level, I have known geographers who worked for the Department of Transportation, the Department of Environmental Management, and the Department of Natural Resources in the Division of Nature Preserves, the Division of Reclamation, and the Division of Water. At the local level, I have known geographers who worked in city planning departments, county planning departments, and tax agencies. In business, I have known geographers who worked for the electric power industry, the natural gas industry, telephone companies, map publishing companies, and surveying companies. Geographers I have known who worked for nonprofit groups were employed by the Central Indiana Land Trust and the Indiana Nature Conservancy.

Is Geography an Art or Is It a Science?

Geography is both an art and a science. It is an art because often the patterns found on Earth are a matter of interpretation or opinion. For example, if one attempts to define a regional boundary by observing various types of earth features, an opinion is often involved. One person may define a boundary using criteria another person believes is inappropriate. Artistic work is highly prized in geography. It makes being part of the discipline exciting, creative, and fun.

Geography is also a science. It involves data collection, testing of hypotheses, and the building of theories. Using the scientific method to communicate the results of research is required so that other people might replicate the research method and arrive at identical results.

Module 1 Objectives

You should now be able to:

- Define what the word *geography* means

- Compare how a modern definition of geography is different from the literal meaning of the word

- List the two major earth features studied by geographers

- Identify the four spheres of the physical world

- Describe the *First Law of Ecology*

- Compare and contrast the two approaches used by geographers to study earth features

- Describe how *analysis* is different from *synthesis*

- List the three main categories of geography courses and classify geography courses into one of the three categories

- Compare and contrast why geography can be viewed as being either an art or a science

****

6

MODULE 2: EARTH'S GRID

The network of parallels and meridians superimposed on Earth's surface used to locate earth features is known as the earth's grid, the geographic grid, the latitude-longitude grid, or the *graticule*. Geographers are constantly using the earth's grid to communicate the location of earth features to other people. Students who complete this course should be able to use the latitude-longitude grid.

Latitude

Latitude is defined as the "angular distance measured north and south of the Equator." To understand this definition, it is first necessary to know a couple of things about Earth. First, the *Equator* is the line that divides Earth into a north half and a south half (Fig. 2-1). This is not an arbitrarily defined line, for it is positioned halfway between the

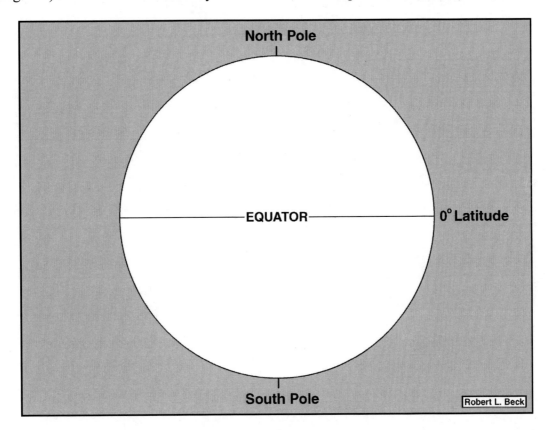

Figure 2-1. The Equator

North Pole and the South Pole, but which North Pole and which South Pole? Perhaps you already know there are two north poles and two south poles. These two types of poles are (1) the rotational poles and (2) the magnetic poles. Use the world map shown in *Goode's World Atlas* (p. 20) to find these two poles. One is labeled "North Pole" and one is

7

labeled "North Magnetic Pole."[1] The Equator is the line halfway between the **rotational poles** and not the magnetic poles. Figure 2-1 shows both the north rotational pole and the south rotational pole. In this book every time I mention the phrases "North Pole" or "South Pole," they specifically refer to the rotational poles and not to the magnetic poles.

The latitude of the Equator is 0°. It is 0° because we are measuring distances north and south of it. Find the Equator on the "Average Annual Temperature Range" map in **Goode's World Atlas** (p. 33). Its label is shown as "0" on the right-hand side of the map.

The imaginary straight line connecting the North Pole with the South Pole is known as the **polar axis** (Fig. 2-2). I show this as a hidden line (dashed line) because it goes through Earth's interior and is not shown on maps. The polar axis intersects the Equator at the center of Earth if the Equator is viewed as a plane instead of a line. Rather than calling this point of intersection "the center of Earth," I call it the **vertex**, which is a term used to define the center of any circle. Figure 2-3 shows the polar axis intersecting the Equator at the vertex (center of Earth).

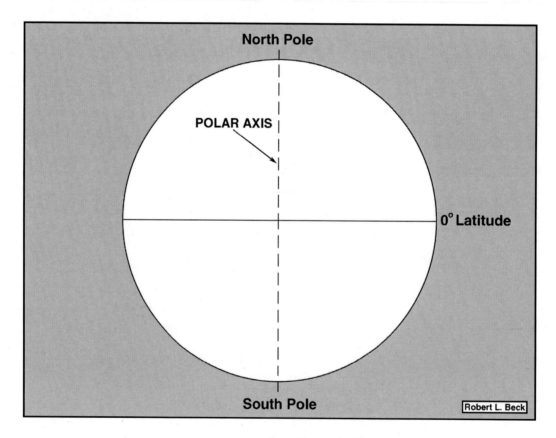

Figure 2-2. The Polar Axis

---

[1]Please be advised that the magnetic poles migrate. The North Pole is currently positioned over the Arctic Ocean, so its location shown in **Goode's World Atlas** is incorrect.

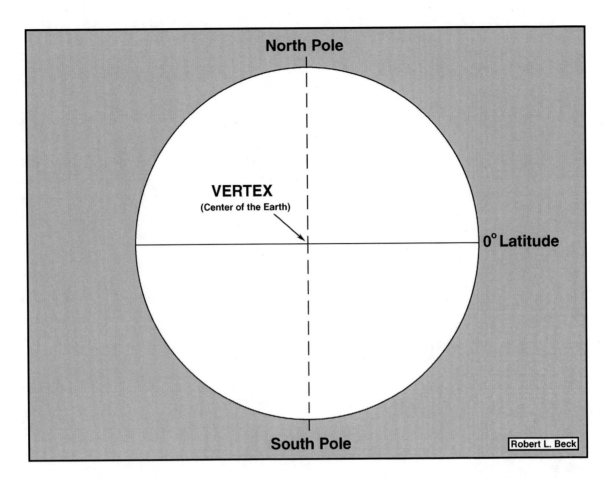

Figure 2-3. The Vertex

****

DRAWING THE EARTH'S GRID

I will now draw a sample latitude line on the globe, and I will use a 30°–60°–90° triangle to demonstrate how to do so. I start with laying a side of the triangle on the Equator and positioning the 30° point of it at the vertex (Fig. 2-4). Next I draw a straight line connecting the vertex with the point where the long side of the triangle intersects the circumference of the circle. I then remove the triangle (Fig. 2-5). Please note I now have a 30° angle shown on the drawing. The final step is to draw a line **parallel** to the Equator connecting the 30° point on the circumference with a point on the opposite side of the circle (Fig. 2-6). I have now plotted the 30° degree North Latitude line on the globe. Remember that latitude is an **angular distance**, and in this case it is an angular distance north of the Equator. Latitude lines run east to west across the globe, but they measure distances north and south of the Equator because they are angular distances measured north and south of the Equator.

9

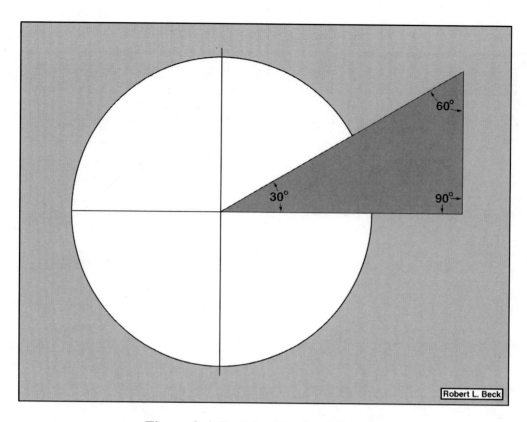

Figure 2-4. Positioning the Triangle

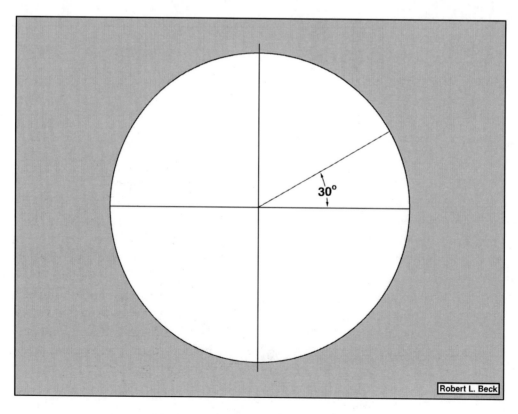

Figure 2-5. Drawing a 30° Angle

Figure 2-7 shows a few examples of latitude lines. Some are labeled north latitude and some are labeled south latitude. All, however, run parallel to the Equator, so latitude

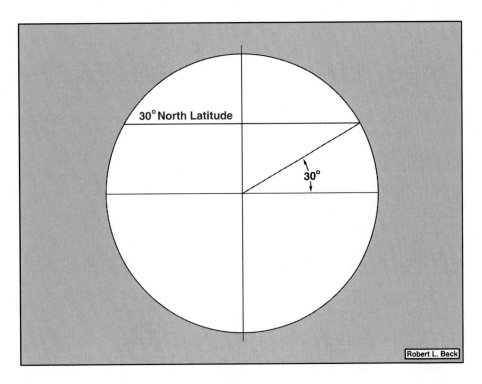

Figure 2-6. The 30° North Latitude Line

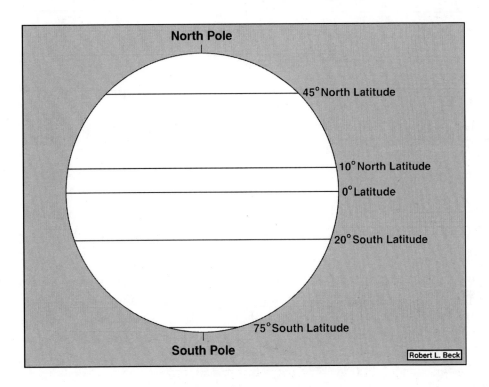

Figure 2-7. Latitude Lines

lines are also known as *parallels*. Please note that the Equator is the longest latitude line and that the lines become progressively shorter as one moves toward either pole. In fact, the North Pole and the South Pole are points and not actually lines.

What is the latitude of the North Pole? Answer: 90° North Latitude.

The 60° latitude line is useful for quickly assessing area distortions on maps, for this latitude line is almost exactly one-half the length of the Equator. This can be shown using a globe or it can be shown on a drawing. An examination of the drawing in Figure 2-8 reveals the length of the 60° North Latitude line ($X + Z$) is one-half the length of the Equator ($X + Y$).

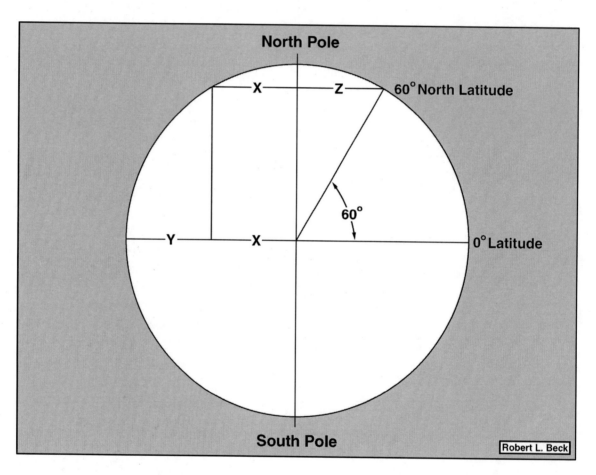

Figure 2-8. The 60° North Latitude Line

In my traditional lecture class I like to show this using a globe. The Equator is nearly 25,000 miles long, so the length of a 60° latitude line is about 12,500 miles. On many maps the 60° latitude line is the same length as the Equator (when it should be one-half the length). This means that polar areas on some maps appear much larger than they actually are. For example, the continent of South America is over eight times larger than the island of Greenland, but on some maps South America appears to be about the same size as Greenland (see Miller Cylindrical Projection, *Goode's World Atlas*, p. 12).

Indianapolis is situated at 39°46′ (thirty-nine degrees, forty-six minutes) North Latitude, which is listed in the Pronouncing Index of ***Goode's World Atlas*** (p. 339). There are 60 minutes of latitude between every degree and 60 seconds of latitude between every minute.

If Indianapolis were situated 14 minutes north of its present location, what would its latitude then be? Answer: 40° North Latitude.

Longitude

Longitude is defined as the "angular distance measured east and west of the Prime Meridian." The ***Prime Meridian*** is the 0° longitude line because angular distances are measured east and west of it. The Prime Meridian begins at the North Pole, runs through the Royal Observatory in Greenwich, England (London area), and then continues south until it reaches the South Pole (Fig. 2-9). It therefore only goes halfway around the earth, as do all other longitude lines.

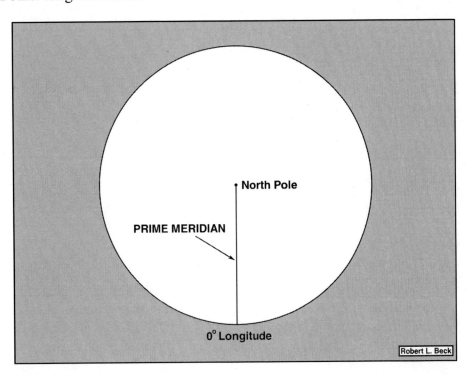

Figure 2-9. The Prime Meridian

Latitude lines run all the way around Earth forming circles, but longitude lines only go halfway around Earth, forming half-circles. Find the Prime Meridian on the "Average Annual Temperature Range" map in ***Goode's World Atlas*** (p. 33). Its label is shown as "0," near the center of the map at the top. Now find the point of intersection of the Prime Meridian and the Equator off the southern coast of West Africa. The Prime Meridian (0° Long.) is also shown on the "British Isles" map in ***Goode's World Atlas*** (p. 191). Note it goes through the London area and also note that as you move either west or east of it, the longitude lines shown on the map increase by increments of 2°.

13

A longitude line is drawn just like a latitude line, but the point of the triangle is situated at the North Pole (or South Pole) when plotting the line (Fig. 2-10). Removing the triangle after drawing the line reveals the longitude line (Fig. 2-11). You should now

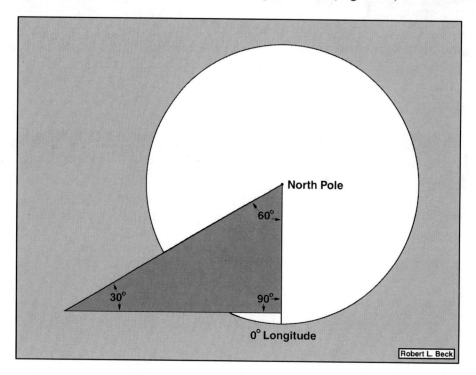

Figure 2-10. Drawing a 60° Angle

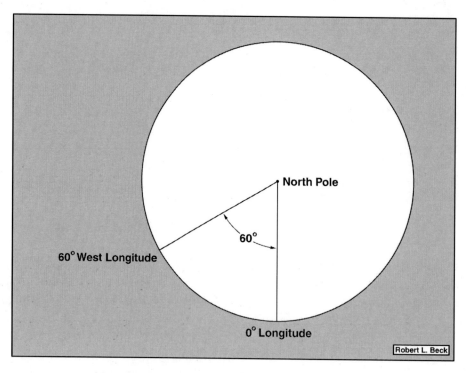

Figure 2-11. The 60° West Longitude Line

14

be able to see that another difference between drawing latitude lines and longitude lines is that with latitude lines you have to draw a second line parallel to the Equator, which is the actual latitude line. With longitude lines you do not have to draw a second line; drawing the line from the North Pole (or South Pole) to the circumference of the circle is the longitude line.

The 180° longitude line is the highest numbered longitude line. It is located opposite the Prime Meridian on the globe (Fig. 2-12). A circle is formed if one joins the Prime Meridian and the 180° longitude line. The 180° longitude line is sometimes known as the *International Date Line*, because when you cross it the day of the week changes. Traveling west across the International Date Line adds a day, while traveling east

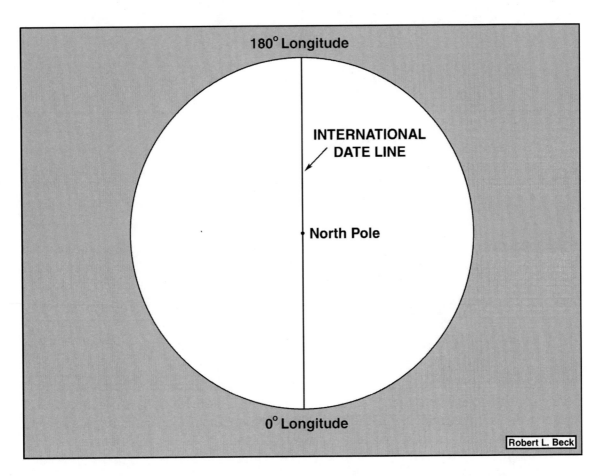

Figure 2-12. The 180° Meridian

subtracts a day. For example, if it is Monday, October 10, east of the International Date Line then it is Tuesday, October 11, west of the International Date Line. All our calendar days begin and end at the International Date Line. Although it commonly said that "the 180° longitude line is the International Date Line," that statement requires some explanation. The actual International Date Line (as opposed to the 180° longitude line) zigzags through the Pacific Ocean to avoid splitting countries and island groups (Fig. 2-13).

A piece of Russia is located east of the 180° longitude line (see Asia map, *Goode's World Atlas*, p. 209). The International Date Line was shifted to the east in this area to keep all of Russia west of the line.

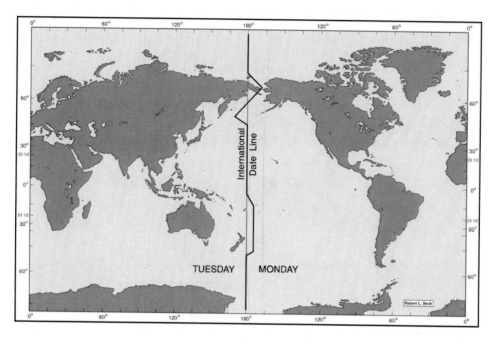

Figure 2-13. The International Date Line, 2010

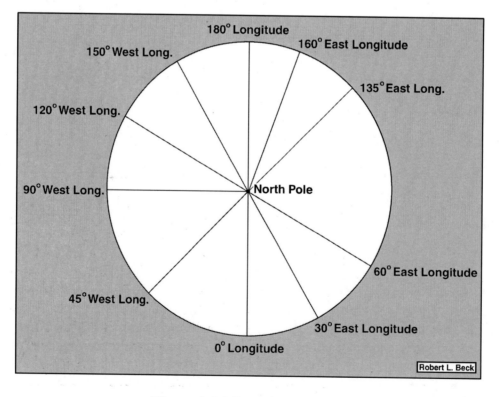

Figure 2-14. Longitude Lines

16

Longitude lines are also known as *meridians*. Unlike parallels, which become progressively shorter as they near the pole, all meridians begin and end at a rotational pole, so they are roughly the same length. Indianapolis is situated at 86°08′ West Long. (see Pronouncing Index, *Goode's World Atlas*, p. 339). A few meridians (longitude lines) are shown on Figure 2-14. Some of them are labeled west longitude and some of them are labeled east longitude.

In what country does the intersection of 15° South Latitude and 65° West Longitude occur? Answer: Bolivia (use a map in *Goode's World Atlas* to verify this).

Great Circle Routes and Great Circles

A Great Circle route is the shortest distance between two points on Earth's surface. They can be easily plotted using a piece of string and a globe. I like to do this by using two cities at approximately the same latitude but a long distance apart. For example, Indianapolis, Indiana, and Madrid, Spain, are both situated at about the same latitude (Madrid is actually a little farther north, but only by a few miles), so on most world maps showing an Equatorial perspective of Earth, it appears the shortest distance would follow the 40° North Latitude line. By laying a taut string on a globe with one point at Indianapolis and the other at Madrid, it can be seen that the Great Circle route passes over the island of Newfoundland. If this is now shown on a world map (that uses an Equatorial perspective), the Great Circle route appears to be longer than the route laid out on the 40° N. Lat. line (Fig. 2-15).

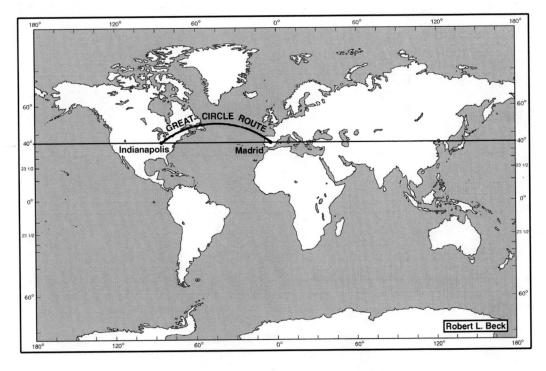

Figure 2-15. A Great Circle Route

17

A Great Circle is any circle that divides Earth into halves. The Equator is a Great Circle because it divides Earth into a northern hemisphere and a southern hemisphere. Is the 30° North Latitude line a Great Circle? No! That latitude line does not divide Earth into halves, for obviously the area north of the 30° North Latitude line is much smaller than the area south of the 30° North Latitude line. The Equator is the only latitude line that is also a Great Circle. How about if we join the Prime Meridian with the 180° meridian, would those two meridians, when joined, form a Great Circle? Yes! All meridians form Great Circles when joined with the opposite meridian on the other side of Earth.

The Great Circle route between any two points on the same meridian follows that meridian. For example, Charleston, South Carolina, and Guayaquil, Ecuador, are both located on the 80° West Longitude line, so the shortest distance between them follows that meridian.

If you convert a Great Circle to a plane and then thrust that plane through Earth, would it intersect the vertex? Yes! The line-of-contact between any plane that intersects the vertex and Earth's surface defines a Great Circle (Fig. 2-16).

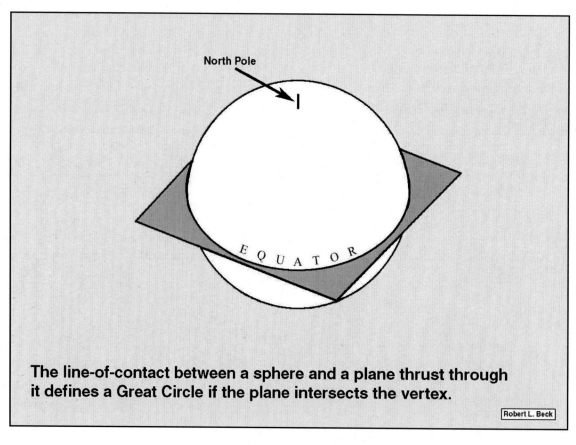

The line-of-contact between a sphere and a plane thrust through it defines a Great Circle if the plane intersects the vertex.

Robert L. Beck

Figure 2-16. Plane Through the Earth

18

Module 2 Objectives

You should now be able to:

- Use the geographic grid to locate earth features on a map

- Compare and contrast *latitude* with *longitude*

- Plot latitude lines and longitude lines on a circle using a triangle

- Determine whether or not a given latitude line is greater than or less than 12,500 miles in length

- Define a *Great Circle route*

- Draw a Great Circle route on a globe

- Determine whether or not a circle on a globe is a *Great Circle*

- Define the following words or phrases: *graticule, polar axis, Equator, Prime Meridian, International Date Line*

Practice Exercise: Using a globe, determine the Great Circle route between Indianapolis and Colombo, Sri Lanka. Draw the Great Circle route on this map with a red pencil.

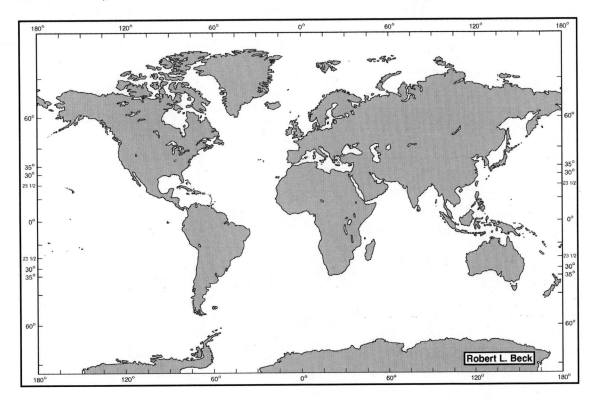

19

Practice Exercise: Using a globe, draw a Great Circle Route between Perth, Australia, and Buenos Aires, Argentina, on this map with a red pencil.

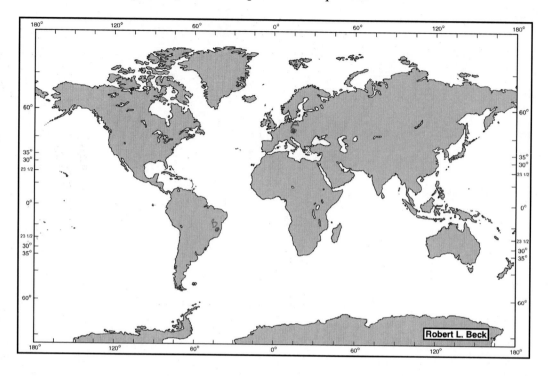

Practice Exercise: Choose two cities on different continents. Using a globe, draw the shortest distance between them on this map with a red pencil.

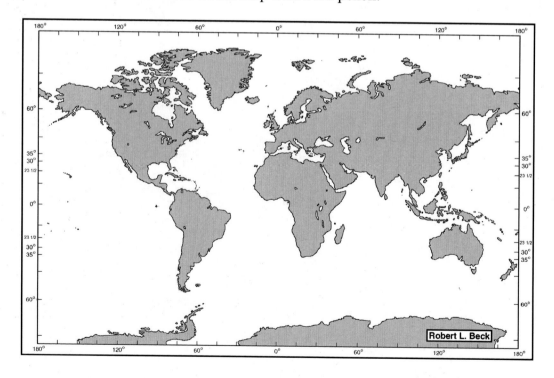

MODULE 3: EARTH–SUN RELATIONSHIPS

This is one of the most important modules in the course, for what you learn here has applications throughout the semester. I like to include this module early in the course for that reason. Many of the geographic patterns observed on Earth are tied, in some way, to the position of the Earth and sun in space. To truly understand these geographic patterns, one needs to comprehend *four major Earth–sun relationships*.

Inclination of the Axis

First, Earth sits at an angle in space. This is known as the *inclination of the axis*. This angle is sometimes said to be 66½° from the plane of Earth's orbit around the sun, but it is more commonly expressed as 23½° from a hypothetical vertical position of the axis (Fig. 3-1). Whenever I purchase a globe, and especially one for use in teaching, I make sure it sits in an inclined position.

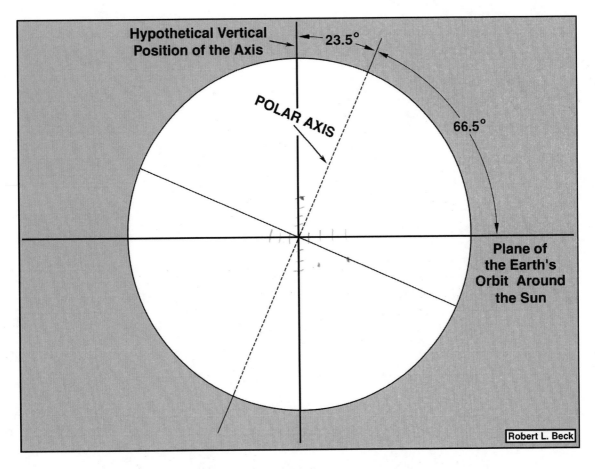

Figure 3-1. Inclination of the Axis

Rotation

Second, as Earth sits in space in an inclined position it spins (or turns) on its axis. This spinning of Earth on its axis is known as **rotation**. It takes about 24 hours for Earth to complete one rotation, which is known as a **solar day**.

Earth rotates in an eastward direction, so if Earth is viewed from over the North Pole it appears to rotate counterclockwise (Fig. 3-2).

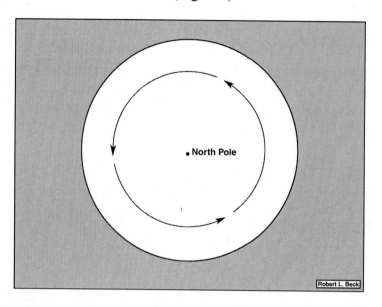

Figure 3-2. Direction of Earth Rotation, North Pole View

When viewed from over the South Pole, Earth appears to rotate clockwise (Fig. 3-3). I like to demonstrate this concept by holding a pencil in my hand while

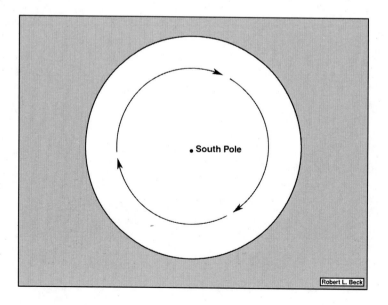

Figure 3-3. Direction of Earth Rotation, South Pole View

rotating it counterclockwise as I view it from the top. If I keep turning the pencil in the same direction as I slowly move it above my head, it now appears to be rotating clockwise as I view it from the bottom.

Not all places on Earth rotate at the same velocity. ***Rotational velocity*** decreases as one moves from the Equator toward a pole. This is easily demonstrated by thinking of a person standing at the Equator for one solar day. In that 24-hour period, he or she travels a distance of nearly 25,000 miles (the Equatorial circumference). That person moves at a rotational velocity exceeding 1,000 miles per hour (24,902 miles / 24 hours = c. 1,038 miles per hour [mph] (Fig. 3-4). A person standing at 60° North Latitude only

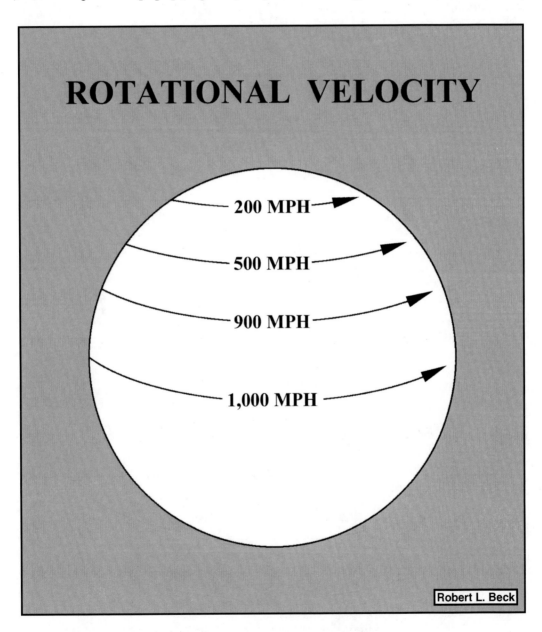

Figure 3-4. Rotational Velocity

moves about 12,500 miles in a 24-hour period (remember that 60° North Latitude is only one-half the length of the Equator). He or she therefore only moves at about 520 miles per hour (12,500 miles / 24 hours = c. 521 mph).

Which city, Miami or Chicago, moves at the greatest rotational velocity? Answer is: Miami. It is closer to the Equator.

The ***Coriolis effect*** is one of the physical effects of rotation and refers to the apparent deflection of a free-moving object in response to Earth's rotation. The free-moving object we are most concerned about in this course is the wind. Free-moving objects, including the wind, move along straight lines, but as they move Earth rotates underneath them seemingly causing them to be deflected from their original paths.

Figure 3-5 shows some examples of the Coriolis effect. In the figure free-moving objects attempt to move along the black lines, but they appear to move along the slightly longer gray lines. In the Northern Hemisphere, free-moving objects 1–4 appear to deflect

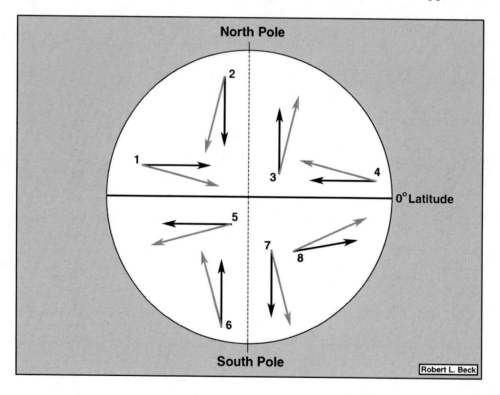

Figure 3-5. Coriolis Effect

to the right, regardless of their direction of motion. An object moving from west to east (#1, Fig. 3-5) appears to deflect to the southeast; an object moving from north to south (#2, Fig. 3-5) appears to deflect to the southwest; an object moving from south to north (#3, Fig. 3-5) appears to deflect to the northeast; and an object moving from east to west (#4, Fig. 3-5) appears to deflect to the northwest. In the Southern Hemisphere the deflection is to the left (#5–#8, Fig. 3-5).

24

To demonstrate how the Coriolis effect works, think of a situation involving bird hunting. Imagine you are going pheasant hunting with a shotgun. As you walk through the field, a pheasant startles you as it springs from its hiding spot and flies from the right to the left in front of you. You quickly raise the shotgun, aim it directly at the pheasant, and pull the trigger. Will you hit the pheasant? No. You miss it because the shotgun pellets cannot instantly travel from the gun to hit the pheasant. The shotgun pellets traveled in a straight line, but from the eye of the pheasant the shotgun pellets seem to have been deflected.

The Coriolis effect is strongest at the poles and nonexistent at the Equator. The rotational velocity at the poles is 0 mph, so wind that originates near the poles is subjected to rapidly increasing velocities as it travels toward the Equator, thus enhancing the Coriolis effect. Air that moves along the Equator is not subjected to the Coriolis effect, for the Equator is a Great Circle and by traveling along it you are taking the shortest distance to another point on the Equator. This means that as you travel your rotational velocity would remain constant whether traveling to the east or to the west. This constant rotational velocity eliminates the Coriolis effect.

As Earth rotates, it exerts a ***centrifugal force*** on all earth objects. You might have felt this centrifugal force if you have ridden on a merry-go-round. Trying to walk on a merry-go-round as it moves can be tricky, especially if you are moving from its center to the edge. The merry-go-round exerts a centrifugal force as it turns, so it tries to throw you off it! Earth while rotating tries to throw the loose objects on it out into space. So why are we still here? Are not people loose objects that are subjected to the centrifugal force of rotation? Well, we remain on Earth because gravity holds us on. Gravity is about 289 times stronger than the centrifugal force of rotation. If we did not have gravity on Earth, we would be thrown out into space.

Which city, Miami or Chicago, is subjected to the greatest centrifugal force of rotation? Answer is: Miami. The centrifugal force of rotation is greater in Miami than in Chicago because, again, it is closer to the Equator. Miami rotates at a higher velocity, so it also has a greater centrifugal force exerted on it.

Earth's rotation is thought to have influenced the **shape of the planet**. We usually think of Earth as being a sphere, but it is really an oblate ellipsoid. The distance from the North Pole to the South Pole through the Earth's center (following the polar axis) is about 7,900 miles (Fig. 3-6). This is known as the polar diameter. The Equatorial diameter, from the Equator on one side of the Earth to the Equator on the opposite side of the Earth, is about 7,927 miles (Fig. 3-6). Earth has a "bulging Equator" that was probably formed when the semiliquid materials in Earth's interior were thrust out by the centrifugal force of rotation caused by the high rotational velocities at the Equator. The bulging Equator means Earth's poles are slightly flattened.

Most geographers do not pay much attention to Earth's bulging Equator, for the bulge is too slight to greatly influence the distribution of earth features. Cartographers typically depict Earth as a sphere on maps and not as an oblate ellipsoid; however, data tables are sometimes published in cartography textbooks that give the accurate lengths of the parallels and meridians of the non-spherical Earth. **Geodesy** is the branch of mathematics dealing with the size, shape, and gravity of Earth. People who study geodesy are therefore very much interested in Earth's bulging Equator.

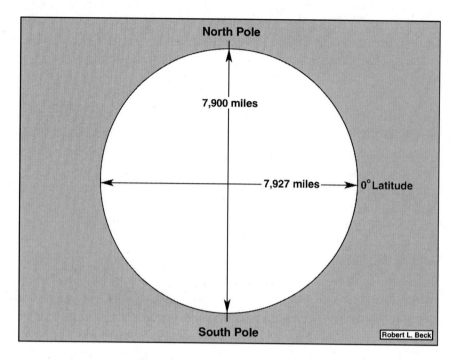

Figure 3-6. Earth Diameters

Earth's shape influences the strength of **gravity** over its surface. A person standing at the North Pole is located closer to Earth's center (vertex) than a person standing at the Equator, for the distance from the North Pole to the vertex is about 3,950 miles (7,900 / 2), whereas the distance from the Equator to the vertex is about 3,963.5 miles (7,927 / 2). The pull of gravity is stronger on the person standing at the North Pole than on the person standing at the Equator. The person at the North Pole is located closer to Earth's center of gravity because he or she is closer to Earth's center. Gravity is strongest at the poles and weakest at the Equator. People first had some inkling about this using pendulum clocks. Near the Equator the clocks would register a different time than the same clocks used in Europe. It was reasoned gravity affected the movement of the pendulum thus resulting in time differentials.

Which city, Miami or Chicago, is closest to the center of Earth? Answer is: Chicago. It is closer to the North Pole.

Places on Earth experience the gravitational attraction of the moon and sun as Earth rotates. The **tides** are mostly explained by rotation, for the gravitational fields of the moon and sun interact in complicated ways as they attempt to pull Earth's water to them, which cause the tides. The shape of coastlines, the water depth, and the configuration of the seafloor also contribute to the complexity of tides. There are many types and names of tides—high tides, low tides, ebb tides, flood tides, diurnal tides, semidiurnal tides, compound tides, mixed tides, spring tides, and (the favorite of the crossword puzzle designer) neap tides. Tides are complicated, and I do not know much about them. One must have a good background in physics and mathematics to understand them well.

Earth wobbles a little bit as it rotates. This wobble of Earth on its axis is known as *precession.* Right now Earth's polar axis sits at an angle of about 23½° in space, but sometime in the future it might sit at a different angle, perhaps 25° or maybe 22°. Precession is thought to cause long-term changes in the inclination of Earth's polar axis.

Rotation imposes a *daily pattern of activity* on most life-forms. Plants and animals adjust to the cyclical rhythms of light, darkness, heat, humidity, and wind. For example, I raise a few chickens. Every day they head to the chicken house to roost for the night at about the same time in the late afternoon.

Revolution

As Earth rotates on its axis it also moves in orbit around the sun. The movement of Earth around the sun is known as *revolution*, which is the third major Earth–sun relationship. The fact that Earth rotates as it revolves is sometimes known as the "double motion of the earth." The work of Galileo Galilei and Johannes Kepler helped define this double motion.

Earth revolves around the sun counterclockwise when viewed from above the North Pole (Fig. 3-7). It takes Earth about 365.25 days to complete one revolution, or one

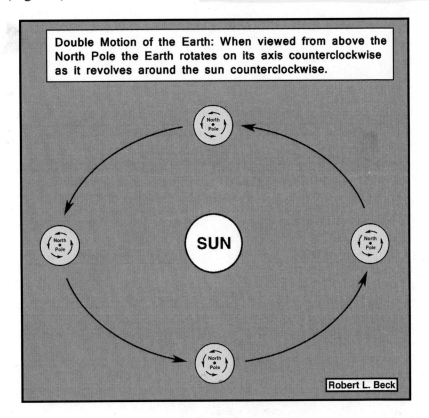

Figure 3-7. Revolution

time around the sun. This is known as a ***tropical year***. A calendar year is usually composed of 365 days, but every fourth year the calendar has 366 days (leap year) to account for that extra ¼ day that occurs every tropical year.

Earth makes an elliptical orbit around the sun, and not a circular one (Fig. 3-8). The point at which Earth is closest to the sun in the course of the tropical year is known as the ***perihelion***. This occurs on January 3, and at that time Earth is about 91.5 million

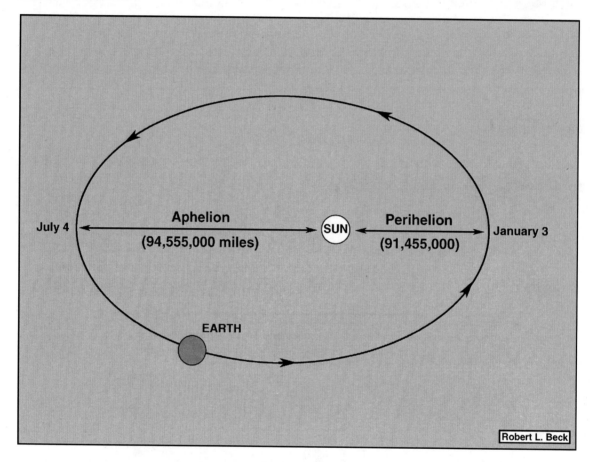

Figure 3-8. Earth's Elliptical Orbit

miles away from the sun. The point at which Earth is farthest away from the sun is known as the ***aphelion,*** which occurs on July 4. At that time Earth is about 94.6 million miles away from the sun. It is commonly said that the average distance between Earth and the sun is 93 million miles.

Is Earth closer to the sun on August 10 or on December 10? Answer is: Dec. 10. It is nearing perihelion.

Note that when Earth is closest to the sun, on January 3, winter is occurring in the Northern Hemisphere. Our seasons then cannot be explained on the basis of the distance from Earth to the sun. Some people have the mistaken notion that we have summer when Earth is close to the sun and winter when Earth is far away from the sun.

Parallelism of the Axis

As Earth revolves around the sun, its polar axis remains pointing to the same spot in outer space. It does not matter if it is May 5, August 11, September 25, or December 27— during every day of the year the North Pole remains pointed at the same spot in the sky. Many people know that the North Pole is always pointing at a distant star, Polaris (also known as the North Star). The fact that the polar axis remains pointing at the North Star during its complete revolution means that linear extensions of the axis are shown as parallel lines (Fig. 3-9) on a two-dimensional drawing depicting Earth in various positions around the sun. Thus, the fourth Earth–sun relationship is *parallelism of the axis*.

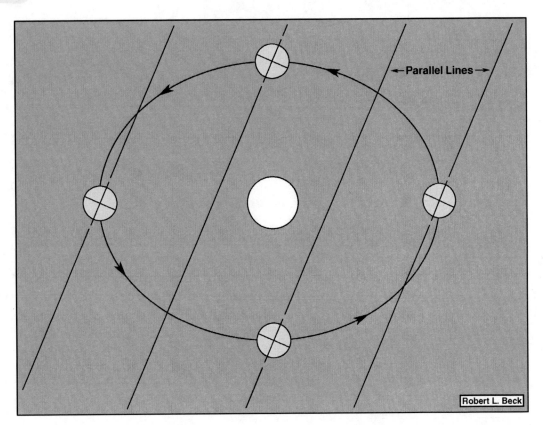

Figure 3-9. Parallelism of the Axis

Polaris is directly overhead if you are standing at the North Pole. Its light strikes you at a 90° angle, so you have to turn your head and look straight up to see it. Remember that the latitude of the North Pole is also 90°, so if the light of Polaris strikes the North Pole at a 90° there is a one-to-one correspondence between the angle that Polaris's light strikes Earth and the latitude of the Earth. Indianapolis and Madrid are both positioned at about 40° North Latitude, so the light of Polaris strikes both of those cities at an angle of 40° above the horizon (Fig. 3-10). This relationship was especially handy for people who, years ago, navigated using only the stars. If the night was clear, and you were able to see Polaris, it was a relatively simple matter to determine its angle above the horizon and thus determine your latitude.

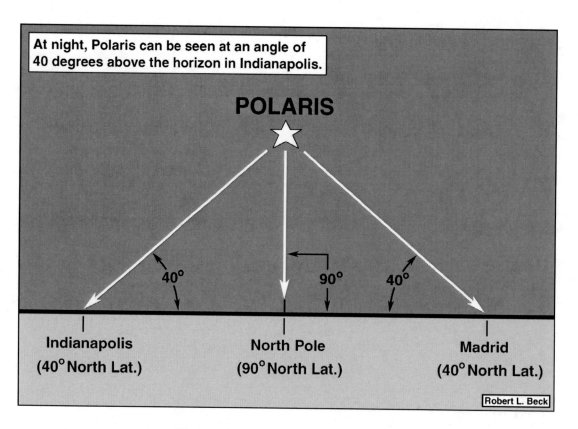

Figure 3-10. The Angle of Polaris

Before there were adequate maps to guide sailors across the ocean, and also before a method was developed to accurately determine longitude at sea, it was apparently a fairly common practice to "ride the latitude" while sailing from Europe to North America. For example, a ship might debark from a southern Spanish port and thence sail along the coast of Africa to perhaps 25 degrees N. Lat. (***Goode's World Atlas***, p. 284). From there it could turn west and chart a course across the middle of the Atlantic Ocean. Every night a sighting was made to make sure Polaris remained at 25 degrees above the horizon. If it was not found to be at that angle then an adjustment was made to steer the ship back into position so that Polaris might be seen at an angle of 25 degrees the next night. Maintaining a Polaris angle of 25 degrees enabled the ship to make land in the Bahamas. Of course this is a much longer distance than following the Great Circle route from Spain to the Bahamas, but it could be done accurately using the available technology. Taking the Great Circle route was riskier, for the latitude is constantly changing as the ship follows the shorter route along the Great Circle.

What is your latitude if one night, while sailing on the ocean, you observe Polaris positioned at an angle of 10° above the horizon? Answer is: 10° North Latitude.

Where is Polaris seen if you are located on the Equator? Answer is: On the horizon.

Can you see Polaris in the Southern Hemisphere? Answer is: No. It is positioned below the horizon in the Southern Hemisphere, for it would be more than 90 degrees in latitude away from your position.

Module 3 Objectives

You should now be able to:

- Explain the meaning of the phrases *inclination of the axis* and *parallelism of the axis*

- Discuss the difference between *rotation* and *revolution*

- List the major physical effects of rotation

- Define, and briefly explain, the *Coriolis effect*

- Discuss why gravity and rotational velocities vary over the earth's surface

- Determine the angle above the horizon at which Polaris is seen in the night sky for any place on Earth

- Define or identify the following terms: *solar day, centrifugal force of rotation, double motion of the earth, tropical year, oblate ellipsoid, precession, geodesy*

- Compare and contrast the *perihelion* with the *aphelion*

- Describe the shape of Earth's orbit around the sun

- Discuss why the North Star was a valuable navigation aid before the invention of sophisticated navigation instruments

****

"A year indoors is a journey along a paper calendar; a year in outer nature is the accomplishment of a tremendous ritual. To share in it, one must have a knowledge of the pilgrimages of the sun, and something of that natural sense of him and feeling for him which made even the most primitive people mark the summer limits of his advance and the last December ebb of his decline . . . . We lose a great deal, I think, when we lose this sense and feeling for the sun. When all has been said, the adventure of the sun is the great natural drama by which we live, and not to have joy in it and awe of it, not to share in it, is to close a dull door on nature's sustaining and poetic spirit." — Henry Beston, ***The Outermost House***, 1928

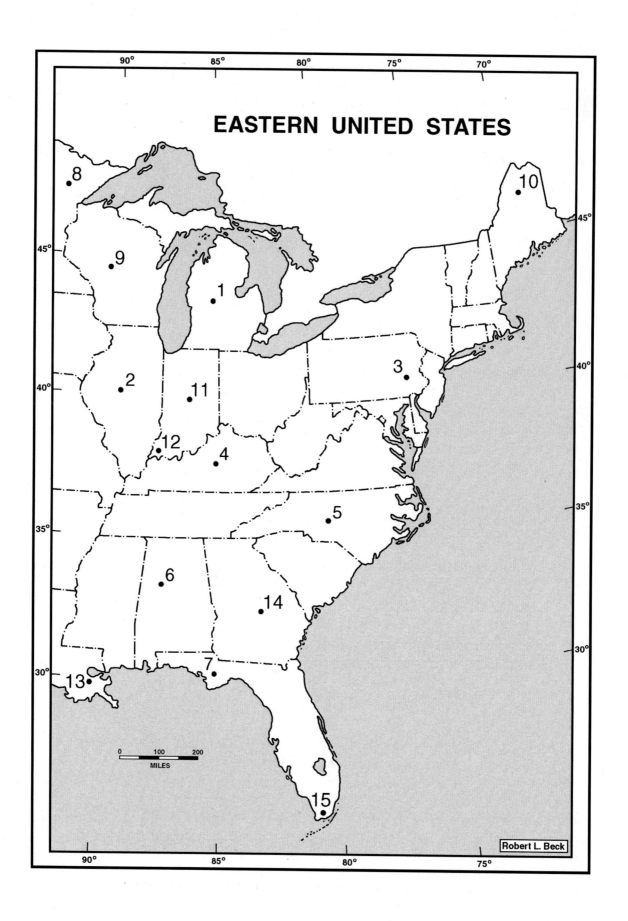

EASTERN UNITED STATES

Robert L. Beck

32

MODULE 4: SOLAR RADIATION

This is another critical module for understanding physical geography. ***Study this module thoroughly!*** The concepts presented in this module will have a direct bearing on understanding both weather and climate.

The Sun

The sun is a gigantic nuclear reactor, for in its center hydrogen atoms fuse to form helium atoms (Fig. 4-1). This fusion releases energy that works its way through the body of the

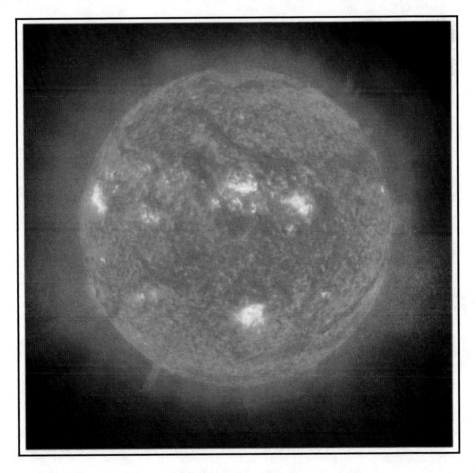

Figure 4-1. The Sun
(NASA photo)

sun and eventually through the surface of the sun and then into space. Some of this energy is occasionally released as huge solar flares (Fig. 4-2). Earth, being about 93 million miles from the sun, is hit with some of this solar radiation, but only a small fraction of the total amount of energy emitted. Observe in Figure 4-2 how small Earth is when compared to the sun. Of course, the distance between Earth and the sun in that figure is not to scale.

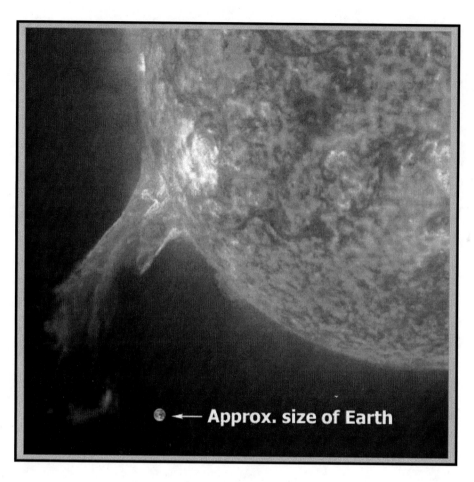

Approx. size of Earth

Figure 4-2. A Solar Flare
(NASA photo)

Subsolar Point

Some of the solar radiation that strikes Earth hits it at a 90° angle. The place where this occurs is known as the ***subsolar point (SSP)***. Geographers also use the phrases "the direct rays of the sun" or "the vertical rays of the sun" to refer to the 90° angle. I like to use the term ***SSP***, so that is what I will call it in this course.

The SSP is well named, for there is only **one** point on Earth where this occurs. As you move away from the SSP, in any direction, the angle the sun's rays strike Earth will decrease. Imagine you have a round ball and a flat wooden board lying on the ground. If you place the ball on the board, it will come into contact with the board at only one point, for a sphere can only come in contact with a plane at a single point (Fig. 4-3). If we now think of solar radiation as a "plane of energy" moving toward Earth, there is only one place where that plane can strike Earth at a 90° angle. The rest of that "plane of energy" would strike Earth at less than a 90° angle.

34

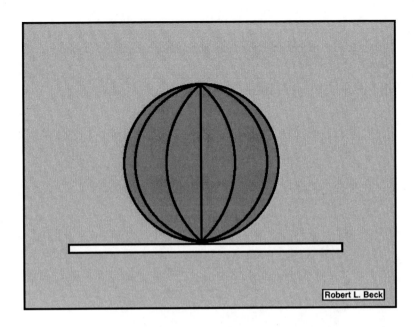

Figure 4-3. A Plane and a Sphere

As Earth rotates, the SSP moves across Earth's surface from east to west. It also moves either north or south as Earth revolves in orbit around the sun. If Earth sat in space with its polar axis in a vertical position, the SSP would always be on the Equator (Fig. 4-4). However, Earth sits in space at angle of 23½°, and it maintains parallelism of

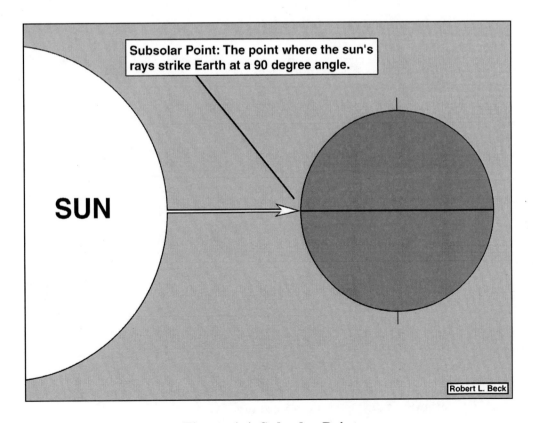

Figure 4-4. Subsolar Point

the axis as it revolves around the sun, so at one time during the year the North Pole leans into the sun and at another time it leans away from the sun (Fig. 4-5 and Fig. 4-6). From our perspective on Earth, the SSP appears to migrate either to the north or to the south as revolution occurs.

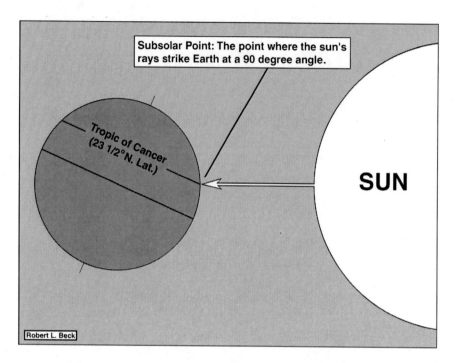

Figure 4-5. North Pole Leaning Toward the Sun

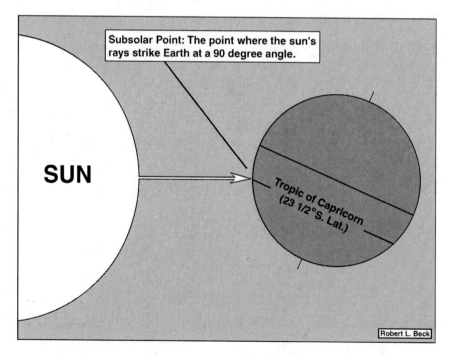

Figure 4-6. North Pole Leaning Away from the Sun

The ***analemma*** is used to find the latitude of the SSP for any day of the year (Fig. 4-7). I want you to be able to use the analemma, so I will explain how it works. As you see, the analemma looks somewhat like a number 8. The number 8 is broken down

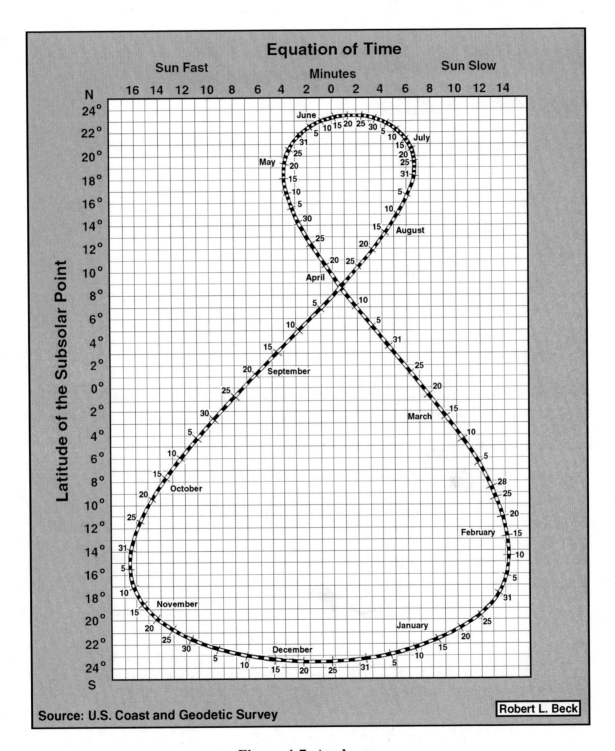

Figure 4-7. Analemma

by months, and each month is broken down by days. Please find the month of October on the analemma (lower left-hand side). Now find the 10th day of October. Note that a line intersects October 10, and further note on the left-hand side of the graph that this line is labeled 6°. This means that on October 10 the SSP is located at 6° South Latitude. The analemma also shows fast sun and slow sun, but we are not concerned with that concept in this course.

Now note that the SSP reaches its maximum northern position on June 21, when it is on 23½° North Latitude *(Tropic of Cancer)*. On December 22 it is on 23½° South Latitude *(Tropic of Capricorn)*, its maximum southern position. The SSP then is either on or between 23½° North Latitude and 23½° South Latitude every day of the year. Twice per year the SSP is on the Equator—once when it is moving north and once when it is moving south.

In which two months is the SSP on the Equator? Answer is: March and Sept.

The SSP migrates to 23½° North Latitude and to 23½° South Latitude because Earth is inclined at an angle of 23½°. If Earth were inclined at an angle of 15°, then the SSP would only migrate to 15° North and South Latitudes. The distance that the SSP migrates in a tropical year is directly related to the inclination of Earth on its axis and to the parallelism of the axis.

Circle of Illumination

The *Circle of Illumination* is the line that divides Earth into day and night (Fig. 4-8). It is also a great circle if we ignore *twilight* (the period of time before sunrise and after sunset when the sun is below the horizon but still providing enough light for us to see).

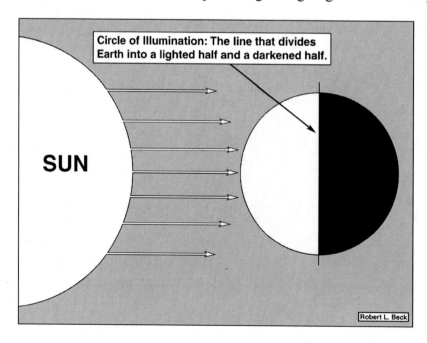

Figure 4-8. Circle of Illumination

The Circle of Illumination is used to define both the *Arctic Circle* and the *Antarctic Circle*. On June 21 the North Pole leans toward the sun. On that day, as you recall, the SSP is on 23½° North Latitude. Now note that on June 21 the Circle of Illumination connects 66½° North Latitude with 66½° South Latitude (Fig. 4-9). All the area north of 66½° North Latitude (the Arctic Circle) is in continuous light and all the area south of 66½° South Latitude (the Antarctic Circle) is in continuous darkness.

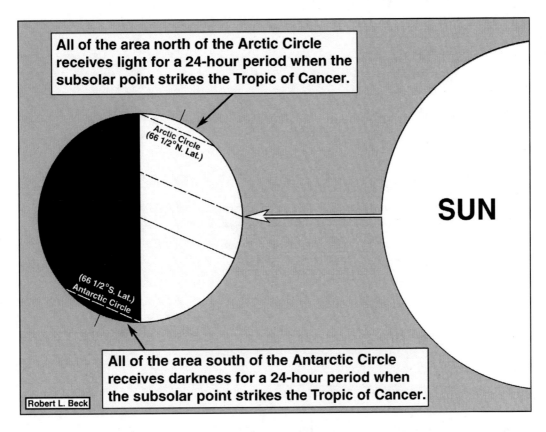

All of the area north of the Arctic Circle receives light for a 24-hour period when the subsolar point strikes the Tropic of Cancer.

Arctic Circle (66 1/2° N. Lat.)

SUN

(66 1/2° S. Lat.) Antarctic Circle

All of the area south of the Antarctic Circle receives darkness for a 24-hour period when the subsolar point strikes the Tropic of Cancer.

Robert L. Beck

Figure 4-9. The Arctic Circle and the Antarctic Circle

You should now be able to understand why Alaska is sometimes known as the "land of the midnight sun." If you look up the latitude of Barrow, Alaska, in the Pronouncing Index of *Goode's World Atlas*, you find it is listed as 71°18′. This is obviously north of 66½°, so Barrow, Alaska, has several days of continuous light in the summer.

When the North Pole leans away from the sun, as it does in the Northern Hemisphere's winter, then the area north of the Arctic Circle is in continuous darkness and the area south of the Antarctic Circle is in continuous light. Again, please remember, when the SSP strikes the Tropic of Cancer (23 1/2 degrees) the Circle of Illumination is positioned at 66 1/2 degrees—these two numbers have to add up to 90. Please review the following practice questions to make sure you understand the concepts I covered in this section.

Practice Questions:

- *At what latitude would the Tropic of Cancer be located if Earth sat in space at an angle of 30 degrees (instead of 23 1/2 degrees)? Answer is: at 30 degrees.*

- *Where would the Circle of Illumination be located if the SSP was striking 30 degrees latitude? Answer is: 60 degrees. These two numbers have to add up to 90.*

- *If the SSP is located at 20 degrees N. Lat. then at what latitude is the Circle of Illumination located? Answer is: at 70 degrees.*

- *If the Circle of Illumination is located at 90 degrees latitude then at what latitude is the SSP located? Answer is: at 0 degrees. They have to add up to 90.*

- *Old Crow, Yukon Territory, is located at about 68 degrees N. Lat., so it is positioned north of the Arctic Circle. People who live in Old Crow cannot see the sun when the SSP strikes the Tropic of Capricorn on December 21, for 68 + 23 1/2 = 91.5 degrees. A person cannot see the sun if the SSP is more than 90 degrees of latitude away from his or her position. Since the people of Old Crow cannot see the sun on December 21, on what day might they be able to see the sun when the SSP begins its migration north? Answer is: January 12. You figure this by subtracting 68 from 90, which means the sun will be on the horizon in Old Crow when the SSP is positioned at 22 degrees S. Lat. (68 + 22 = 90); next you use the analemma to determine that on January 12 the SSP is positioned at 22 degrees S. Latitude.*

Seasons

You should now be able to understand why Earth has four seasons. The seasons are caused by the four Earth–sun relationships and not by Earth's variance in distance from the sun.

The **solstices** occur when the SSP strikes a 23½° latitude line. This is the beginning of either summer or winter, depending on which hemisphere is involved. The word *solstice* means "sun standing still." Ancient observers of the setting sun noticed that it seemed to be moving either north or south, for it would set at different positions on the horizon almost every day. For six months it moved north, but then it stood still one day before reversing itself to move south. For the next six months it moved south, but then it stood still one day before reversing itself to move north. These two times during the year when the setting sun stood still on the horizon became known as the solstices. In some cultures religious or civil ceremonies were held to mark these occasions.

In the Northern Hemisphere the beginning of summer occurs on June 21 when the SSP strikes the Tropic of Cancer (23½° North Latitude). This is known as the **summer solstice**, but in the Southern Hemisphere it is the beginning of winter and is known as the winter solstice. All during the months of January, February, March, April, May, and the first three weeks of June, the SSP moves north, but on June 21 the SSP stands still on 23½° North Latitude.

On June 22 the SSP reverses and starts to move south. As the SSP moves south, it eventually reaches the Equator (on about September 23), and on that day all latitudes of the Earth have the same length of day and night. This is known as an *equinox* (equal night). In the Northern Hemisphere this is known as the *autumnal equinox* (the beginning of fall) and in the Southern Hemisphere it is known as the vernal equinox (the beginning of spring). When an equinox occurs, the Circle of Illumination connects the North Pole with the South Pole.

The SSP continues to move south during the rest of September and also during the months of October, November, and the first three weeks of December. When it reaches the Tropic of Capricorn (23½° South Latitude) on December 21, the second solstice of the calendar year occurs. This is the beginning of winter in the Northern Hemisphere, so it is known as the *winter solstice*, but in the Southern Hemisphere it is the beginning of summer, so it is known as the summer solstice.

On December 22, the SSP starts to move back north, and on about March 21 it is back on the Equator. This again causes all latitudes to have the same length of day and night, so we have another equinox. This equinox marks the beginning of spring in the Northern Hemisphere, and it is known as the *vernal equinox*, but in the Southern Hemisphere it is known as the autumnal equinox, the beginning of fall.

Insolation

The receipt of solar radiation by the earth is known as *insolation*. The amount of solar radiation received by Earth at any point is influenced by two factors: (1) the length of exposure (amount of daylight) and (2) the sun angle.

The length of daylight influences the amount of insolation because if the sun shines on an area for 20 hours, that area is likely to receive more solar radiation than an area receiving only 6 hours of sunshine. Clearly then, Barrow, Alaska, receives a lot more solar radiation on June 21, when it has 24 hours of daylight, than on December 22, when it has zero hours of daylight.

The *angle* at which the sun strikes the earth also plays a strong role in influencing the amount of solar radiation that an area receives. I like to use a flashlight to demonstrate this concept. Imagine I have a flashlight in my hand as I turn it on. The amount of light energy emitted by the flashlight is constant (assuming that you have a charged battery). It does not matter which direction I aim the flashlight—it still emits the same amount of light energy (for example, 400 units). Now imagine I hold the flashlight so that it hits a tabletop at a 90° angle. The 400 units strike the tabletop and are confined to a fairly small area seen by the human eye as an illuminated circle. In this example, the 400 units of energy might be confined to an area of 100 square centimeters—each square centimeter would be receiving four units of energy. Next, imagine I turn the flashlight so it strikes the tabletop at an angle of 30°. Now the beam of the flashlight (400 units of energy) spreads out over a much larger area, maybe 400 square centimeters. In this case each square centimeter receives only one unit of energy (Fig. 4-10).

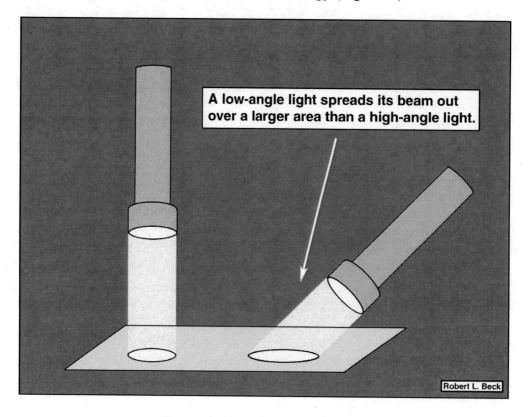

A low-angle light spreads its beam out over a larger area than a high-angle light.

Robert L. Beck

Figure 4-10. Angle of Radiation

The sun is similar to the flashlight. It emits only a certain amount of energy, so when it strikes Earth at a 90° angle (at the SSP), the sun's beam is concentrated in a small area of Earth and is therefore intensively heating that small area. On the other hand, a place on Earth receiving the sun's rays at an angle of 30° is less intensively heated. A **high sun** (or high-angle sun) occurs when the sun strikes Earth at a high angle and a **low sun** (or low-angle sun) occurs when the sun strikes Earth at a low angle. The sun striking Earth at a 90° angle is an example of a high-angle sun, and the sun striking Earth at a 30° angle is an example of a low-angle sun.

CALCULATION OF SUN ANGLES

You need to be able to calculate sun angles. To do this one must know: (1) the day of the year, (2) the latitude of the SSP, and (3) the latitude for which you are trying to determine the sun angle. For example, let us assume you are trying to calculate the sun angle for Indianapolis at noon on February 5. Now go back and fill in what you need to know: (1) day of the year = February 5, (2) the latitude of the SSP = consult analemma and determine that on February 5 the SSP is at 16° South Latitude, and (3) the latitude for which you are trying to compute the sun angle = Indianapolis (40° North Latitude, listed in *Goode's World Atlas* as 39°46′ N. that I round up to 40° N.).

To **calculate** the sun angle you next have to perform two steps. First, determine the difference in latitude between the SSP and the latitude for which you are trying to determine the sun angle, Indianapolis in this case. Indianapolis is located at 40° North Latitude, and the analemma tells us that the SSP is located at 16° South Latitude on February 5, so the difference in latitude would be 56° (40° + 16° = 56°, but note, if the two locations are in the same hemisphere you must subtract instead of add). Second, subtract the difference in latitude from 90°. In this case: 90° − 56° = 34°. This tells us at noon on February 5 the sun strikes Indianapolis at an angle of 34°. You should now be able to take any city on Earth and with the help of the analemma and *Goode's World Atlas* calculate the noon sun angle for that city on any day of the year.

The high sun in Indianapolis occurs on June 21, when the SSP strikes the Tropic of Cancer. On that day the city is 16½° in latitude away from the SSP (40° − 23½° = 16½°) so the sun angle at noon would be 73½° (90° − 16½° = 73½°). The low sun in Indianapolis occurs on December 22, when the SSP strikes the Tropic of Capricorn. On that day the city is 63½° in latitude away from the SSP (40° + 23½° = 63½°), so the sun angle at noon is 26½° (90° − 63½° = 26½°) (Fig. 4-11).

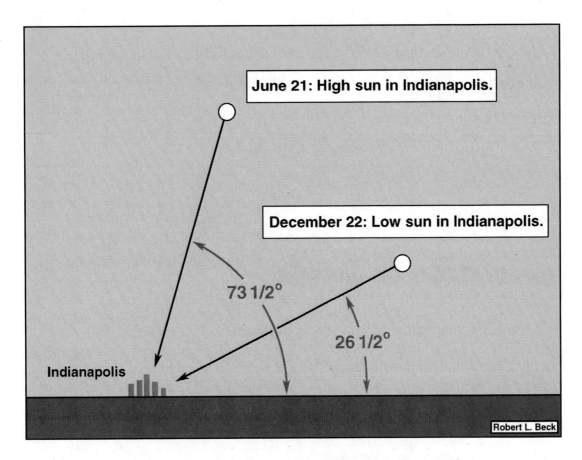

Figure 4-11. High Sun and Low Sun in Indianapolis

43

Latitude Zones

I will refer to various latitude zones as we move through the course (Fig. 4-12). The boundaries between the zones should be perceived as transitional areas rather than as well-defined lines.

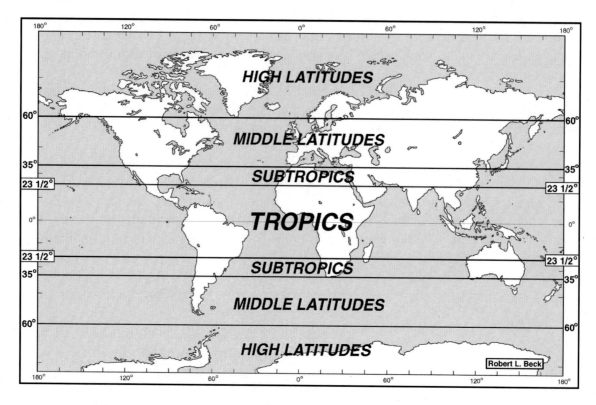

Figure 4-12. Latitude Zones

The tropical zone is Earth's largest latitude zone. It covers the area of Earth between the Tropic of Cancer and the Tropic of Capricorn, so the tropical zone is that portion of Earth receiving the SSP at least once per year. Most of the tropical zone receives the SSP twice per year, once when it moves north and a second time when it moves south. The tropical latitudes are sometimes also known as the **low latitudes**, for they have a low latitudinal number (0° to 23½°).

The subtropics are adjacent to the tropics. The subtropics are generally quite hot, but the SSP never ventures into them. Miami, for instance, is situated at 25°45′ North Latitude, so it is situated in the subtropical latitudes and not in the tropical latitudes. The subtropical latitudes extend poleward from the tropics to about 35° North and South Latitudes (Fig. 4-12).

The middle latitudes begin where the subtropics end and extend poleward to about 60° North and South Latitudes. These latitudes are generally characterized by alternating hot and cold weather—hot in the summer and cold in the winter. Indianapolis, at 40° North Latitude, is situated in the middle latitudes, as is most of the United States.

The high latitudes are located poleward of the middle latitudes in both the Northern and Southern Hemispheres. The high latitudes are cold most of the year and they are also known as the polar latitudes. The high latitudes are named for their high latitudinal numbers (60° to 90°).

Electromagnetic Spectrum

All objects that have a temperature above absolute zero (0° K) emit radiation. Your body emits radiation, your notebook paper emits radiation, your desk emits radiation, your pen emits radiation, and so on. Everything we come in contact with emits radiation. Some radiation is harmful to human health, but most of it is not. Our bodies are constantly being hit with various forms of radiation.

The *electromagnetic spectrum* classifies radiation by wavelengths. Radiation is thought to travel by waves, so the distance from one wave crest to the next is known as a *wavelength* (Fig. 4-13). Hot objects emit *shortwave radiation*, which contains the types

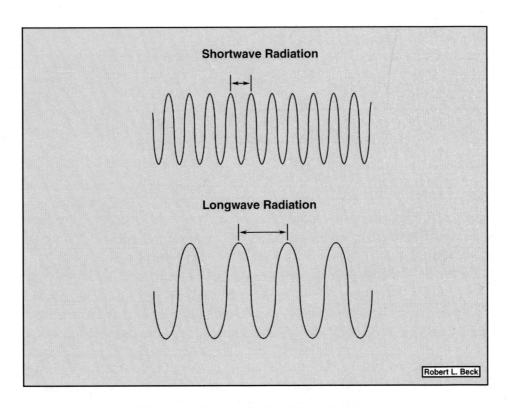

Figure 4-13. Radiation Wavelengths

of radiation harmful to human health. Cold objects emit *longwave radiation*, which is generally not harmful to human health. Figure 4-14 shows the bands of the electromagnetic spectrum arranged from longwave to shortwave.

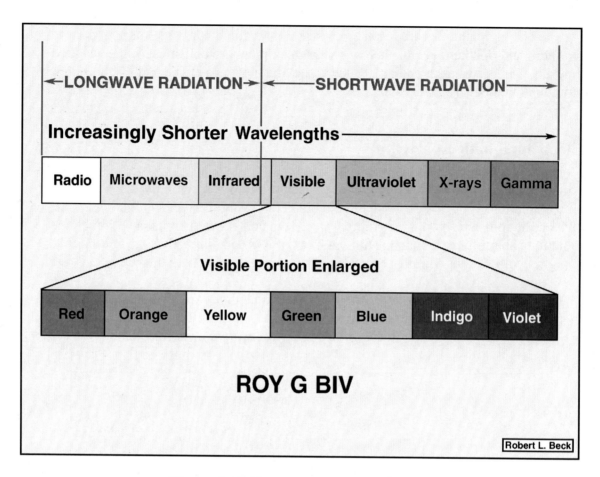

Figure 4-14. Electromagnetic Spectrum

Gamma rays are the shortest of shortwave radiation, so they are emitted by very hot objects, such as the sun. X-rays are longer than gamma rays. Ultraviolet rays are longer than x-rays. Next are visible light rays followed by infrared rays and then microwaves. Radio waves are the longest form of longwave radiation. Within the visible light portion of the spectrum, the individual colors of light are also arranged by wavelengths. Many students know these colors of light as ROY G BIV (an anagram for a fictional name of the person who inhabits that portion of the spectrum). R = red, O = orange, Y = yellow, G = green, B = blue, I = indigo, and V = violet. Red is a cooler color than green, which is a cooler color than blue.

Imagine that you build a bonfire so that the center of it is quite hot. When you look into it you might be able to see the color blue in it. If you do not add wood and slowly let the fire burn itself out, the next color you should see is green, followed by yellow, then orange, and finally red, when only coals remain. After the fire appears to go out, you then put your hand over it and are surprised to feel heat coming from it. You do not see the radiation coming from the seemingly dead fire, but you sure can feel it. You are feeling infrared radiation, the portion of the electromagnetic spectrum on the longwave side of red.

Practice Exercises:

- Draw the four seasons on a blank piece of paper. To do this, first draw the sun as a small circle near the center of the paper. Now draw Earth in four positions around the sun—directly above, directly below, straight to the left, and straight to the right. Next draw the Equator and the polar axis on the earth. Be sure to maintain parallelism of the axis as you draw it in. Place a dot on the earth where the SSP is located on each of the four Earth positions. Label the solstices and the equinoxes. Finish the drawing by labeling the four seasons.

- Compute the sun angle in Indianapolis at noon on your birthday.

- Compute the sun angle in Perth, Australia, at noon on your birthday.

- Compute where the Circle of Illumination is located on some random day of the year.

- Select a city positioned north of the Arctic Circle. Use **Goode's World Atlas** to determine its latitude. Calculate the number of days per year a person who lives in that city will not be able to see the sun.

Module 4 Objectives

You should now be able to:

- Define the *subsolar point*

- Use an *analemma* to find the latitude of the subsolar point for any day of the year

- Define the *Circle of Illumination*

- Plot, on a globe, the position of the Circle of Illumination for any day of the year

- Use the subsolar point and the Circle of Illumination to define the seasons

- Compute sun angles

- Place any point on Earth's surface identified by latitude and longitude into a latitude zone

- Arrange the bands of the *electromagnetic spectrum* in the correct sequence from longwave to shortwave

- Calculate the length of time per year a person who lives in a city north of the Arctic Circle will not be able to view the sun

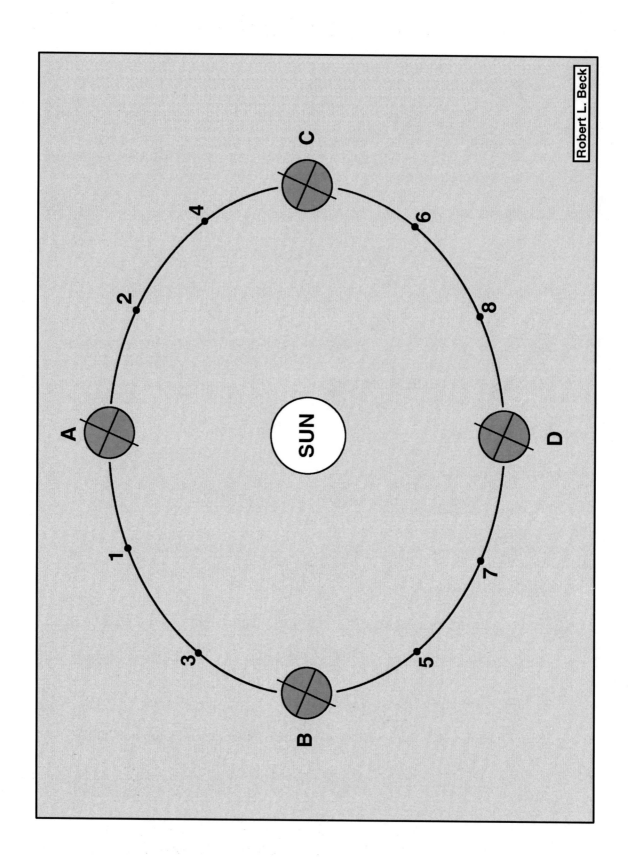

MODULE 5: ATMOSPHERE

Earth formed about 4.6 to 5.0 billion years ago. The atmosphere probably started to form at about the same time, but the atmosphere as we know it is much younger than Earth. Most gases in the atmosphere escaped from the rocks of the earth as they started to decompose during weathering processes. These gases were held to Earth by its gravitational attraction, and over time they kept accumulating to form the modern atmosphere.

Thickness of the Atmosphere

There is considerable disagreement about the thickness of the atmosphere. In this course we assume the atmosphere to be about 300 miles thick, for above that height gas molecules can migrate to outer space by escaping Earth's gravitational attraction. But 300 miles is not thick when compared to the diameter of Earth (Fig. 5-1). Three hundred miles is only about the length of the state of Indiana. As we stand on the ground and gaze up into the atmosphere, it seems really thick, but when astronauts first see Earth from space, they are shocked at how thin the atmosphere is. Viewed from space, the atmosphere appears to be a very thin layer of gas clinging to the earth. The atmosphere is thicker over the Equator than over the poles.

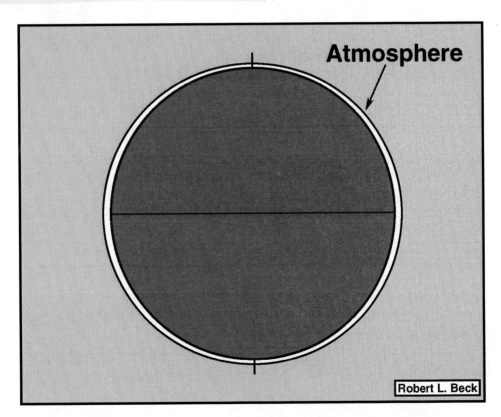

Figure 5-1. In this drawing, the thickness of the atmosphere is shown to scale with respect to the diameter of Earth.

Constituents of the Atmosphere

When people consider the atmosphere, they usually think of it as composed of gases, but the atmosphere also has an abundance of solids and liquids in it, collectively known as *particulates*. The solids in the atmosphere include solid forms of water such as ice and hail, but they also include dust particles, pollen, bacteria, viruses, volcanic ash, smoke and soot particles, organic debris, and minerals of various sorts. Some of the smaller solids can remain floating in the atmosphere for months or even years. *Cloud droplets* and *raindroplets* account for most of the liquids in the atmosphere. Cloud droplets are too lightweight to fall, so they might remain suspended in the atmosphere for a couple of days. *Gases* in the atmosphere include nitrogen (N_2), oxygen (O_2), argon (Ar), carbon dioxide (CO_2), water vapor (H_2O), methane (CH_4), ozone (O_3), and many others. By volume, nitrogen dominates as it accounts for 78% of the atmosphere. Oxygen is second at 21%. All other gases, when combined, make up only about 1% of the atmosphere's volume (Fig. 5-2).

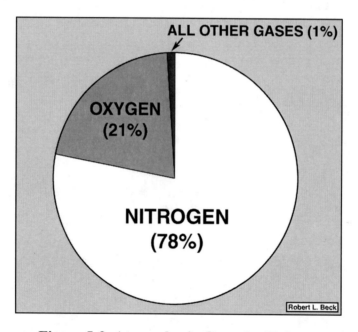

Figure 5-2. Atmospheric Gases by Volume

Earth Radiation

Earth's surface radiates energy just as any other object does that has a temperature above absolute zero ($0°K$). Compared to the sun, Earth's surface is much cooler, so it emits *longwave radiation*. Please keep in mind that solar radiation = shortwave radiation and earth radiation = longwave radiation. Earth radiation is sometimes also known as *terrestrial radiation*.

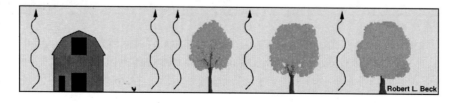

Greenhouse Effect

Incoming solar radiation has to go through the atmosphere before it can hit Earth's land–sea surface. The outer atmosphere absorbs the harmful gamma rays and x-rays the sun sends toward Earth. It also absorbs some, but not all, of the ultraviolet radiation emitted by the sun. The atmosphere, however, does **not** do a good job of absorbing infrared radiation and visible light. The atmosphere lets a lot of solar radiation strike Earth's surface from the infrared, visible, and ultraviolet portions of the electromagnetic spectrum (Fig. 5-3).

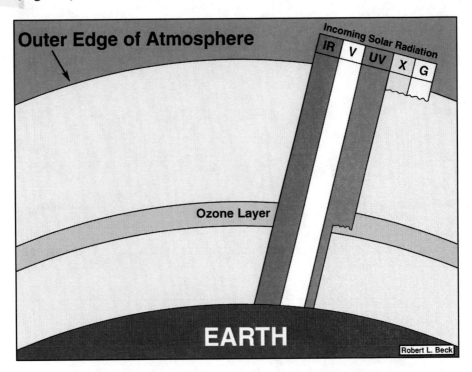

Figure 5-3. Effects of the Atmosphere on Incoming Solar Radiation

You **feel infrared** radiation when you expose your body to sunlight—you feel the heat of the sun. You **see visible** radiation when you expose your eyes to sunlight—you see the light of the sun. You **cannot see or feel ultraviolet** radiation, just as you cannot see or feel an x-ray when you go to the dentist. Ultraviolet radiation is the form of solar radiation that causes skin cancer.

Solar radiation passing through the atmosphere hits Earth's surface, both land and sea. Of course, Earth's surface starts to get warm with exposure to the sun, and in doing so it radiates heat back to space. Earth radiation is **longwave** radiation, not shortwave. The atmosphere does not let this outgoing, longwave radiation pass easily through it. In fact, the atmosphere absorbs most of this earth radiation. This concept is known as the *greenhouse effect* (Fig. 5-4).

A greenhouse lets sunlight in, but it does not easily let heat out. I have a small greenhouse, and I have found on average the temperature inside my greenhouse is about

51

30°F warmer than the outside temperature during a sunny day. If the outside air temperature is 25°F, the air temperature inside the greenhouse is likely about 55°F. Earth's atmosphere lets solar radiation in, but it does not easily let earth radiation out. The atmosphere holds onto earth heat just as the greenhouse holds the heat inside it.

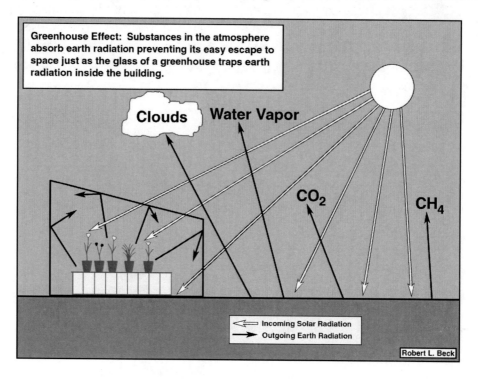

Figure 5-4. Greenhouse Effect

With the greenhouse effect comes one of the most important points about physical geography and meteorology (the study of weather)—***Earth's atmosphere is heated mainly by the earth and not by the sun!*** In other words, (1) the sun heats the earth and (2) the earth heats the atmosphere. As one moves away from the earth's surface and up into the atmosphere, he or she expects the air temperature to drop. I discuss this concept in greater detail in the module on air temperature (Module 7).

Carbon dioxide, water vapor, methane, and certain other gases are sometimes known as the ***greenhouse gases***. They are the ones that retard longwave earth radiation from passing through the atmosphere and escaping to space. These gases help the atmosphere hold onto Earth's heat. The greenhouse gases are similar to throwing another blanket on your bed during a cold night. The blanket helps trap your body heat underneath your bedcovers and prevents it from escaping to the bedroom.

Carbon is an element found in plants, animals, and the remains of plants and animals such as in fossil fuels of coal, oil, and natural gas. Carbon is also found in certain types of rocks. When humans burn trees or any of the fossil fuels, the burning process releases the carbon stored in those organic substances to the atmosphere, where it readily combines with atmospheric oxygen to form carbon dioxide, a common atmospheric gas. Humans started burning large amounts of fossil fuels with the beginning of the Industrial

Revolution about 200 years ago. This action, scientists argue, has led to an increase in the amount of carbon dioxide in the atmosphere helping the atmosphere retain heat, which is the principal cause of *global warming*.

An abundance of data and evidence supports the idea that global warming is occurring. Older adults know that our winters today are not nearly as severe as the ones experienced 80 to 100 years ago, observed global surface air temperatures steadily increased throughout the twentieth century (Fig. 5-5), and plants and animals have shifted

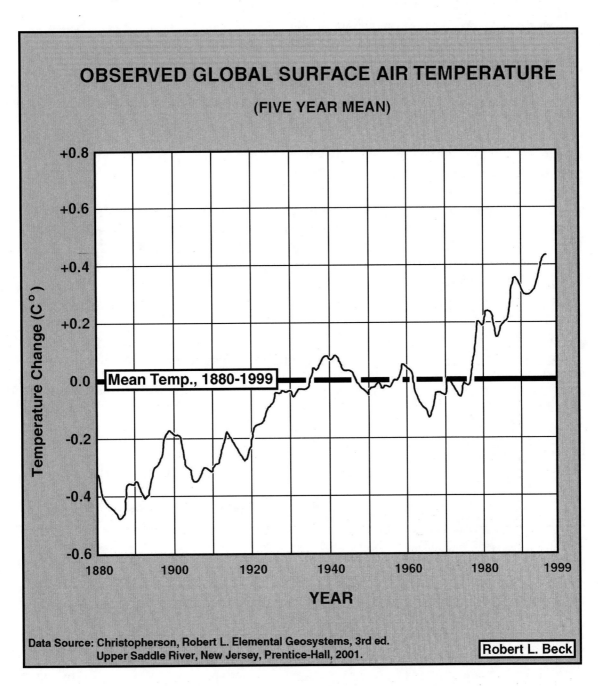

Figure 5-5. Observed Global Surface Air Temperatures

their ranges to adjust for this increased heat. See this website for evidence of global warming: http://www.climatehotmap.org/. Global warming is occurring, but how much of a role humans have played in this process is not known. Is the global warming we experience today simply the result of a natural process, or are humans mostly responsible for it? Virtually all atmospheric scientists are now convinced that humans are, indeed, largely responsible for it. Everyone must see Al Gore's movie, *An Inconvenient Truth*, to learn more about global warming and the threats to some of the world's most populated areas if the ice caps melt away entirely.

People who are concerned about global warming can do many things to help reduce it. You can drive less and walk more. You can use less energy to heat and cool your house or apartment by lowering the thermostat in the winter and raising it in the summer. In the winter this might mean you have to wear heavy clothes to keep warm, something more and more people seem reluctant to do. Many people today want to wear only T-shirts and open footwear such as sandals and flip-flops even in winter, but they also want to keep warm, so they keep their living quarters much warmer than what would be necessary if they wore proper winter clothing. Also, replacing incandescent lightbulbs with fluorescent lightbulbs reduces use of electricity.

Planting trees is another good way to reduce global warming. You already know trees help cool the atmosphere by shading the earth, but trees also reduce the amount of greenhouse gases in the atmosphere by pulling carbon dioxide out of it. I am a member of The National Arbor Day Foundation. Every year that organization gives me the opportunity to buy ten little trees for a few dollars. I plant the trees in a small garden nursery in my backyard. Little trees are easily killed by lack of water, so I make sure my nursery bed is heavily mulched, which helps retain rainwater. After one year I transplant the surviving young trees to a favorable site somewhere on or near my property or give them as gifts to friends and acquaintances. I enjoy watching how their growth progresses over the years and in doing so helps to lower the carbon content of the atmosphere.

Earth's Albedo

About 31% of solar radiation entering the outer edge of the atmosphere is reflected or scattered to space by substances on the ground or in the air. When viewed from space, Earth appears to shine. This *earthshine* is actually reflected or scattered solar radiation. The reflectivity of an object is known as its *albedo*, which is expressed as a percentage. Earth's albedo is about 31%, but individual surfaces on Earth have different albedos. For example, black surfaces (such as asphalt parking lots) have low albedos because they absorb almost all solar radiation that hits them; their albedos are often in the range of 5% to 8%. White, or light-colored, surfaces have high albedos because they are good reflectors of solar radiation. Fresh snow has albedos that range from about 80% to 95%; grass about 25% to 30%; forest around 10% to 20%; and bare soil about 8% (Fig. 5-6). Albedos of water bodies are highly variable depending on the angle of solar radiation. If the sun strikes a water body at a high-angle most of its radiation will be absorbed by the water, so the albedo will be low; however, if the sun strikes a water body at a low-angle then the water will be a good reflector—almost like a mirror. Clouds also have highly variable albedos depending on the type of cloud and the angle of solar radiation. (Fig. 5-6).

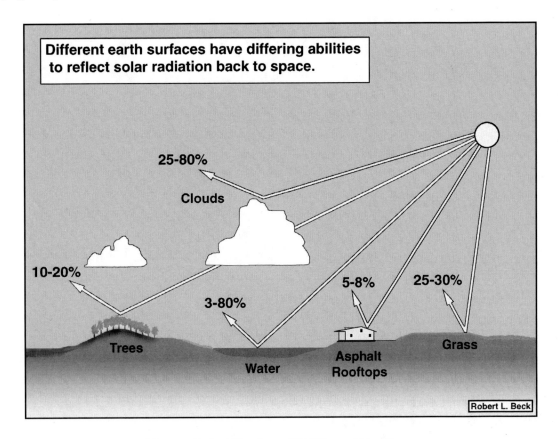

Figure 5-6. Albedos of Different Surfaces

Layers of the Atmosphere

A few schemes have been developed to classify the layers of the atmosphere. The one we use in this course is based on temperature changes as one proceeds from Earth's surface and up into the air above it.

Years ago, before the Second World War, it was thought the atmosphere consisted of only one layer, which was based on temperature changes. People reasoned the atmosphere was hot near Earth's surface and that it kept getting colder, and colder, and colder with increasing distance from the source of atmospheric heat, which is the surface of the earth. The invention of sophisticated rockets changed this belief, for data collected from weather instruments attached to the rockets showed that in certain places atmospheric air temperatures actually increased with increasing elevation.

The *troposphere* is the layer of the atmosphere nearest Earth's surface and the one in which we live. It is named for the Greek word *tropos*, which means "turn," for in this layer the air is constantly turning over vertically and moving about horizontally. The troposphere contains most of the atmosphere's mass and almost all its water vapor and dust particles. Virtually all our weather events occur in the troposphere, so when you look up and see a cloud, even the very highest one, it is located in the troposphere (Fig. 5-7).

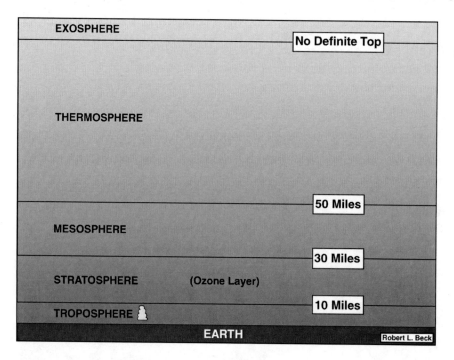

Figure 5-7. Average Thickness of the Atmospheric Layers

The troposphere is **not** evenly thick over Earth's surface; it is thinner over the poles and thicker over the Equator. Over the poles, its thickness is only about 5 miles (8 km), whereas over the Equator it is about 11 miles (18 km) (Fig. 5-8). What causes this variation in thickness? First, gravity is stronger over the poles, so it has a tendency to pull the atmosphere closer to Earth's surface. Second, the rotational velocity is greater at the Equator. This causes the centrifugal force of rotation to be greater there than at the poles, so air is thrown out to a greater degree at the Equator than at the poles. Third, the SSP is usually hovering about the Equator; the high sun angle at this latitude produces hot surfaces, and they in turn heat the air above those surfaces causing it to rise. Fourth, the poles are cold. The cold surfaces chill the air above them causing it to become heavy and desirous of sinking toward Earth's surface.

The defining characteristic of the troposphere is that, on average, air temperature decreases with increasing elevation. In most instances the higher one rises in the troposphere the colder the air becomes. This expected change of air temperature with increasing elevation is known as the ***normal lapse rate***, which says for every one kilometer increase in elevation air temperature drops 6.5°C (Fig. 5-9). The normal lapse rate is a worldwide average, for the actual rate of air temperature change above any specific point on Earth's surface probably will not be 6.5°C.

The ***stratosphere*** lies just above the troposphere (Fig. 5-7), and in it one finds layers of gases separated by weight. The Latin word *stratum* implies a layered condition.

There is little vertical mixing of air in the stratosphere, so air movements are primarily horizontal. Few aircraft fly in the stratosphere, but one that did was the Concorde, the SST (supersonic transport) jointly built by Great Britain and France. People flying in the stratosphere have smooth rides, for they experience little vertical air turbulence.

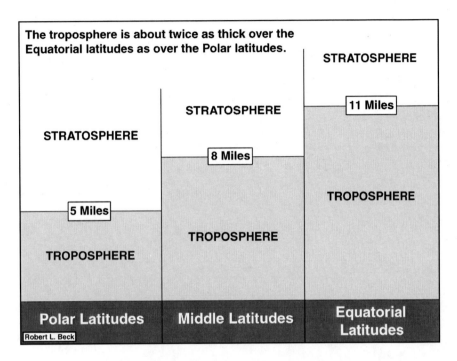

Figure 5-8. Thickness of the Troposphere

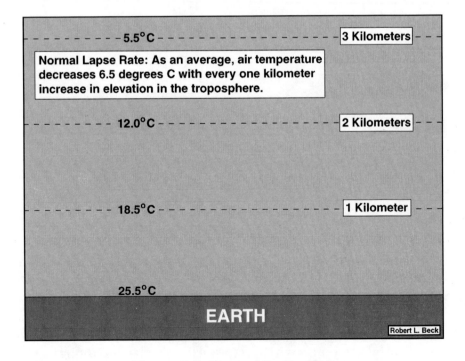

Figure 5-9. Normal Lapse Rate

57

One of the distinctive stratospheric layers is the ***ozone layer.*** Ozone (O_3) is a gas that absorbs ultraviolet radiation, so it helps protect humans from this harmful radiation emitted by the sun. The absorption of solar radiation by ozone warms the stratosphere and as a result air temperatures actually increase as one moves up into it from the troposphere.

Many scientists now believe the ozone layer is thinning because of human actions. Chlorofluorocarbons (CFCs) released to the atmosphere from aerosol sprays and refrigerants migrate to the stratosphere from Earth's surface. Once there, when subjected to solar radiation, CFCs break down the ozone molecules causing the layer to thin (Fig. 5-10). Humans in the future might have to live in an environment subjected to much

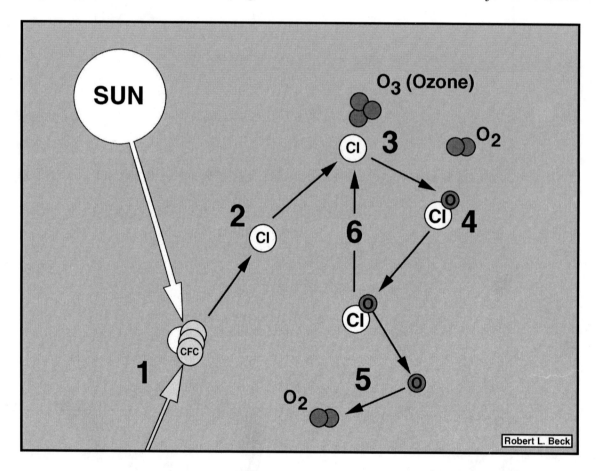

Figure 5-10. The destruction of stratospheric ozone occurs in a sequence of steps as follows: (1) CFCs enter the ozone layer, (2) ultraviolet light from the sun hits a CFC molecule and breaks off a chlorine atom, (3) the chlorine atom reacts with an ozone molecule, pulling an oxygen atom from it, (4) a chlorine monoxide molecule is formed when the chlorine atom and the oxygen atom join, (5) an oxygen atom floating in the atmosphere pulls the oxygen atom off a chlorine monoxide molecule, which produces an atmospheric oxygen molecule (O2), (6) the chlorine atom left floating in the atmosphere reacts with another ozone molecule to further break down the ozone content of the stratosphere.

larger doses of ultraviolet radiation than what we now experience. Holes in the ozone layer have been discovered in Earth's polar regions (Fig. 5-11).

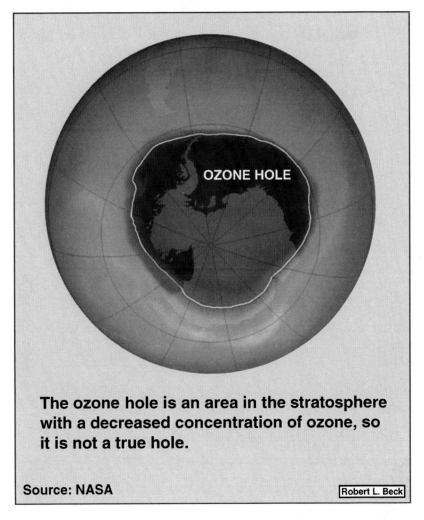

OZONE HOLE

The ozone hole is an area in the stratosphere with a decreased concentration of ozone, so it is not a true hole.

Source: NASA

Robert L. Beck

Figure 5-11. Antarctic Ozone Hole

The *mesosphere* is the layer above the stratosphere (Fig. 5-7). In it, temperatures again decrease with increasing elevation. The Greek word *meso* means middle. The mesosphere is the third of five layers of the atmosphere.

The fourth atmospheric layer is the *thermosphere*, another layer in which temperatures rise with increasing elevation. Gamma rays and x-rays are absorbed by the atmospheric gases in this layer. The Greek word *therm* means "heat."

The outer layer of the atmosphere is the *exosphere*, which merges into interplanetary space. The normal concept of temperature does not apply in this layer, for the air molecules are far apart, and some of them can extend thousands of miles into space. Some physical geographers do not include the exosphere as one of the atmospheric layers. They put the outer edge of the atmosphere at the top of the thermosphere.

Between the bottom three layers of the atmosphere (troposphere, stratosphere, and mesosphere) are zones in which the air temperature remains fairly constant with increasing elevation. These zones are known as *pauses*. The *tropopause* lies between the troposphere and the stratosphere, the *stratopause* lies between the stratosphere and the mesosphere, and the *mesopause* lies between the mesosphere and the thermosphere (Fig. 5-12).

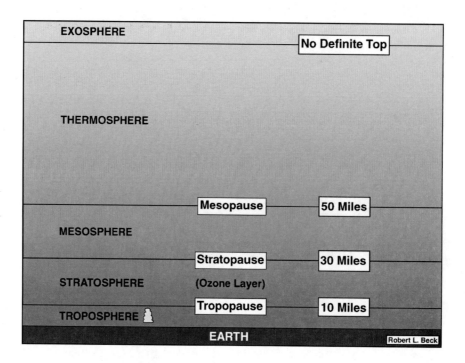

Figure 5-12. Atmospheric Pauses

Module 5 Objectives

You should now be able to:

- List the types of substances found in the atmosphere

- Compare and contrast *earth radiation* with *solar radiation*

- Describe the *greenhouse effect* and explain why it occurs

- Identify albedo differences between various earth surfaces

- List some reasons why scientists believe that global warming is occurring

- Compare and contrast the different layers of the atmosphere

- List four actions a person can take to reduce global warming

60

MODULE 6: HEAT

Heat is a form of energy produced by the random motions of atoms and molecules of substances. Hot substances have more vigorous motions than cold substances. *Temperature* is a measure of heat, and there are three common temperature scales for doing so—*Fahrenheit, Celsius,* and *Kelvin* (Fig. 6-1). Many people mistakenly use the words *heat* and *temperature* as if they mean the same thing, but they are **not** synonymous—heat is a form of energy, and temperature is a measure of heat.

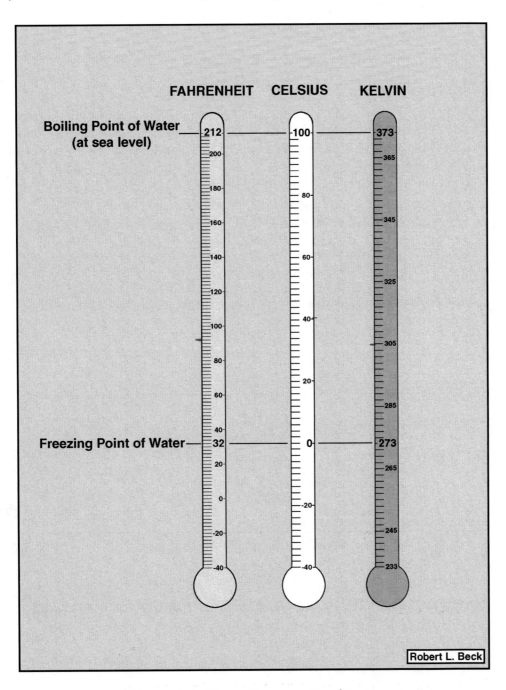

Figure 6-1. Three Temperature Scales

Types of Heat

In this course we consider three types of heat. **Sensible heat** is the heat we feel with our senses. It is the heat measured with a thermometer. When we say, "The day is hot," we are talking about sensible heat. **Latent heat** cannot be measured directly. It is energy stored within atoms and molecules as rapid motions of particles. The word *latent* is from Latin and it means "lying hidden." **Specific heat** is the amount of heat (or energy) needed to raise 1 gram of a substance 1°C. If we take 1 gram of land and 1 gram of water, we find it takes more heat to raise the gram of water 1°C than it does to raise the gram of land 1°C. Water has a higher specific heat than land.

Water Conversions

Water is one of the few substances on Earth existing naturally in three states—solid, liquid, and gas. Changing the state of water either releases energy to the environment or takes energy out of the environment (Fig. 6-2). For example, changing ice into liquid water requires heat. The heat that performs this change of state (sensible heat) comes from the environment, and it goes into the liquid water as rapid motions within molecules. According to the **Law of Conservation of Energy**, also known as the

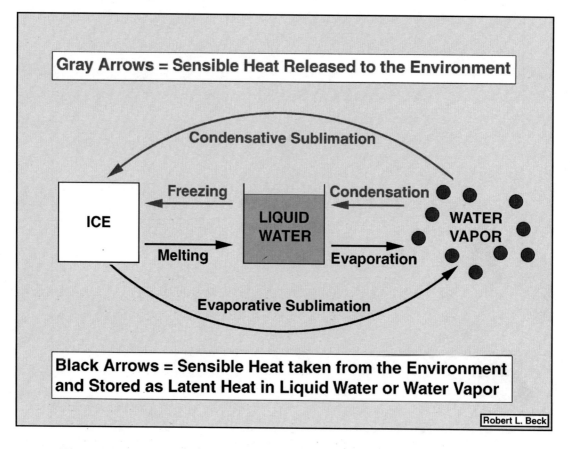

Figure 6-2. Water Conversions and the Storage and Release of Heat

First Energy Law, heat cannot be created or destroyed, only changed in form. The sensible heat that converts ice into liquid water is stored in the liquid water as latent heat. Just as sensible heat is required to turn ice into liquid water; sensible heat is also required to convert liquid water into water vapor. Sensible heat is taken from the environment, which might be the atmospheric environment, to turn the liquid water into water vapor, and that heat is stored in the water vapor as latent heat.

The water conversion process also works in reverse to release heat back into the environment. Converting water vapor to liquid water releases latent heat, so it goes back into the environment as sensible heat. Changing liquid water into ice also releases latent heat (stored in the liquid water), so it too goes back into the environment as sensible heat (Fig. 6-2).

Turning ice into liquid water is known as *melting*; turning liquid water into water vapor is known as *evaporation*; and turning ice directly into water vapor (bypassing the liquid state) is known as *sublimation*. All of these processes are **cooling processes**—they take energy from the environment and store it as latent heat in a liquid or gas. You feel the process when you step out of the shower before drying off. Beads of water cover your body, and they start to evaporate almost immediately after you turn off the shower. Your body feels cool because evaporation occurs. The same process is used to chill wine in wine skins and water in water bags. With both the wine and water examples, some of the liquid permeates the skin or bag and is exposed to the atmosphere. The droplets then start to evaporate, thereby cooling the remainder of the liquid in the skin or bag. Ice works the same way. Some people like to put ice in a glass of tea; as the ice melts it chills the tea.

Heating processes occur when water is converted in the other direction. Water vapor turns back into liquid water through a process known as *condensation*; liquid water turns back into ice through a process known as *freezing*; and water vapor can turn directly back into ice (once more bypassing the liquid state) in a process again known as *sublimation*. When these actions occur, sensible heat is released to the environment. Freezing is a heating process, for if you have ever touched a freezer with your hand after having put a large number of containers of water in it you know it feels warm. The freezer is converting the water in those containers back into a solid state thus releasing sensible heat; the freezer is simply discharging the sensible heat back into the environment.

·Condensation is an especially important process in redistributing global energy. Consider all the warm water in the Gulf of Mexico during the summer. The Tropic of Cancer passes through the Gulf of Mexico, so the SSP also goes through it in June and July. A lot of evaporation occurs during this period. As the water evaporates it is loaded with tropical energy stored in the water vapor as latent heat. When this energy-laden water vapor is drawn into Indiana by a midlatitude cyclone (which I discuss in a later module), it condenses as it hits a weather front. This releases sensible heat to Indiana originally stored as latent heat over the Gulf of Mexico (Fig. 6-3). Any time liquid water or water vapor is moved around the globe by ocean currents or air masses, huge amounts of energy are transferred. Imagine a person carrying a glass of water in your house from one room to another. Do you realize that person carried not only water to another room but also energy to another room? When I teach this course in the classroom, I literally carry a small amount of water in a cup or bottle from the classroom and out into the hallway to hammer home the point that liquid water has heat in it. This little demonstration so impressed one older student that she told me a couple of months later she would never, in all her life, forget that liquid water has heat in it.

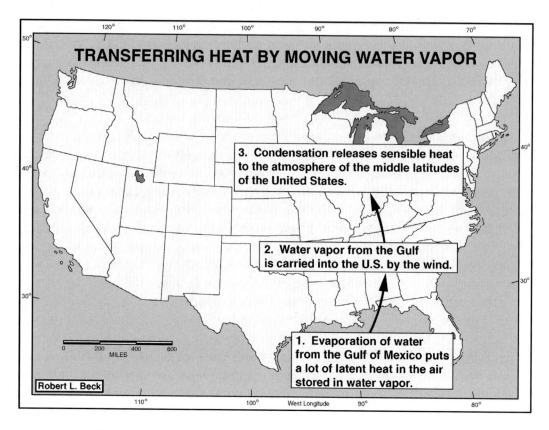

Figure 6-3. Transferring Heat by Moving Water Vapor

Geothermal furnaces and heat pumps take advantage of the ability of water to transfer heat. My wife and I installed a geothermal furnace in our house in 2008 to lower our heating bills. Tubes filled with water and antifreeze are buried in our front yard five feet underground (Fig. 20-23, p. 264). Water is constantly circulating in the tubes, which are connected to our geothermal furnace. During the winter, the water in the tubes absorbs heat from the ground and is transferred into the house through the use of a little pump. Heat is extracted from the tubes by the furnace, which sends it into our rooms through heating ducts. During the summer the furnace works in reverse. Heat from our rooms is transferred to our water heater (through the furnace) and cool water is brought into the house via the underground tubes, which our furnace converts into cool air. We never have to turn on a furnace or an air conditioner—the geothermal furnace constantly monitors and regulates the temperature of our house. In the winter of 2010–2011 we saved about $1,000 by having a geothermal furnace, instead of a furnace consuming costly heating oil. Geothermal furnaces, however, are very expensive. It will take many years to recoup our investment, but I was really tired of seeing the oil truck back up to our house knowing a hefty bill would be handed to me in a few minutes for the 220 gallons just pumped.

Latitudinal Differences in Heat

Earth experiences a net annual *surplus of heat* from the Equator to about 38° North Latitude and from the Equator to about 38° South Latitude. More incoming shortwave radiation is received in these latitudes than what is lost to space as outgoing longwave radiation. High sun angles are mostly responsible for this surplus heat (Fig. 6-4).

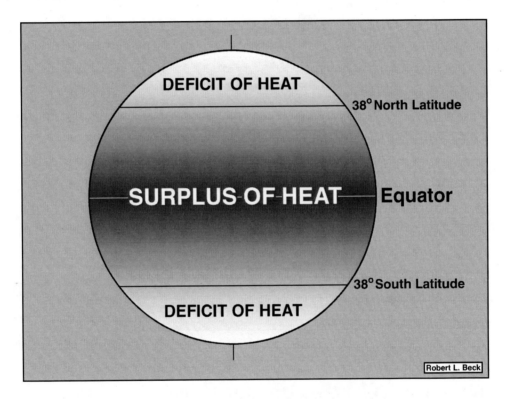

Figure 6-4. Latitudinal Differences in Heat

Earth experiences a net annual *deficit of heat* from about 38° North Latitude to the North Pole and from about 38° South Latitude to the South Pole. More outgoing longwave radiation is lost to space in these latitudes than what is received as incoming shortwave radiation. Low sun angles are mostly responsible for this deficit of heat (Fig. 6-4).

Water is a key element in redistributing this global imbalance of heat. Ocean currents move warm water poleward, and they also move cold water equatorward. Air masses move water vapor (and the heat in it) from the tropical regions to the midlatitude and polar regions, where it condenses releasing the heat of the tropics over, for example, central Indiana. Without water the tropics would probably be much hotter than they are and the poles would be much colder. We need water to balance out our latitudinal differences in heat.

Heat Transfer Processes

Heat is transferred in more than one way. **_Radiation_** is the transfer of heat by the movement of waves. Waves are classified by their wavelengths, and they are shown as bands on the electromagnetic spectrum. Solar radiation and earth radiation transfer heat by the movement of waves (Fig. 6-5).

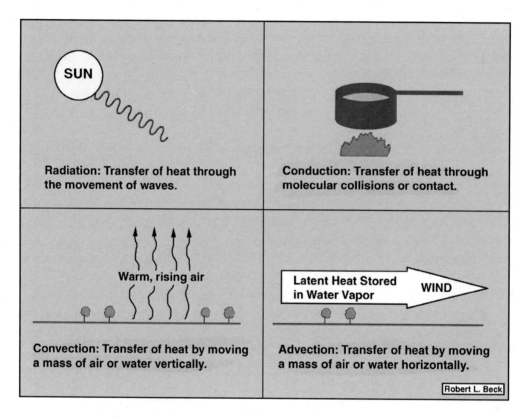

Figure 6-5. Heat Transfer Processes

Conduction is the transfer of heat by molecular collisions. A hot molecule collides with a cold molecule and in doing so transfers some of its heat. Air is a poor conductor, for air molecules are widely spaced. About the only place in the atmosphere where conduction is important occurs at the line-of-contact with Earth's surface. This basal layer of the atmosphere is either heated or cooled by conduction, depending on the temperature of the earth.

The transfer of heat by the movement of a mass is known as **_convection_**. In physical geography we are most concerned with the movement of air masses and water masses. Convection is a major process in redistributing global imbalances of heat. As convection occurs, water vapor and liquid water are moved around the globe. Technically, convection can occur in any direction, but a physical geographer who uses that word is specifically referring to the **upward** movement of a mass, usually a volume of air. **_Advection_** is the term used to describe the **horizontal** movement of a mass. Advection, in effect, is horizontal convection. Advection in the atmosphere is more

66

commonly known as the wind. When the wind blows, water vapor is transferred latitudinally over Earth's surface, resulting in the transfer of heat.

Module 6 Objectives

You should now be able to:

- List the three types of temperature scales for measuring heat

- Describe the difference between *temperature* and *heat*

- Compare and contrast three types of heat

- Briefly discuss the Law of Conservation of Energy

- Describe what happens to heat when water is changed from one form to another

- Describe how energy is moved around Earth and explain how water is involved

- List four heat transfer processes and describe the differences between them

Bald eagle perched near its nest in Putnam County, Indiana.
(Robert L. Beck photo, 2007)

SOUTH AMERICA

0   300   600
MILES

West Longitude

Robert L. Beck

68

MODULE 7: AIR TEMPERATURE

Modules 7, 8, 9, 10, and 11 focus on the four weather elements, which should be studied in a specific order. If you ever teach physical geography or meteorology, always study weather by beginning with *air temperature*, for differences in air temperature produce differences in *air pressure*, which generate *winds*, resulting in the movement of water vapor, ultimately producing *precipitation*. Of course, differences in air temperature are mostly caused by Earth–sun relationships, so that is why I covered that topic early in the course.

Mean Daily Temperature

Mean daily temperature (MDT) is the standard building block for compiling mean temperatures for longer periods of time such as mean monthly temperature and mean yearly temperature. You need to be able to compute MDT, for I have at least one exam question on it. MDT is easy to compute. All you have to do is take the maximum temperature of the day, add to it the minimum temperature of the day, and divide by 2. The given formula is:

Maximum Temperature + Minimum Temperature / 2 = MDT

For example, let us assume for a certain 24-hour period Indianapolis had a high temperature of 60° and a low temperature of 44°. The MDT for Indianapolis on that day would therefore be 52° (60 + 44 / 2 = 52).

Thermometers that record both the daily high temperature and the daily low temperature have long been standard weather instruments. These thermometers are known as maximum/minimum thermometers. Inexpensive ones can be purchased in many hardware stores. I have one hanging in my greenhouse, but in the winter I use it in my chicken house to see how well my heat lamps are performing.

Daily Cycle of Air Temperature

Air temperature reflects a balance between incoming, shortwave solar radiation and outgoing, longwave earth radiation—the sun sends energy in and the earth sends energy out. This balance can be seen in the daily cycle of air temperature for virtually any place on Earth.

Let us assume we are studying a midlatitude city during clear weather at the time of equinox. Remember at that time all places on Earth have the same length of day and night, about 12 hours of each. At equinox the sun rises at 6 AM, will reach its zenith at

12 noon, and sets at 6 PM (black line on Fig. 7-1). The solar radiation curve (black line) represents incoming energy, but the atmosphere is mainly heated by outgoing earth radiation (gray line).

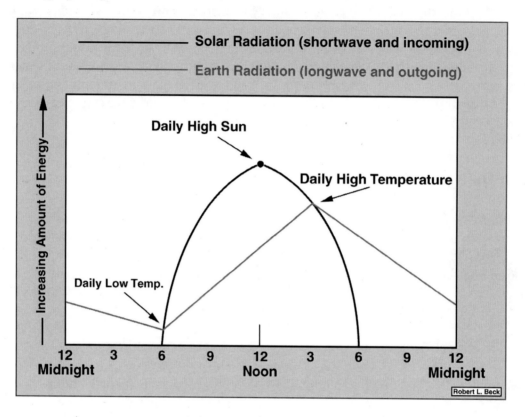

Figure 7-1. Daily Cycle of Air Temperature

The **daily low temperature** usually occurs about 10 to 15 minutes **after** sunrise and is shown on the graph where the black line intersects the gray line shortly after 6 AM (Fig. 7-1). At daybreak, the sun is on the horizon, so it strikes the ground at a very low angle; Earth continues to lose more heat to space than what it receives from the sun during this 10- to 15-minute period . . . air temperature continues to fall. By about 6:15 AM the sun reaches a high enough angle to send to Earth the same amount of energy as Earth loses to space. The daily low temperature occurs at a time when incoming solar radiation equals outgoing earth radiation.

All during the morning hours, from 6 AM to 12 noon, the sun rises higher in the sky. The angle at which it strikes our city continues to increase. The earth gets warmer and warmer with each passing hour, so the earth radiation curve starts a gradual upward climb (Fig. 7-1). At 1 PM the sun begins its daily descent, and in a few hours it sets. During the initial few hours of this descent (from 12 noon to about 3 to 4 PM) the sun sends more energy to Earth than what Earth loses to space, so the earth radiation curve continues to rise, even though the sun angle is diminishing.

The **daily high temperature** is reached at about 3 to 4 PM when the sun is again sending the same amount of energy to Earth as what Earth is losing to space (Fig. 7-1).

70

The daily high temperature occurs when incoming solar radiation equals outgoing earth radiation. There is about a 3- to 4-hour lag between daily high sun and daily high temperature. The daily high temperature does not occur when the sun is highest in the sky, for again *the atmosphere is heated mainly by the earth and not by the sun!*

The temperature of the atmosphere starts to fall in the late afternoon, and it continues to do so after the sun sets at 6 PM. All during the nighttime hours the earth sends smaller and smaller amounts of radiation to the atmosphere, so the air temperature falls and falls and falls until it bottoms out a few minutes after sunrise of the next day.

My preceding example assumes a clear sky. Cloudy weather has a delaying effect on the daily lows and daily highs. Clouds prevent the sun from quickly warming the earth, so the daily low temperature might be an hour or two after sunrise. Clouds also hold onto earth radiation causing the daily high temperature to occur much later in the afternoon.

Annual Cycle of Air Temperature

The annual cycle of air temperature is similar to the daily cycle in that it, too, has a time lag between high sun and high temperature. In the annual case, however, there is about a 30- to 40-day lag. I live in Greencastle, Indiana, where, as a long-term average, July 20 is the hottest day of the year, even though the high sun occurs on June 21, the summer solstice. June 2012 was an extremely hot month relative to most Junes, and I remember one year in the mid-1990s that June was hotter than July in central Indiana. We had a rainy July that year with an accompanying cloud cover, which reflected a lot of solar radiation back to space, thus lowering the mean July temperature. August is also a hot month in Indiana, but usually not as hot as July. Exceptions do occur, for a heat wave hit Indiana in August 2007 making it hotter than July 2007. The longest heat wave on record in central Indiana (of daily high temperatures of 90°F or more) occurred in 2011. The heat wave ran 23 days from July 17–August 8; it beat the old record of 19 days set in the Dust Bowl year of 1936.

The coldest month of the year in central Indiana and the United States is usually January, not December when the winter solstice occurs. In Greencastle, the coldest day of the year, again as a long-term average, is January 19. Occasionally, the month of February is colder than January. This happened in 2007, when Earth had the warmest January on record. Daily low temperatures ranging from 20°F to zero or below, a lingering snow cover produced by a major snowstorm on February 13, and cold blasts of Arctic air made February colder than January. The first crocus to bloom in my yard usually occurs on about February 20, but in 2007 the first crocus did not bloom until March 5, one day after the arrival of the first robin on March 4. Fourteen inches of February snow and bitterly cold air delayed the arrival of the late winter colors of purple, white, and yellow.

January and July are the coldest and hottest months of the year, respectively, throughout most of North America. World temperature maps, such as those shown in

Goode's World Atlas, usually show the January and July patterns of temperature because those months represent temperature extremes.

Temperature Singularities

Sudden jumps or drops of air temperature occurring seasonally over many years are known as *temperature singularities*. Many of these temperature singularities are named, and they are most closely associated with certain areas of Earth. **Indian Summer** is a temperature singularity that occurs when warm temperatures arrive in late October and early November in the eastern United States. Frost in western and central Europe in May is known as an **Ice Saint**. In New England, warm temperatures often affect the region sometime between January 20 and January 23. This brief warm spell is known as the **January Thaw**.

The causes of temperature singularities are not known. It is presumed the controls of weather and the influences of land, water, sun angles, and topography influence the same place more often than not year after year.

Normal Condition of the Atmosphere

In the troposphere, as an average, air temperatures decrease at a rate of 6.5°C per 1 kilometer increase in elevation. This rate is known as the **normal lapse rate** (or *average lapse rate*). If the temperature near Earth's surface is 25°C, then according to the normal lapse rate, the temperature 1 kilometer up is 18.5°C, and at 2 kilometers the temperature will be 12.0°C (Fig. 7-2). The normal lapse rate is an average, so it is an **expected** value based on many observations of temperature changes in the troposphere.

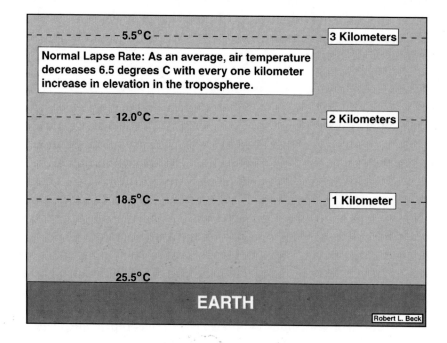

Figure 7-2. Normal Lapse Rate

The actual change in temperature with increasing elevation is known as the **lapse rate** (or *environmental lapse rate*), and it might be more or less than 6.5°C. For example, one day the lapse rate might be 3.9° per kilometer and on another day it might be 7.8° per kilometer (Fig. 7-3). The lapse rate, then, is the **observed** value of temperature change. To repeat, the normal lapse rate is what we expect, but the lapse rate is what we observe. Many factors contribute to this variance between the expected lapse rate and the observed lapse rate. Among them are upper-level winds, snow cover, clouds, and atmospheric disturbances.

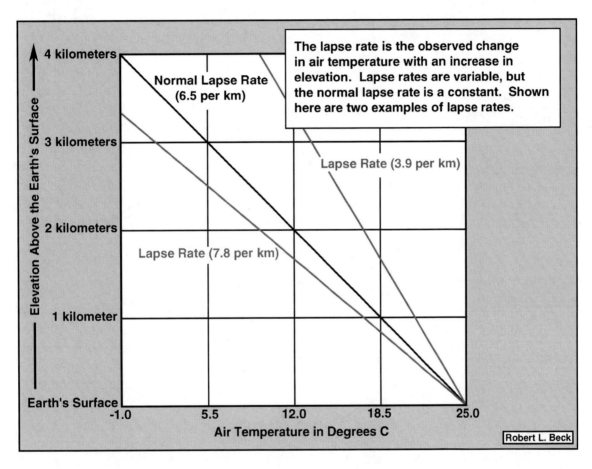

Figure 7-3. Lapse Rate

Temperature Inversions

One expects the temperature of the atmosphere to be highest near Earth's surface, for as you know, **the atmosphere is heated mainly by the earth and not by the sun.** The normal condition of the atmosphere has hot or warm temperatures near Earth's surface and cool or cold temperatures farther up (Fig. 7-4). Occasionally, however, this normal temperature pattern is reversed so that cool or cold temperatures are found near Earth's surface and hot or warm temperatures farther up (Fig. 7-5). This is an inverted (turned around) condition and is known as a **temperature inversion**.

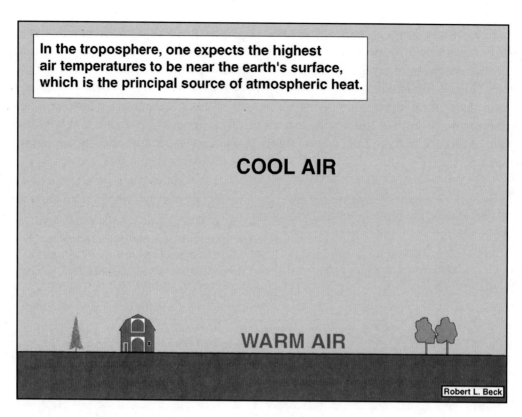

Figure 7-4. Normal Condition of the Atmosphere

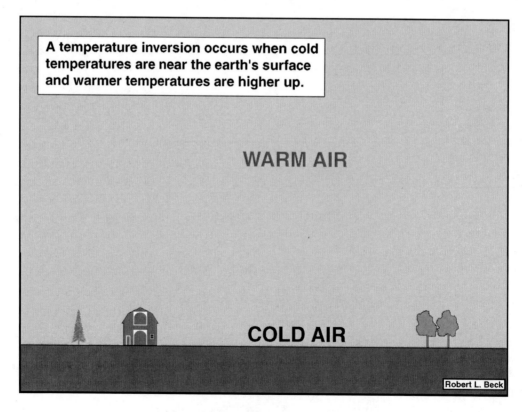

Figure 7-5. Temperature Inversion

There are two main types of temperature inversions—surface inversions and upper-level inversions. A *surface inversion* forms when the base of the atmosphere becomes cooler than the air above it. Surface inversions typically form during winter nights, especially when the sky is clear, the air is dry and calm, and there is a snow cover. Winter nights are long, so the earth loses a lot of heat to space, which chills the surface through a process known as *radiation cooling*. Dry air has a lack of water vapor in it, a greenhouse gas that holds heat. A clear sky enables earth heat to escape to space much more easily than what would be the case under a cloudy sky. Calm air helps concentrate cold air at the basal layer of the atmosphere instead of being mixed with warm air above, as windy conditions would do. A snow cover cools the air with which it comes in contact.

Surface inversions retard the development of rain-bearing clouds, for the cold air at the base of the atmosphere does not want to rise. Cold air is dense and heavy when compared to warm air. It is commonly said that "warm air rises." When warm air is positioned above cold air, as it is in a temperature inversion, this produces a highly *stable atmosphere*, for both the warm air and the cold air want to remain where they are.

One can see how far these inversion layers extend upward if you drive into Indianapolis, Chicago, or many other large American cities during a winter morning. The previous night, as the inversion formed, pollutants entered the atmosphere from power plants, furnaces, automobiles, and other sources. These pollutants, now in the cold air at the base of the atmosphere, continue to remain there after sunrise, for the cold air is not going to rise and disperse the pollutants downwind. A brown haze often marks the upper boundary of the surface inversion. Above the boundary the air is clear, but below it the air is hazy. Surface inversions usually extend upward a few hundred feet above the earth's surface (Fig. 7-6).

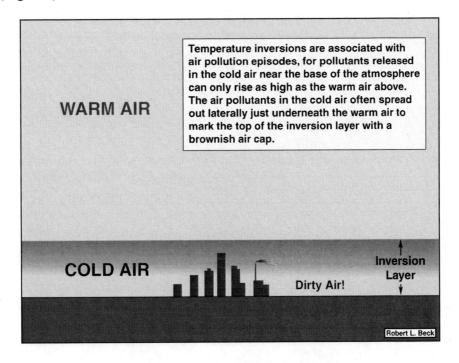

Figure 7-6. Surface Inversion

Many modern power plants have smokestacks that are about 1,000 feet tall. They were built that way so their emissions can be discharged into the atmosphere above surface inversions (Fig. 7-7). These emissions are then dispersed downwind. Old power plants often had smokestacks that were only about 200 feet tall. Emissions discharged from those smokestacks during a temperature inversion simply hung around the local environment, sometimes producing a deadly air pollution episode.

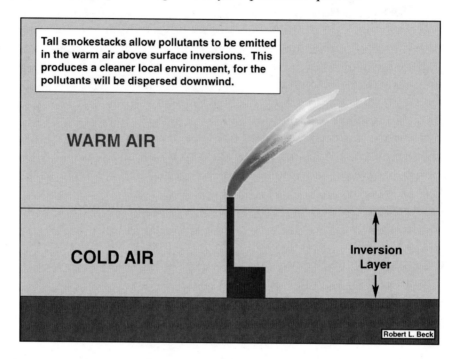

Figure 7-7. Smokestacks and Surface Inversions

A surface inversion forms when surface air becomes cold, but an ***upper-level inversion*** forms when upper-level air becomes warm. The two types of inversions thus have different formation processes.

Subsiding air (air sinking toward Earth's surface) in a high pressure cell sometimes forms an upper-level inversion. The classic place in the United States where this occurs is Los Angeles, California. Every summer the California High migrates northward (Fig. 7-8), and its eastern edge settles over the west coast of California and Oregon. Subsiding air in that high pressure cell is heated as it descends, for (1) it comes under greater air pressure as it descends and (2) it gets closer to the source of atmospheric heat, Earth's surface. Sometimes the descending air is heated to the point where it is warmer than the colder air beneath it, thus producing an upper-level inversion at about 5,000 feet (Fig. 7-9). Upper-level inversions occasionally form over Indianapolis in the summer, usually August, when an anticyclone (high pressure cell) is positioned over the city for several days.

The Los Angeles-area mountains help trap the pollutants beneath the inversion layer. One of the best places to breathe clean air in Los Angeles is high in the mountains surrounding the city. This inversion layer has formed virtually every summer for

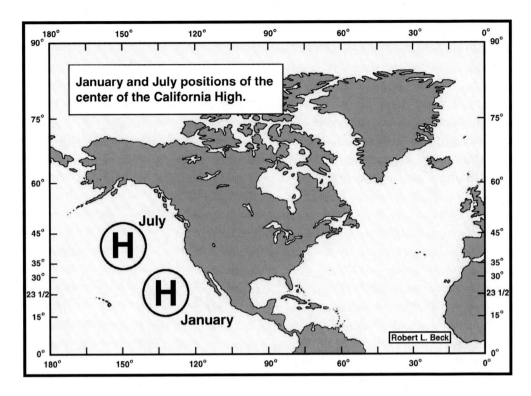

Figure 7-8. Migration of the California High

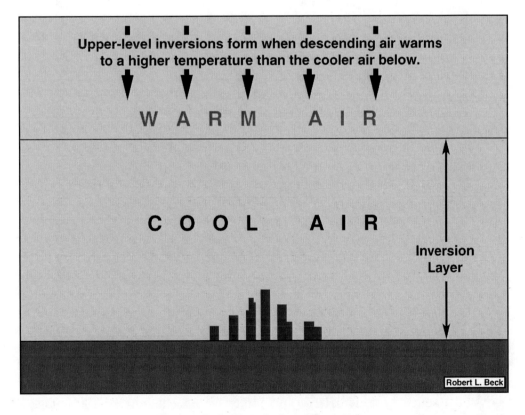

Figure 7-9. Upper-level Inversion

thousands of years. American Indians called the Los Angeles basin the "Bay of Smokes," for they observed this meteorological condition years before American or European settlers arrived.

Both surface inversions and upper-level inversions are associated with air pollution episodes, for both types of inversions produce stable atmospheres in which air wants to remain in place with the pollutants trapped in it. The lack of vertical mixing between the cool surface air and the warm upper air is the cause of the problem. Surface inversions usually form in the winter, but upper-level inversions usually form in the summer.

Air Drainage

In hilly areas at night, cold air frequently settles to the bottoms of valleys or depressions in the earth's land surface. This process is known as *air drainage* (Fig. 7-10). The topographic conditions of southern Indiana make this area of the state much more susceptible to air drainage than central Indiana, where the land is flatter. The first fall frosts and the last spring frosts in Indiana typically occur in bottomlands.

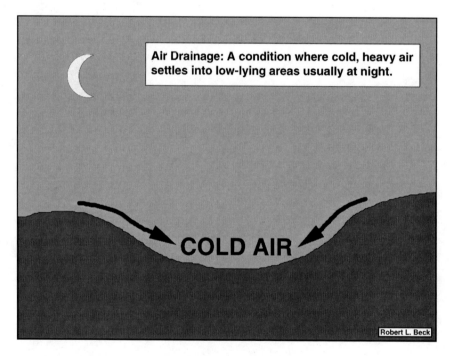

Figure 7-10. Air Drainage

Fruit trees and other temperature-sensitive crops should be planted on hilltops or on hillslopes in the midwestern and southern United States. I once had a student in class whose father owned and operated an apple orchard in Missouri, near the Missouri River. I asked this student one day if his father's apple trees were located in the bottomlands along the river. He said, "Oh no, they wouldn't survive there. They are planted on the hillsides facing the river." In Florida, an elevational difference of just 20 feet between the top of a hill and the lowlands adjacent to it was enough to produce significant differences as to whether or not an orange tree was able to survive the severe 1962 freeze. The trees at the top of the hill survived with virtually no damage, but those in the lowlands were killed off.

Air Temperature on Mountaintops

Mountaintops tend to have large daily air temperature ranges. The days tend to be hotter than expected and the nights colder than expected. Air molecules are far apart near the summits of mountains. In the daytime hours, solar radiation has an easy time penetrating this thin atmosphere and striking the mountain, which causes it to warm to a temperature greater than what one expects given the normal lapse rate. At night, earth radiation can easily escape to space through the thin atmosphere, which chills the air above the mountain to a point lower than what one expects given the normal lapse rate.

Polar Front

Most people know the poles are cold and the tropics are hot. But cold air does not easily mix with hot air, so what lies between the poles and the tropics? Please do not say, "warm" or "cool"! What lies between? A line-of-contact between the cold air and the hot air known as the *polar front* (Fig. 7-11). The polar front, in effect, separates the cold

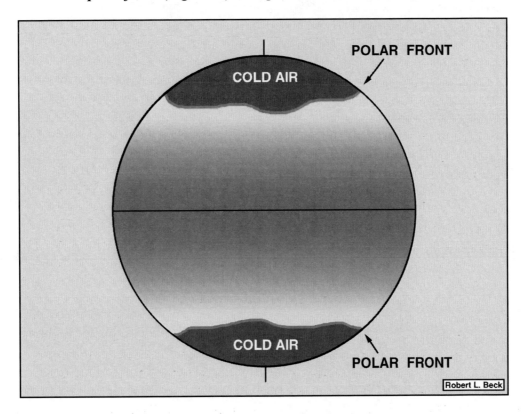

Figure 7-11. Polar Front

air of the poles from the hot air of the tropics and subtropics. A polar front is found in both the Northern and Southern Hemispheres.

Air moving along the polar front, in most instances, travels from west to east. This moving air is sometimes known as the *polar front jet stream* or, more simply, the *jet stream*. However, there are two jet streams in the Northern Hemisphere—the polar front jet stream and the subtropical jet stream.

The polar front develops large waves in it at times. These large waves are known as **Rossby waves,** and they occasionally swing south deep into the middle latitudes or subtropics (Fig. 7-12). When that happens, cold masses of air invade the middle latitudes. If a Rossby wave develops over the United States, it is quite possible for Indianapolis to

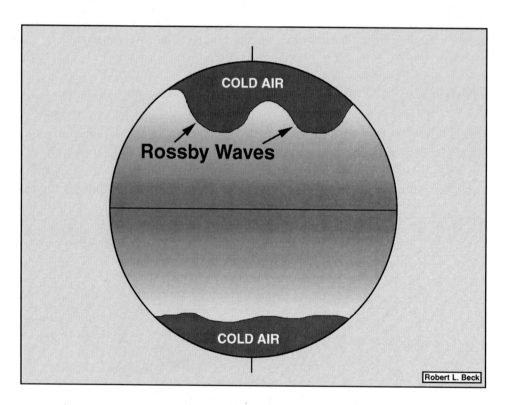

Figure 7-12. Rossby Waves

be cold for an extended period of time while Kansas City, roughly at the same latitude as Indianapolis, is quite warm during that same period (Fig. 7-13).

The polar front migrates seasonally. In the winter the area of cold air at the North Pole expands, so the polar front pushes to the south. In the summer the area of cold air at the North Pole contracts, so the polar front retreats back to the north. The polar front is usually situated in the Gulf Coast states in the winter, and in the summer it is often located somewhere in Canada (Fig. 7-14).

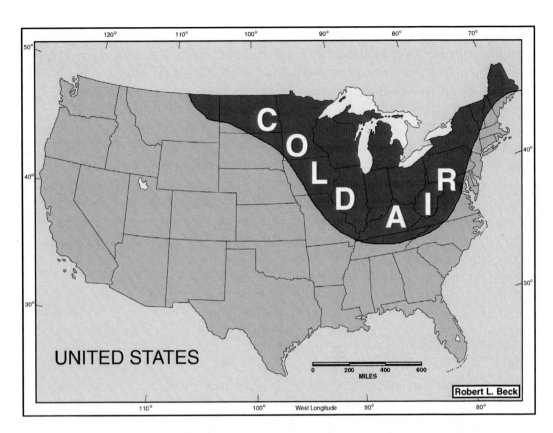

Figure 7-13. A Rossby Wave over the Midwestern United States

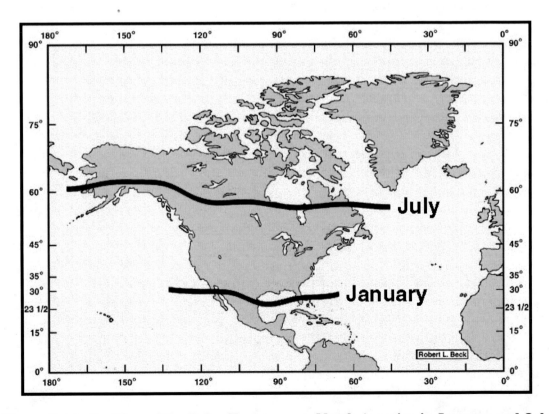

Figure 7-14. Position of the Polar Front across North America in January and July

Indiana is normally situated north of the polar front in January and south of it in July, but the polar front can also fluctuate wildly across North America in a matter of a few days. The average position of the polar front in the winter might be in the Gulf Coast states, but it can move all the way north to Michigan in a short period of time.

Temperature Zones

The tropics are hot, for the SSP is always located somewhere within its boundaries. The subtropics are also hot with occasional outbreaks of cold air in the winter. The poles are always cold. The middle latitudes are where the great temperature contrasts occur, for in these latitudes the polar front is almost always located. The middle latitudes tend to have both hot periods and cold periods—hot summers when they are positioned south of the polar front and cold winters when they are positioned north of the polar front.

Land and Water Contrasts

Land and water heat and cool differently. People who live in the middle of a continent have a much different climate than people who live on a windward ocean coast, even if they live at the same latitude. Land is stationary, so when the sun's rays strike it, the energy remains concentrated on the surface; water is fluid, so its mobility redistributes heat throughout its mass. Land is opaque, the sun's rays do not penetrate it very far; water is transparent, the sun's rays penetrate dozens of feet. Land transfers its heat by conduction, a slow process that lets heat build up on the land surface. Water transfers its heat by convection, a relatively fast process that moves heat through the movement of water masses. Land has a lower specific heat than water, which gives land the ability to heat quickly; water has a higher specific heat than land, so it takes water a long time to warm up. All these factors mean that *land heats more quickly than water!*

It takes water a long time, relative to land, to get warm. But once it is warmed, water tends to hold onto its heat. Land, on the other hand, loses its heat quickly. The heat of land is concentrated in the upper few inches of the surface. This heat is quickly lost when autumn starts to appear. Water has its heat distributed throughout its mass; it takes a long time for the whole mass to cool relative to those few inches over the land. This means then that *land cools more quickly than water!*

Land-dominated areas have temperature extremes—cold winters and hot summers. Water moderates temperature; climates that are water modified have cool winters and mild summers. Areas dominated by land, with temperature extremes, have *continental climates*. Areas dominated by water, with temperature moderation, have *marine climates.* Compare the climographs of two cities located approximately on the same latitude—Wichita, Kansas, and San Francisco, California (Fig. 7-15). Note that Wichita, near the center of North America, has a continental climate with much colder winters and hotter summers than San Francisco.

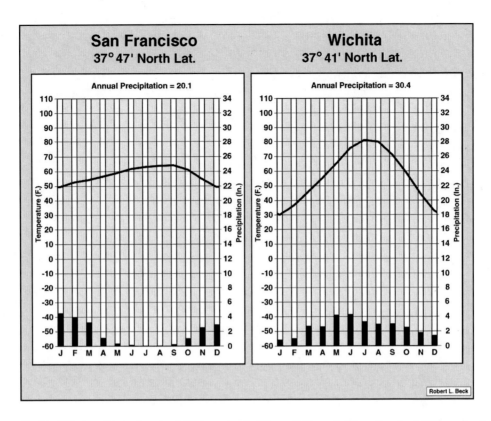

Figure 7-15. Water-Dominated Climate (left) and Land-Dominated Climate (right)

****

Isotherms

It is difficult and quite inconvenient to find geographic patterns when all you are looking at are numbers on a map. Weather data are collected at weather stations, which are points when shown on a map (Fig. 7-16). To reduce the complexity of such a cartographic portrayal, geographers find it useful to convert these data points to *isolines* so that geographic patterns emerge.

An isoline is a general term for any line that connects points of equal value. An isoline connecting points of equal air temperature is known specifically as an *isotherm*. Isothermal world maps (reduced to sea level) of the "Average January Temperature" and the "Average July Temperature" are shown in *Goode's World Atlas* on page 32. The sinuous white lines are the isotherms. Note on the July map the 95 degree isotherm encircles an area in the western Sahara Desert in North Africa. The area inside that

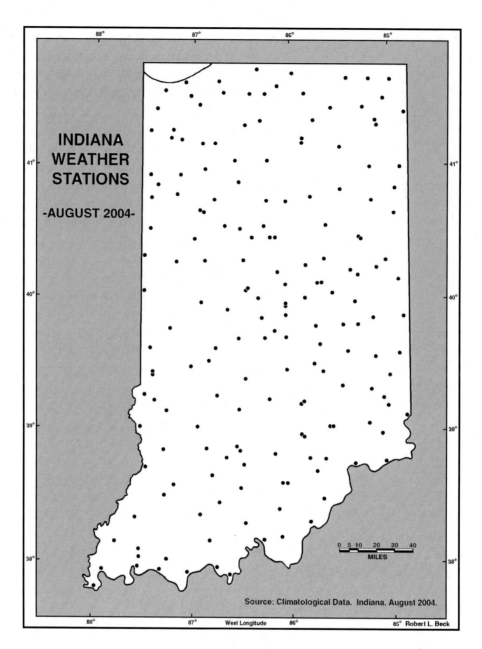

Figure 7-16. Indiana's Weather Stations

isotherm is shaded dark orange, so the average July temperature in that area is above 95°F. Any point on the white line surrounding the dark orange area has an average July temperature of 95°F (35°C). To convert from degrees F to degrees C you can use the following formula: (°F − 32) ÷ 1.8 = °C; and to convert from degrees C to degrees F you can use this formula: (°C × 1.8) + 32 = °F.

*What is the value of the isotherm that goes through Lake Michigan as shown on the July map in **Goode's World Atlas**, p. 32? Answer is: 68°F (20°C).*

Plotting an isotherm (or any isoline) on a map requires some thought, for it is often necessary to place the line in an assumed position based on temperature readings from nearby weather stations. Assume we have some weather stations with temperature readings as shown in Figure 7-17. Further assume that we want to place isotherms at 5° intervals on the map beginning with the 55° isotherm. Where would it be placed? There is only one data point shown as 55°! Beginning at the 55° point, notice that the

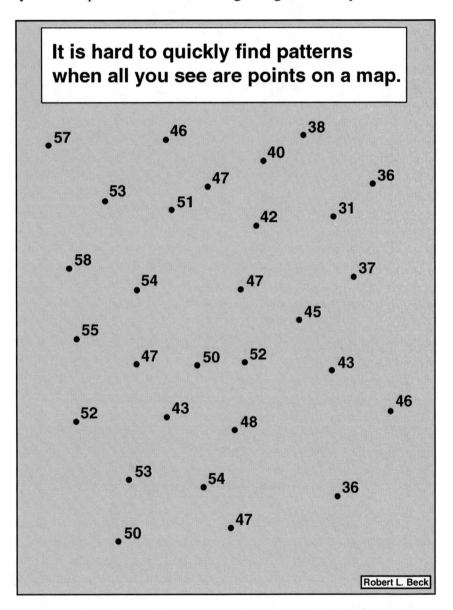

Figure 7-17. Air Temperatures at Hypothetical Weather Stations

isotherm trends toward the northeast because it has to be positioned somewhere between the 54° and 58° data points. This is an assumed position; we do not actually know what the temperature is between those two points, but halfway between should be 56° and the 55° point is theoretically positioned halfway between 56° and 54°. The isotherm then

85

curves to the northwest because it is assumed there is a 55° temperature somewhere between the 58° point and the 53° point, and also between 57° and 53° (Fig. 7-18).

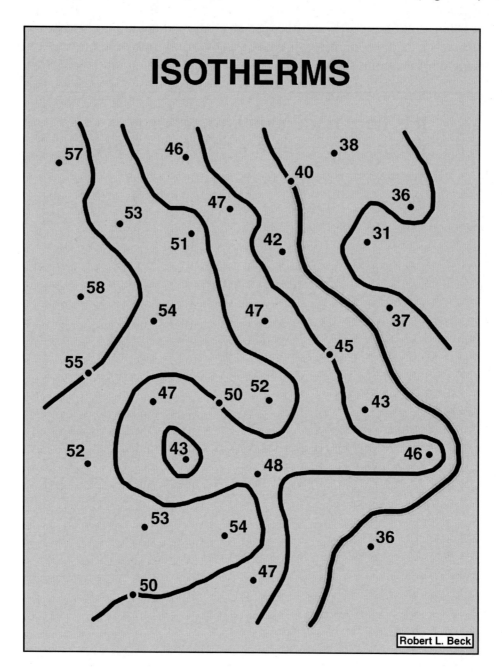

Figure 7-18. Isotherms with Data Points

When the map is completed with isotherms plotted at 5° intervals, and the data points removed, it is fairly easy to see that a warm air wedge extends across the map from the northwest to the southeast with cold air in the northeast and a cold pocket of air in the southwest (Fig. 7-19). Such a pattern is hard to see when looking at the data points alone.

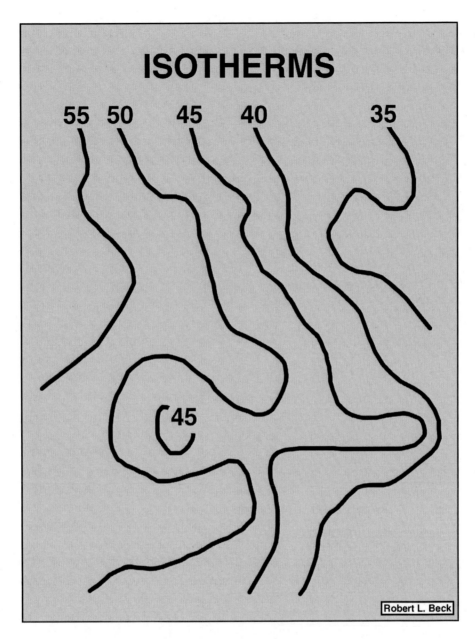

Figure 7-19. Isotherms without Data Points

Global Patterns of Air Temperature

Isotherms are useful when trying to find temperature patterns on a small-scale map such as Earth. What are some temperature patterns that can be observed on the "Average January Temperature" and on the "Average July Temperature" maps shown in ***Goode's World Atlas*** on page 32?

One pattern is that isotherms tend to run in an east-west direction. This makes sense, for as we move from the Equator to the poles air temperature decreases. A second pattern is that the isotherms in the Southern Hemisphere from about 20° South Latitude to 60° South Latitude have fewer fluctuations than the isotherms in the Northern

Hemisphere at the same latitudes. What might explain this difference? The Southern Hemisphere's oceans at those latitudes redistribute heat, whereas at the same latitudes in the Northern Hemisphere we find large areas of land, which bring temperature extremes causing the isotherms to bend.

A third pattern is that the coldest place on earth in January occurs over land in eastern Siberia, with a mean January temperature less than −49°F. The North Pole, over water, is not as cold as this area in eastern Siberia. Remember that land-dominated areas bring temperature extremes. A fourth pattern is that the world's hottest places, also over land, are shown on the July map. One of these places is over the western Sahara Desert in North Africa and the other is in the Arabian Peninsula, with neither place located on the Equator.

A fifth pattern concerns the direction that isotherms bend. An **equatorward** bend indicates the presence of a cold spot, and a **poleward** bend indicates the presence of a hot spot. For example, on the January map the 32°F isotherm is positioned at about 60° North Latitude in the Pacific Ocean (off the southern coast of Alaska) and at about 67° North Latitude in the Atlantic Ocean (off the northern coast of Iceland). That same isotherm is located at about 40° North Latitude over North America (running through central Illinois). North America is cold in the winter, so the 32°F isotherm bends equatorward. Also note that over North America in the summer (July) the isotherms are now bending toward the North Pole, which indicates the continent is now hot.

Does the bend of the 68°F isotherm at about 30° South Latitude off the west coast of South America on the July map represent a cold ocean current or a warm ocean current? Answer is: A cold ocean current—the isotherm is bending equatorward.

A sixth pattern concerns the spacing of the isotherms. Please observe on the January map there are nine isotherms between southern Florida and northern Alaska, but on the July map there are only four. The ***temperature gradient***, or the change in temperature between two places, is more pronounced in North America in January than in July. One final point concerning these two maps is that the continent of Antarctica is not shown, so the maps do not show the world's coldest temperatures are found over Antarctica—a landmass at a high latitude. Use the practice exercise on page 246 of this textbook to study temperature gradients and isotherms in more detail.

Heating Degree Days

When the mean daily temperature (MDT) of an area falls below 65°F, it is assumed the people who live there will heat their homes. The ***heating degree day*** concept was developed to measure the potential demand for fuel, to compare consumption patterns between cities, and to look at how fuel usage changes with time. Heating degree days are easy to compute, and they are often listed in local newspapers during the winter. All you have to do to compute the heating degree days, for some place on Earth, is subtract the MDT of that place from 65°F to derive the total number of heating degree days for that day. This would be given by the formula: 65° − MDT = heating degree days. For example, assume that Indianapolis had a MDT of 60° last October 21. If you subtract this from 65°, you get 5 heating degree days (65° – 60° = 5 heating degree days). On Oct. 21, Indianapolis would have registered five heating degree days. When you add all the heating degree days in a heating season, for many places around the country, one can begin to compare fuel needs. Indianapolis typically has around 5,500 heating degree days in a heating season, but Los Angeles has less than 2,000. I once asked the truck driver who filled our heating oil tank how he knew when to fill it, for there is no exterior gauge on it. He told me "heating degree days."

Module 7 Objectives

You should now be able to:

- Compute the *mean daily temperature* for any city on Earth using weather data

- Identify the times of the day when the daily high temperature and daily low temperature usually occur and explain why they occur at those times

- Identify the principal source of atmospheric heat

- Identify the month of the year that has the highest average monthly temperature and the month of the year that has the lowest average monthly temperature and explain why they occur in those months

- List three *temperature singularities* and explain the temperature singularity concept

- Discuss the *normal lapse rate* and use it to estimate vertical temperature variations

- Explain how the *normal lapse rate* is different from the *lapse rate*

- Describe a *temperature inversion*

- Compare and contrast the two main types of temperature inversions

- Discuss the concept of *air drainage*

- Explain why mountaintops bring temperature extremes

- Define the *polar front* and discuss some of its main characteristics

- Explain why land and water heat and cool differently

- Define an *isotherm* and use an isothermal map

- Discuss some of the major global patterns of temperature

- Compute the *heating degree days* for any city on Earth using weather data

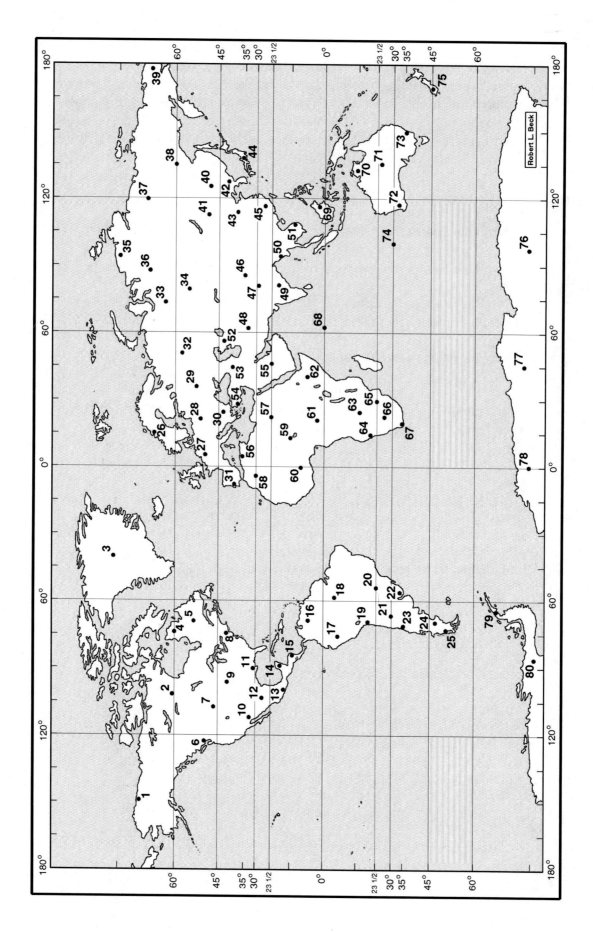

Robert L. Beck

MODULE 8: AIR PRESSURE

Differences in air temperature produce differences in air pressure, so a module on air pressure logically follows a module on air temperature. Air pressure is the second weather element.

Two Ways to Perceive Air Pressure

One way to perceive **air pressure** is to view it as a force of collisions. Air is a material substance in which its molecules move about rapidly, and every time they collide with an object, which might be another air molecule, they exert a certain pressure as a result of that collision. Faster-moving molecules exert greater pressure because the force of the collision is greater. Imagine you pour some water in a saucepan, put the lid on it, set the saucepan on a stove's burner, and turn the heat on. The water vapor molecules inside the pan soon start to move at a faster rate, and in a few minutes the water vapor increases the pressure on the lid so that you might hear it rattle. The pressure inside the pan increases through the application of heat energy. The air molecules travel faster, which then increases the pressure (force of collisions) on the lid.

The second way to perceive air pressure, and the way I want you to view it in this course, is to think of air pressure as the weight of overlying air. Consider a fish at the bottom of the ocean (Fig. 8-1). That fish has the whole weight of the water above it pressing down on it. Clearly, the fish is under a lot of water pressure. One cannot imagine a situation in which a fish at the bottom of the ocean is under less water pressure than a fish near the surface of the ocean. The atmosphere is like an ocean, but it is an ocean of

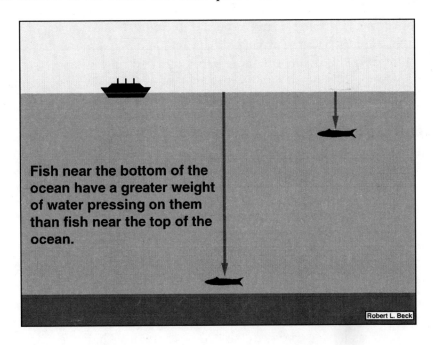

Figure 8-1. Water Pressure in the Ocean

91

air and not one of water. People living at the bottom of the atmosphere, as most of us do, have the entire weight of the atmosphere above us pressing on our bodies. We are like the fish at the bottom of the sea (Fig. 8-2).

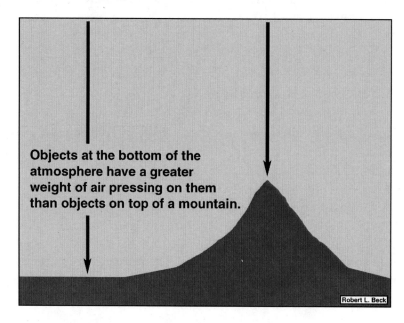

Objects at the bottom of the atmosphere have a greater weight of air pressing on them than objects on top of a mountain.

Robert L. Beck

Figure 8-2. Air Pressure in the Atmosphere

Vertical Distribution of Air Pressure

Air pressure always decreases with an increase in elevation; air pressure inversions in the atmosphere do **not** exist. Air pressure at the top of a mountain is always less than the air pressure over an adjacent valley because the atmosphere is thinner over the mountaintop. A 1-inch column of air extending from the base of the atmosphere (at sea level) to the outer edge weighs about 15 pounds. Every square inch of a person who lives at sea level has that amount of weight pressing on his or her body at all times. People who live in mountainous environments do not have as much air pressing on them as people who live at sea level.

The density of air molecules also decreases with an increase in elevation. At the base of the atmosphere air molecules are closely packed. With increasing elevation the molecules are farther and farther apart (Fig. 8-3). It is estimated that about 50% of the atmosphere's air molecules exist within 3½ miles (18,500 feet) of Earth's surface.

Measurement of Air Pressure

The **barometer** is the instrument used to measure air pressure. Evangelista Torricelli, an Italian, invented the *mercurial barometer* in 1643. Torricelli used a column of mercury confined in a 36-inch glass tube as his barometer. When the tube was turned over into a dish, the mercury at first flowed out the bottom of the tube and into the dish. Air pressed down on the mercury as it tried to rise in the dish. Eventually a balance was reached between the weight of the atmosphere pressing down in the dish and the hydrostatic

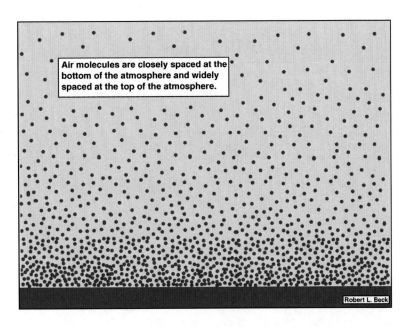

Figure 8-3. Density of Air Molecules in the Atmosphere

pressure of the column of mercury pressing up from the bottom of the tube. The mercury in the tube soon stabilized, proving air is a material substance that exerts pressure on objects (Fig. 8-4). People tested Torricelli's barometer by comparing mercury levels at the tops of mountains and in the bottoms of valleys. Of course, it was quickly noted the air pressure on top of a mountain is much lower than the air pressure of an adjacent valley. Torricelli's invention gave chemists an important tool for measuring gases.

It is now known that standard sea level air pressure is 29.92 inches of mercury. The column height of mercury in a barometer fluctuates in response to changes in air pressure. When the atmospheric air pressure increases, some of the mercury from the dish is forced back up into the tube. The mercury in the tube rises when high pressure occurs and the barometer might read 30.5 inches. When the atmospheric air pressure decreases, some of the mercury from the tube drains into the dish until a new balance is reached. The mercury in the tube falls when low pressure occurs, and it might then read 29.2 inches.

Mercurial barometers are accurate, and they give a fast response, but they are also costly, easily broken, and require special handling. A more durable barometer, especially when treated roughly in the field, is the *aneroid barometer*. This type of barometer uses a metal cylinder with a flexible side. The cylinder has most of its air removed so that variations of air pressure are indicated by the relative bulges of the flexible side (Fig. 8-5). Aneroid barometers are used in altimeters in modern aviation. They were also used by explorers to measure the height of mountains and the depth of canyons. John Wesley Powell, for example, used them (and also mercurial barometers) in his explorations of the American West in the 1860s and 1870s—Powell led the first successful expedition down the Colorado River through the Grand Canyon. Aneroid barometers, used mostly as a decoration, hang on the interior walls of many houses in the United States today.

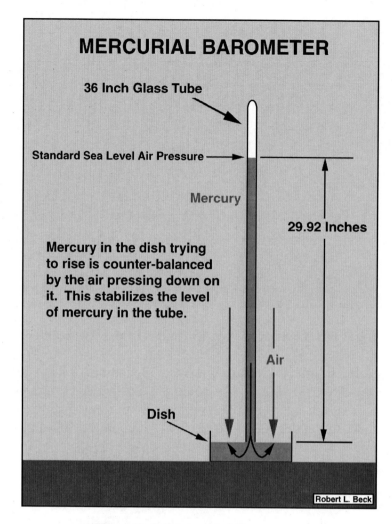

Figure 8-4. Mercurial Barometer

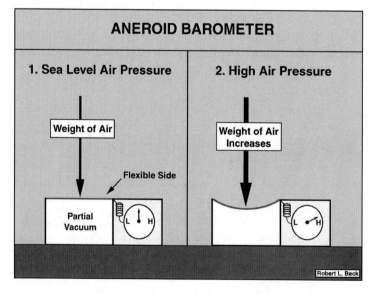

Figure 8-5. Aneroid Barometer

Pressure Systems

Air pressure varies horizontally as well as vertically. For example, the air pressure in Indiana is usually different than the air pressure in California. Variations of air pressure often occur within Indiana. Fort Wayne, Evansville, and Terre Haute usually have different air pressures than Indianapolis.

Pressure systems are known as *lows* and *highs*. Lows, of course, bring low air pressure, but they also bring stormy weather, precipitation, high humidities, and wind. Lows are also known as *cyclones*. Highs bring high air pressure, and they also usually bring clear weather, dry conditions, low humidities, and calm air. Highs are the opposite of lows both in the types of air pressure they bring and in the types of weather they bring. Highs are also known as *anticyclones.*

Both lows and highs are mobile. For example, Indiana might be under the influence of a low pressure system on Monday and under the influence of a high pressure system on Tuesday. Lows and highs can also remain over an area of Earth for an extended period of time, six months or more. When such a situation occurs, it is said to be a semipermanent high or a semipermanent low. The Sahara Desert, in Africa, has a semipermanent high pressure system over it most of the year.

Causes of Horizontal Variations of Air Pressure

What causes these horizontal variations of air pressure? How can one place on Earth have high air pressure and another place have low air pressure? There are two main causes.

DIFFERENTIAL HEATING AS A CAUSE OF
HORIZONTAL VARIATIONS OF AIR PRESSURE

One of the principal causes of horizontal variations of air pressure is *differential heating*. Many factors cause some places to get hot and other places to remain cool. Sun angles vary, so does cloud cover, and do not forget the albedo differences of various Earth surfaces. Figure 8-6 shows two cities with equal-sized columns of air over them. I placed 10 dots in each air column, and each dot represents billions of air molecules. The weight of each column at the earth's surface is identical in both cities (10 dots). Now imagine that City A has a cloud cover and that City B is clear (Fig. 8-7). During the day, more solar radiation reflects back to space over City A (clouds have high albedos) than City B, so it receives more solar radiation and becomes warmer than City A. The air column over City B expands as the city gets hot (air parcels expand when subjected to heat) (Fig. 8-7). The 10 dots are now spread throughout a greater volume of air, but the air pressure at the surface is still the same (10 dots). Air pressure in the upper level of the atmosphere begins to vary horizontally as the air column expands. At the elevation of the dashed line, the air pressure over City A is 2 dots, but the air pressure in the expanded air column over City B is now 5 dots at this same elevation. An upper-level high pressure has formed over City B relative to the upper-level low pressure over City A. The atmosphere tries to equalize this horizontal variation of air pressure by moving, via the

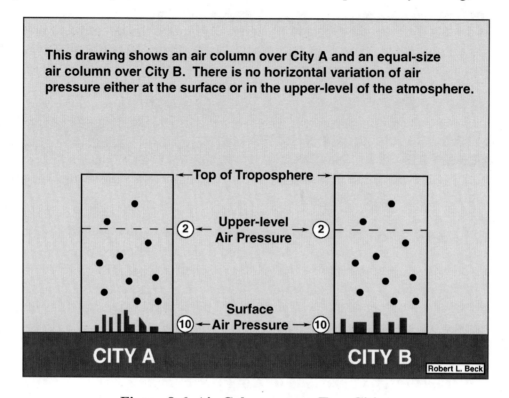

Figure 8-6. Air Columns over Two Cities

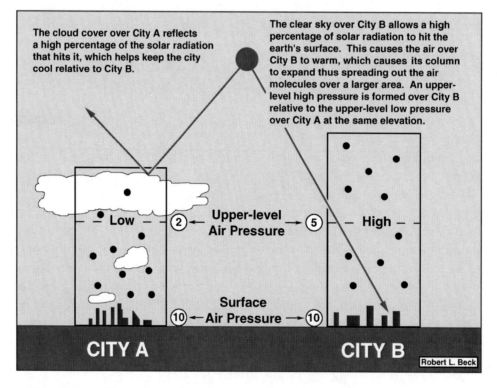

Figure 8-7. Upper-level Air Pressure Variation between Two Cities

the wind, air from City B's upper atmosphere to City A's upper atmosphere. Removing 1 dot from City B's air column drops the surface pressure to 9 dots, and adding 1 dot to

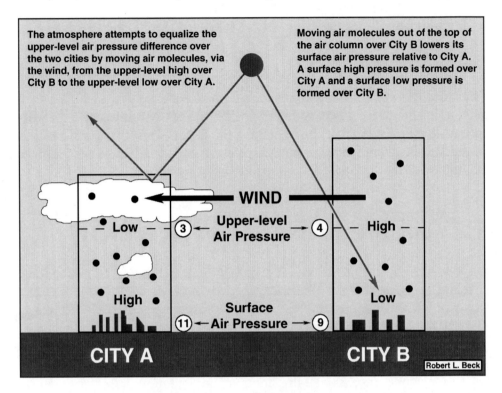

Figure 8-8. Upper-level Wind between Two Cities

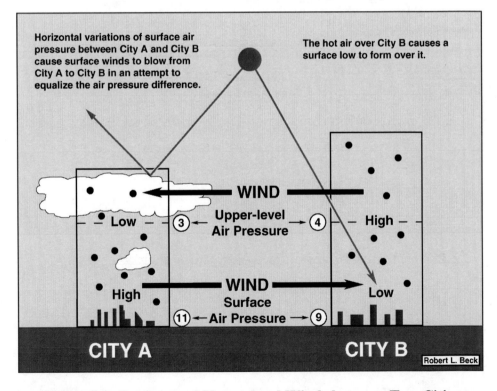

Figure 8-9. Surface and Upper-level Winds between Two Cities

City A's air column raises the surface air pressure to 11 dots, which produces a horizontal pressure variation on the earth's surface (Fig. 8-8). The clear sky over City B meant the city got hot, which ultimately produced a low pressure at the base of its air column. Surface winds move air molecules from City A to City B (Fig. 8-9) in an attempt to equalize the surface air pressure differences as upper-level winds are moving air molecules from City B to City A.

The whole point I am trying to make with this sequence of drawings is that in the atmosphere, as a general rule, *hot surfaces are associated with low air pressures!* There are exceptions to this general rule. For example, the Sahara Desert has some of the world's hottest surface temperatures, but a high pressure system dominates it (except during the middle of the summer) and not a low pressure system.

UPPER-LEVEL AIR MOVEMENT AS A CAUSE OF HORIZONTAL VARIATIONS OF AIR PRESSURE

Upper-level air movement is a second major cause of horizontal variations in air pressure. Upper-level air movement is either convergent (coming together) or divergent (moving apart). *Upper-level air convergence* raises surface air pressure, regardless of the surface temperature. The Sahara Desert, which is very hot all year, is dominated by a surface high pressure because air is converging over it. If you think of an air column extending from Earth's surface to the top of the troposphere and then imagine that billions of air molecules are added to this column near its top, will this raise the surface air pressure? Yes, for air molecules entering the top of the column add weight to the entire column, thus raising air pressure at the bottom of it (Fig. 8-10).

Upper-level air divergence lowers surface air pressure. If air molecules are removed from the top of an air column, then that reduces the weight of the entire column thus lowering the air pressure at the bottom of it (Fig. 8-10).

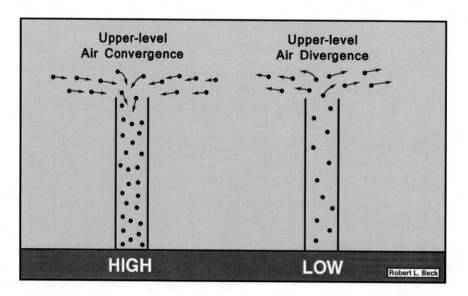

Figure 8-10. Upper-level Air Convergence and Upper-level Air Divergence

Isobars

Lines that connect points of equal air pressure are known as *isobars*, another type of isoline. Isobars are commonly expressed in inches or in millibars. One inch = 34 millibars, so standard sea level air pressure is expressed as either 29.92 inches or 1,017 millibars. Cyclones and anticyclones (lows and highs) are bounded by isobars (Fig. 8-11).

Closely spaced isobars (Fig. 8-12) indicate a rapid change in air pressure over Earth's surface, so this is known as a *strong (or steep) pressure gradient*. Widely spaced isobars (Fig. 8-13) indicate a gradual change in air pressure over Earth's surface, so this is known as a *weak (or gentle) pressure gradient*. Wind speed is directly related to pressure gradients, for when the isobars are closely packed wind speed will be high, and when the isobars are far apart wind speed will be low.

World isobaric maps for January and July are shown in *Goode's World Atlas* on pages 34–35. They are labeled "January Pressure and Predominant Winds" and "July Pressure and Predominant Winds." The months of January and July are typically depicted on world pressure maps because those two months bring temperature extremes, which cause great variances in air pressure. Again, please remember air pressure is related to air temperature.

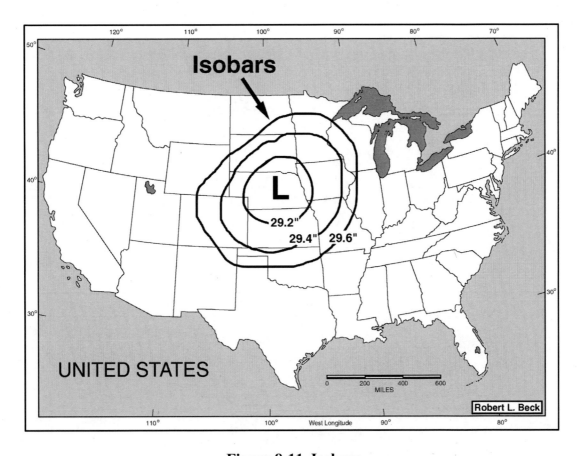

Figure 8-11. Isobars

Figure 8-12. Closely Spaced Isobars

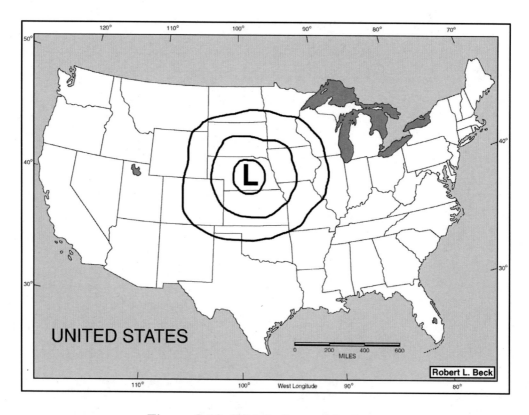

Figure 8-13. Widely Spaced Isobars

Practice Exercise: Answer the following questions using *Goode's World Atlas,* pp. 34–35.

What is the average January air pressure in Indianapolis? Answer is: 1,020 millibars (30.00 inches).

Is the pressure gradient over the Atlantic Ocean north of the 40° parallel steepest in January or July? Answer is: January. There are many more isobars over the ocean in January than in July.

World Pressure Belts

I now present a highly generalized model of the world pressure belts. Please keep in mind there are many specific exceptions to this general model, but I like to teach deductively. I think it is far easier to learn a subject by working from the general to the specific than the other way around.

The SSP is always located either on, or near, the Equator. It does migrate to the Tropic of Cancer and to the Tropic of Capricorn, but for most of the year it is not too far away from the Equator. The Equatorial latitudes are always hot, and as you know, *hot surfaces are associated with low pressures!* A semipermanent low pressure belt is found around Earth at the Equator. This semipermanent belt is known as the *Equatorial Low* (Fig. 8-14).

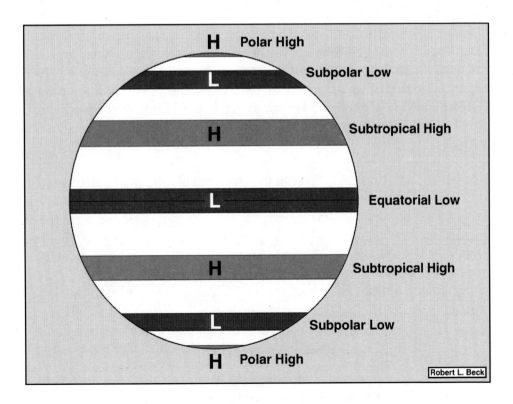

Figure 8-14. World Pressure Belts

The poles are always cold. The air found at the North Pole and at the South Pole is dense and heavy. Such air helps produce semipermanent high pressure cells at both poles. These high pressure areas are known as the **Polar Highs**, for **cold surfaces are associated with high pressures!**

At about 30° North Latitude and 30° South Latitude are semipermanent high pressure belts known as the **Subtropical Highs**. Upper-level air convergence occurs at these latitudes, so the high pressures are produced by upper-level air movement and not differential heating. These latitudes are where Earth's great deserts are located.

The **Subpolar Lows** are semipermanent low pressure areas found at about 60° North Latitude and at 60° South Latitude. The subpolar low in the Northern Hemisphere is especially pronounced over the oceans in winter. The subpolar low around Antarctica is a continuous belt, but in the Northern Hemisphere there are two distinct low pressure cells—the Icelandic Low and the Aleutian Low.

The pressure belts are shown on world maps in **Goode's World Atlas** on pages 34–35. These world maps are labeled "January Pressure and Predominant Winds" and "July Pressure and Predominant Winds." Low pressure areas on these maps are shown as light green, green, and dark green; high pressure areas are shown as light blue, blue, and dark blue.

Observe along the Equator, in both January and July, the existence of a continuous low pressure area, the Equatorial Low, as indicated by the green strip. On both sides of it, in the subtropics, high pressure dominates as indicated by the blue areas. These high pressure areas are stronger over the oceans and weaker over the land, and in some places they are separated from each other by areas of low pressure. The high pressure areas in the subtropics are really cells of high pressure and not true belts. The high pressure cell located over the North Atlantic Ocean is known as the Bermuda High in North America, but in Europe it is known as the Azores High. In the North Pacific Ocean the subtropical high pressure cell is known as either the California High or the Hawaiian High.

Poleward of the subtropics, in both the Northern and Southern Hemispheres, are the subpolar low pressure areas marked with the greenish tint. The low pressure area around Antarctica is continuous year-round, but in the Northern Hemisphere the subpolar lows strengthen in the winter and weaken in the summer. The semipermanent low pressure area in the North Atlantic Ocean is known as the Icelandic Low, and the semipermanent low pressure area in the North Pacific Ocean is known as the Aleutian Low. The map projection cuts off the extreme high latitudes of Earth, so the polar highs are not shown.

Pressure Belt Migration and Reversals

The world pressure belts are depicted in fixed positions on my model (Fig. 8-14), with an alternating belt found at every 30° in latitude—the Equatorial Low at 0°, the Subtropical

Highs at 30°, the Subpolar Lows at 60°, and the Polar Highs at 90°. The belts do not remain fixed in these positions year-round but instead migrate with the direct rays of the sun. As the SSP moves north, the belts shift to the north, and as the SSP moves south, the belts shift to the south. For example, when the SSP is located on the Tropic of Cancer (June 21), the Equatorial Low has mostly migrated into the Northern Hemisphere. At that time of the year, it is not on the Equator as shown on my model. The average positions of the Equatorial Low in January and July are shown in Figure 8-15.

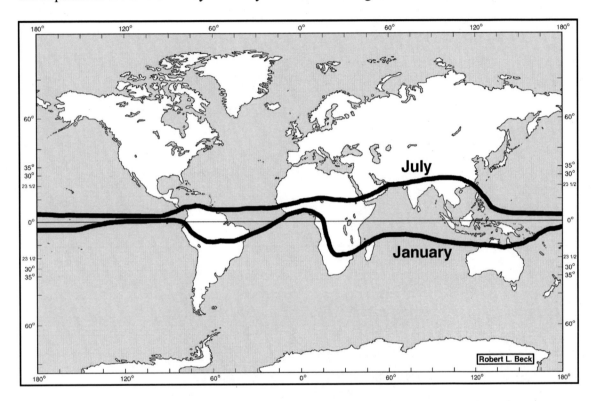

Figure 8-15. Average Positions of the Equatorial Low in January and July

Examine the position of the California High shown on the "January Pressure and Predominant Winds" on page 34 in **Goode's World Atlas**. The center of this high pressure area is positioned at about 30° North Latitude. Now examine the position of the California High on the "July Pressure and Predominant Winds" on page 35 in **Goode's World Atlas**. The center of it is positioned at about 40° North Latitude. Between January and July, the California High shifted to the north about 10° in latitude as the SSP moved north.

Next consider the air pressure changes over Asia between January and July. When central Asia is bitterly cold in the winter (January), a strong high pressure develops over it. This high pressure cell is known as the Central Siberian High, and it reinforces the concept that *cold surfaces are associated with high pressures.* In July, when southern Asia is becoming extremely hot, a low pressure cell develops over southern and southwestern Asia. This low pressure cell is a northern extension of the Equatorial Low, and it reinforces the concept that *hot surfaces are associated with low pressures.* The huge continent of Asia experiences a reversal of air pressure between winter and summer.

Module 8 Objectives

You should now be able to:

- Describe the two ways to perceive *air pressure*

- Explain why air pressure inversions do not exist

- List the two main types of *barometers* and explain how they work

- Compare and contrast the two types of *pressure systems*

- List, and briefly discuss, the two main causes of horizontal variations in air pressure

- Use an *isobaric map* to identify strong and weak pressure gradients

- Plot the *world pressure belts* on a map of Earth

- Discuss why the world pressure belts migrate latitudinally

Figure 8-16. Beech trees are also known as the "initial trees."
Daniel Boone supposedly carved his name in one. Note the smooth bark.
(Robert L. Beck photo, 2007)

MODULE 9: WIND

The **horizontal** movement of air is known as *wind*, the third weather element. Wind is an attempt by the atmosphere to equalize horizontal differences of air pressure; molecules of air are moved by the wind from high pressure areas to low pressure areas. Some of these molecules are water vapor molecules, which contain heat. The wind therefore transfers heat horizontally when it moves water vapor molecules. The horizontal transfer of heat, as you should recall, is known as *advection*.

Cyclonic and Anticyclonic Circulations

Three factors govern the speed and direction of wind: (1) the pressure gradient, (2) the Coriolis effect, and (3) friction. One needs to examine these three factors to understand the world patterns of winds, and cyclonic and anticyclonic circulations in particular.

A high pressure area and a low pressure area, with their accompanying isobars, are shown in Figure 9-1. Pressure gradients always slope out of high pressure areas and

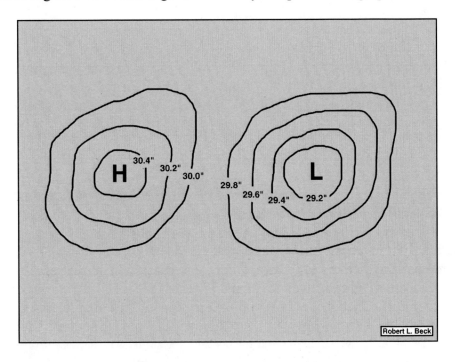

Figure 9-1. Air Pressure Cells

into low pressure areas. There can be an infinite number of pressure gradients sloping out of a high and into a low (Fig. 9-2). The wind tries to blow along the pressure gradients from the high pressure to the low pressure, so it is similar to a ball rolling down a hill and into a hole. Air molecules are like the ball in that they always move, via the wind, away from high pressure areas and into low pressure areas.

105

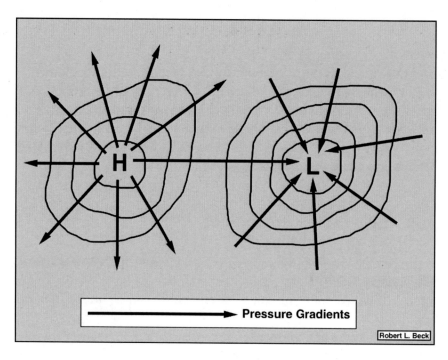

Figure 9-2. Pressure Gradients

Steep pressure gradients occur when isobars are closely spaced. When that happens, there is a rapid change in air pressure over a short distance on Earth, so the wind blows at a high velocity—a ball rolls down a steep hillslope faster than it rolls down a gentle hillslope. Gentle pressure gradients occur when isobars are widely spaced. Such a condition means a gradual change in air pressure over Earth's surface, so the wind blows at a low velocity.

As the wind tries to blow downslope along the pressure gradient, it appears to be deflected by the Coriolis effect. In the Northern Hemisphere the deflection is to the right, and in the Southern Hemisphere the deflection is to the left. Figure 9-3 shows air blowing out of a high pressure area and into a low pressure area in the Northern Hemisphere. The heavy, black lines with arrows show the pressure gradients and the directions they slope. Air tries to move along those lines, but is deflected so that it appears to be moving between the isobars along the little, gray lines.

The frictional drag of air moving over Earth's surface slows it down and pulls it back toward the pressure gradient so that air crosses the isobars at low angles as shown by the thin, black lines with arrows (Fig. 9-3). These lines are the actual surface winds. Please observe these surface winds *converge* (come together) in the low pressure cell and that they *diverge* (move away) from the high pressure cell.

As the surface winds (thin, black lines with arrows) converge on the low pressure cell, they are doing so in a counterclockwise direction (Fig. 9-4). It is commonly said that in the Northern Hemisphere, *"winds blow into a low counterclockwise."* As the surface winds diverge out of the high pressure cell, they are doing so in a clockwise direction, so in the Northern Hemisphere, *"winds blow out of a high clockwise"*

(Fig. 9-4). In the Southern Hemisphere these two patterns are reversed because the Coriolis effect deflects free-moving objects to the left, not to the right.

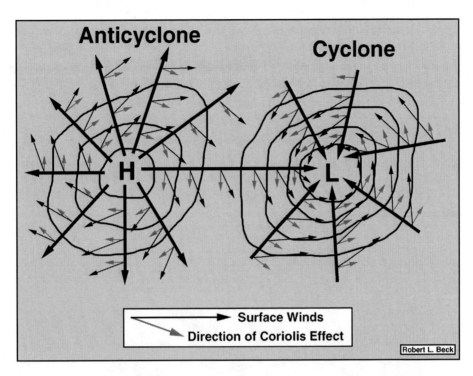

Figure 9-3. Cyclonic and Anticyclonic Circulations with Pressure Gradients and Direction of Coriolis Effect Shown

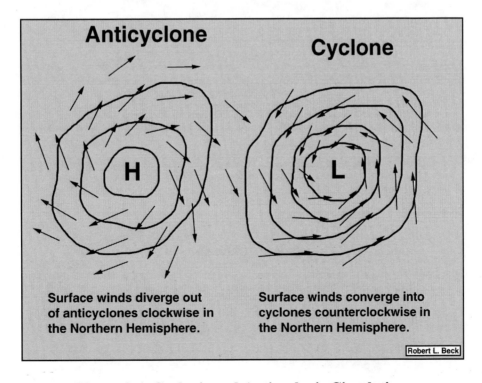

Figure 9-4. Cyclonic and Anticyclonic Circulations

Convection Cells

A cross-sectional view of a *convection cell* (depicting surface winds, upper-level winds, and air pressures) is shown in Figure 9-5. I explain the diagram beginning with the surface low (#1, Fig. 9-5). It has been mentioned many times that *hot surfaces are associated with low pressures*, so hot air rises above the surface low. Hot rising air, in physical geography and meteorology, is known as *convection*. An upper-level high pressure (#2, Fig. 9-5) is positioned above the surface low. The hot rising air diverges from the upper-level high, and upper-level winds carry it to the upper-level low (#3, Fig. 9-5). Air subsides (sinks downward) on top of the surface high (#4, Fig. 9-5) positioned beneath the upper-level low. This subsiding air diverges out of the surface highs, and surface winds carry it to the surface low where it starts the process all over again. Air molecules are constantly moving from #1 to #2 to #3 to #4 and back to #1 in this convection cell model.

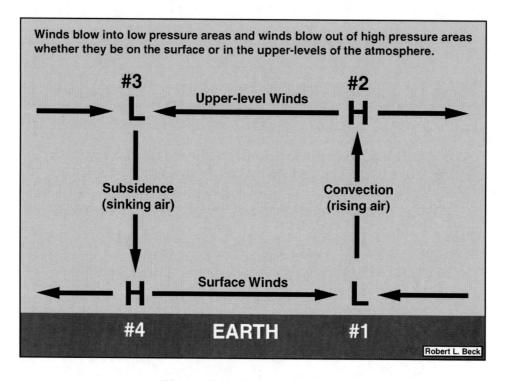

Figure 9-5. Convection Cell

Another major point relating to the movement of air in the convection cell (Fig. 9-5) concerns the terminology describing the air movements. The rising air from #1 to #2 is not wind, for wind is defined as the horizontal movement of air. Rising air is known as *convection*, which is the vertical movement of air. The sinking air from #3 to #4 is also not wind, for the air is subsiding on top of the high pressure cell. Only the air movements from #2 to #3 and from #4 to #1 are winds. Winds converge (come together) in low pressure areas and winds diverge (move apart) in high pressure areas. Wind convergence or wind divergence might be either on the earth's surface or in the upper-levels of the atmosphere.

Practice Exercise: Place a cyclone and an anticyclone on the map of the United States. Draw some isobars around them. Complete the exercise by drawing the winds on the map using lines with arrows.

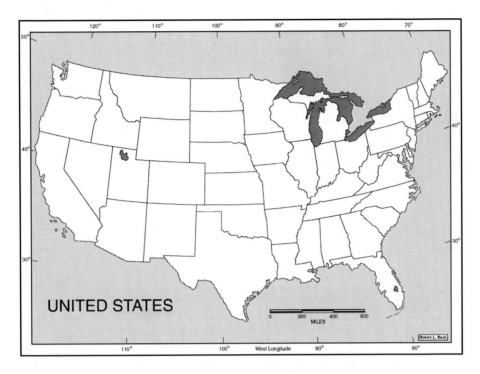

Practice Exercise: What is the direction of the wind in Indianapolis if the low is positioned over southern Kentucky and northern Tennessee as shown in the map below? What is the direction of the wind at the point in the Nebraska panhandle?

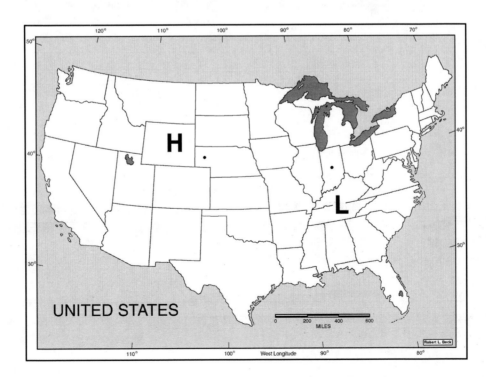

World Wind Belts

The world wind belts are positioned between the world pressure belts, so the blank spaces on my general model of the world pressure belts (Fig. 8-11, p. 101) are where the world wind belts are situated. The heavy, black lines with arrows shown in Figure 9-6 are the pressure gradients sloping from the high pressure areas to the low pressure areas.

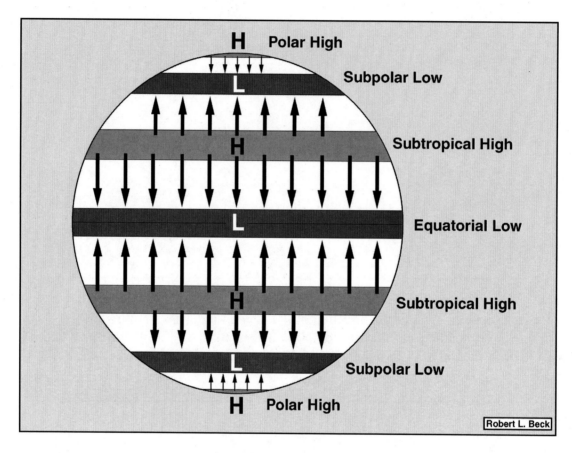

Figure 9-6. World Pressure Gradients

In the tropical areas, air tries to blow along the pressure gradients from the subtropical highs to enter the equatorial low, but the Coriolis effect appears to deflect the air to the right in the Northern Hemisphere and to the left in the Southern Hemisphere. The surface winds converging at the equatorial low are shown as the thin, black lines with arrows in Figure 9-7. The wind belts immediately poleward of the equatorial low are the *trade winds*. In the Northern Hemisphere the trade winds blow from the northeast to the southwest, so they are known as the *northeast trade winds*. European sailors and explorers, such as Columbus, used the northeast trade winds to travel from the Old World continents of Africa and Europe to the New World continents of North America and South America. In the Southern Hemisphere the trade winds blow from the southeast to the northwest, so they are known as the *southeast trade winds*. The trade winds converge at the equatorial low, which is more commonly known as the *Intertropical Convergence Zone (ITC or ITCZ)* (Fig. 9-7). I will refer to it as the ITC.

110

Pressure gradients also slope from the subtropical highs to the subpolar lows (heavy, black lines with arrows shown in Fig. 9-6). Air moving along these gradients is again deflected by the Coriolis effect, and it moves from west to east. These wind belts are known as the *westerlies* (Fig. 9-7). There is a westerlie wind belt in the Northern Hemisphere and another one in the Southern Hemisphere. Indianapolis, and most of the United States, lies in the Northern Hemisphere's westerlie wind belt. Storms that enter

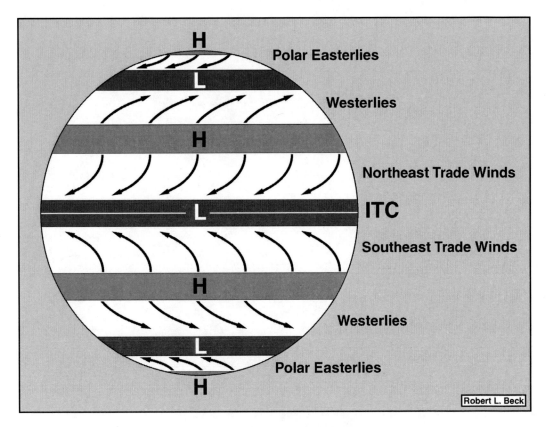

Figure 9-7. World Wind Belts

Indiana are usually pushed into the state from the west by the westerlie winds. People who predict what the weather will be like in Indiana in the near future typically look to the west, for a storm in the central Great Plains might affect the weather of Indiana in a couple of days, but a storm in Pennsylvania has already gone by Indiana; however, the position of the polar front jet stream, and any Rossby waves in it, might alter the direction of storm movement.

The *polar easterlies* are winds that blow from the North Pole and South Pole toward the subpolar lows. Pressure gradients slope from the polar highs to the subpolar lows. Air moving along the gradients is, once again, deflected by the Coriolis effect so the wind is blowing from east to west (Fig. 9-7).

The world wind belts are shown on the world pressure and wind maps in *Goode's World Atlas*, pp. 34–35. The polar easterlies are poorly shown on those maps, which are considerably more complicated than my general model presented above.

Hadley Cells

The two large convection cells found in the tropics are known as the *Hadley cells* (Fig. 9-8). Air rises at the ITC (Equatorial Low) where the trade winds meet. This air is loaded with water vapor, and as it rises it cools, clouds form, and precipitation occurs. The ITC is one of the world's great rain-producing systems. Air diverges out of the top of the ITC, is carried horizontally by upper-level winds, and subsides over the subtropical highs. It then blows out of the subtropical highs as the trade winds to start the cycle all over again.

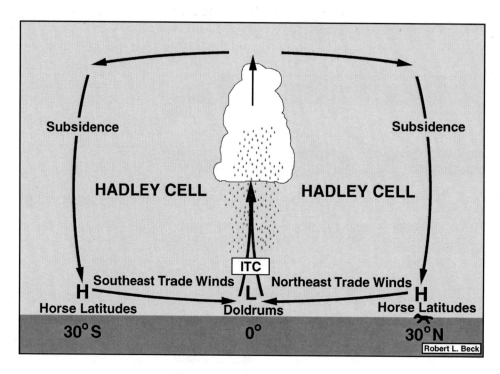

Figure 9-8. Hadley Cells

The subsidence of air over the subtropical highs produces little or no wind at the surface. Ships traveling to the New World from Europe during the colonial period were often heavily laden with various sorts of goods. If they inadvertently sailed into a subtropical high pressure cell, the lack of wind sometimes caused the ship to sit still in the water, possibly for weeks at a time. When that happened, it was sometimes necessary to lighten the load of the ship so that any light wind might move the ship. Heavy objects thrown overboard included horses. This was so common that the latitudes around 30° in both the Northern and Southern Hemispheres were named the *horse latitudes* (Fig. 9-8). They are still called that by some people today.

The *doldrums* is another belt of light or no wind. It is found at the center of the ITC, where the air rises. This mostly windless zone could also cause ships to flounder in the ocean for long periods of time. The doldrums are shown on the world pressure and wind maps in *Goode's World Atlas*, pp. 34–35.

112

Regional and Local Winds

Many regional and local winds are found throughout Earth. Different cultures often have different names for them. I discuss several of them in this section of the course.

The **monsoons** are one of the world's most distinctive and well-known regional winds. Monsoons occur in Africa, East Asia, and Australia, but the monsoons most people have heard of are the ones found in South Asia—India in particular. *Monsoon* is an Arab word meaning "reversal of the winds," so it does **not** mean "rainy season," as many people mistakenly believe. The winds blow one direction in the summer, and they blow in the opposite direction in the winter. Some monsoons bring rain, but others bring drought.

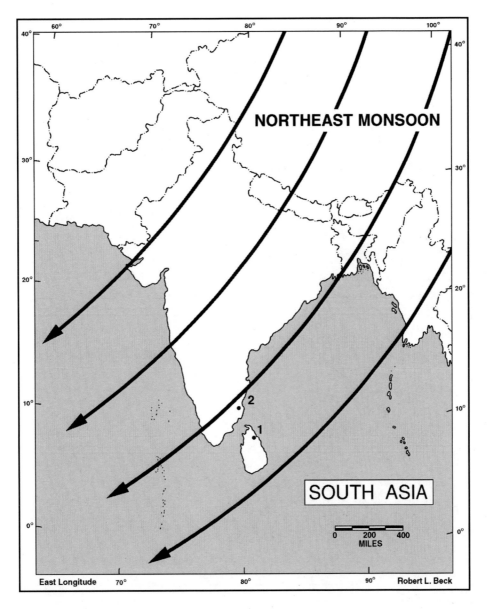

Figure 9-9. Northeast Monsoon in South Asia

The air pressure reversal over Asia between winter and summer is one of the principal causes of the Indian monsoons. When the Central Siberian High dominates Asia, as it does in the winter, the wind blows from land to sea (*Goode's World Atlas*, p. 34). The air lacks water vapor because it originated over the Asian landmass. This *Northeast Monsoon*, as it is sometimes known, brings dry weather to most of India. The air moves across India from the northeast to the southwest (Fig. 9-9).

The wet monsoon in India occurs in the summer when a low pressure cell forms over Pakistan (*Goode's World Atlas*, p. 35). The wind blows into this low pressure cell counterclockwise, so moist air from the Arabian Sea and the Bay of Bengal is carried into India by the *Southwest Monsoon* (Fig. 9-10). As this warm, moist air is forced to rise over the mountains and hills in South Asia, clouds form, and heavy precipitation is produced.

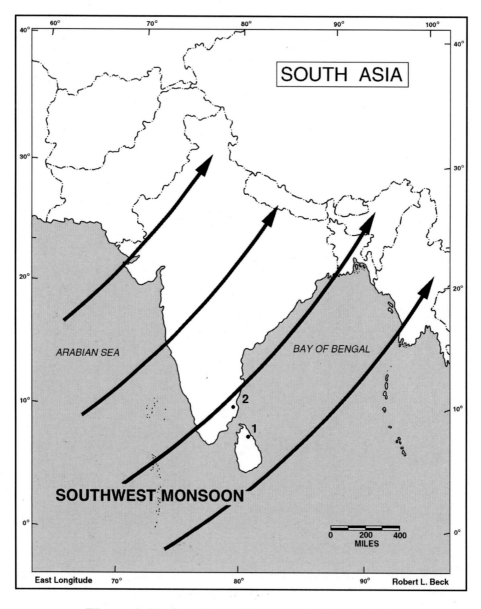

Figure 9-10. Southwest Monsoon in South Asia

114

Cherrapunji, a city in the Khasi Hills in eastern India just north of the Bangladesh border, is the world's second-wettest place. It annually receives about 460 inches of rain, most of which comes with the Southwest Monsoon in the summer. Some people claim this is the world's wettest place, but Mt. Waialeale in Hawaii is probably wetter. The climograph of Cherrapunji is shown in this textbook on page 226.

Sea and land breezes are local coastal winds mostly found in tropical areas throughout the earth. They form because of the differential heating of land and water. During the daytime hours the land heats rapidly, forming a small low pressure cell. A small high pressure area forms over the water because it is cooler than the land. Wind always blows from high pressure to low pressure, and in this case the wind blows from the sea to the land—a *sea breeze* (Fig. 9-11). At night, the process works in reverse

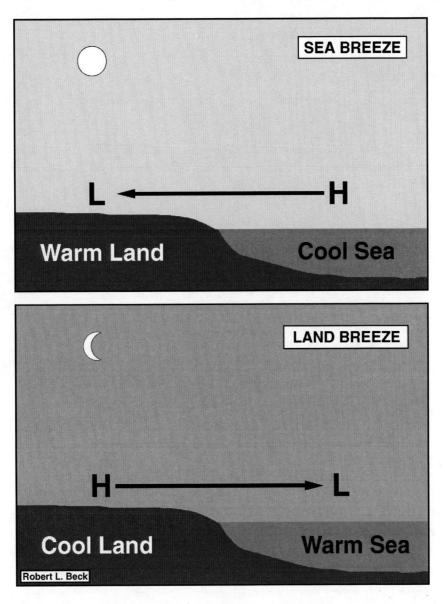

Figure 9-11. Sea and Land Breezes

because the sea is now warmer than the land. Land breezes thus blow from the land to the sea at night (Fig. 9-11). People who swim feel a similar situation in an outdoor pool. During the daytime hours the water feels cold, but at night it feels warm. Florida receives sea breezes from its two coasts in the summer; often these sea breezes converge daily, producing cloudy conditions and precipitation throughout the central part of the state (Fig. 9-12).

Figure 9-12. Florida Sea Breezes
(NASA photo)

Another set of local winds produced by heating variations are ***mountain and valley winds*** (Fig. 9-13). Valley winds form during the day when the mountaintop warms due to its thin atmosphere and sun angle. The warm air rises over the mountain, and air from the valley is drawn upward producing the valley wind. At night, the mountaintop loses its heat rapidly, chilling the air. This cold air blows down the valley as a mountain wind (Fig. 9-13). I had a 68-year-old student several years ago whose mother washed the uniforms of the University of Colorado marching band back in the 1930s or 1940s. She

116

told me her mother hung out the uniforms at night to let them dry. After taking this course, she believed they dried well because of the mountain winds, but it could also be due to the low humidities in Colorado. Hanging your laundry out to dry at night in Indiana is counterproductive, for we do not have mountain winds, and we usually have high humidities at night, so little, if any, evaporation takes place.

I have not personally experienced mountain winds, but I know people who have. Friends of mine who camped in the Rocky Mountains years ago told me they were awakened in the middle of the night by the roar of the wind as it came cascading down the mountain, but when they had pitched their tent at sunset the evening was clear and the air was calm.

Figure 9-13. Mountain and Valley Winds

People in Africa and Europe have regional names for the winds that blow out of the Sahara's subtropical high pressure cell. Winds that blow from the Sahara toward Europe and the Mediterranean Sea are known as the *sirocco winds* (Fig. 9-14). These hot, desert winds are part of the westerlie wind belt and they often deposit dust or fine-grained sand in the Alps, including on the surface of glaciers. Winds that blow from the Sahara toward the Equator are known as the *harmattan winds*, which are part of the northeast trade wind belt. The harmattan winds might bring welcome relief from the high tropical humidities at the beginning of the dry season, but by the end of the dry season they also bring misery in the form of droughts.

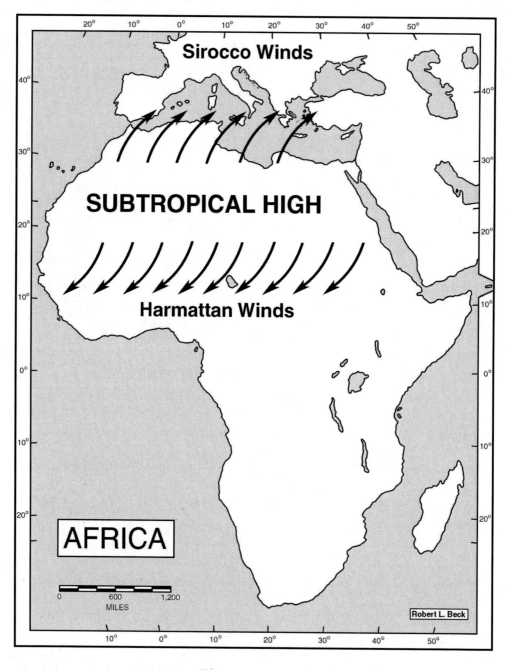

Figure 9-14. African Winds

A cold wind that blows into New England and the northeastern United States from the North Atlantic is known as a *Nor'easter*. These winds occur when a low pressure cell is positioned over the North Atlantic Ocean, and cold air is trying to enter the low in a counterclockwise direction. The wind blows into the northeastern states from a northeasterly direction (Fig. 9-15). On February 12, 2006, a Nor'easter dumped 26.9 inches of snow on Central Park in New York City, which was a record snowfall. Wind speeds in the storm exceeded 60 mph.

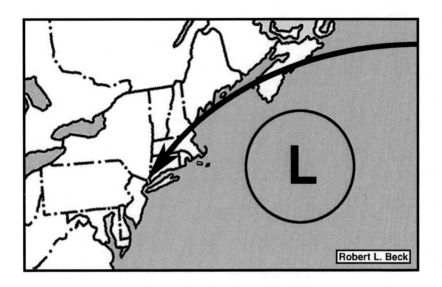

Figure 9-15. Nor'easter

Downslope Winds

Various places around the world have distinctive downslope winds. Different cultures often have different names for these winds. I discuss three downslope winds—chinook winds, Santa Ana winds, and katabatic winds.

A *chinook wind* forms when a low pressure cell is located east of the Rocky Mountains (Fig. 9-16). Air enters this low pressure cell counterclockwise, so some of the air blowing into the low comes from the western side of the Rocky Mountains (Fig. 9-16). When this eastward moving air hits the Rocky Mountains it ascends and might bring orographic precipitation (defined in Module 11), but it will then descend the eastern side of the mountains in its attempt to enter the low pressure cell (midlatitude cyclone). The wind blowing down the eastern side of the Rocky Mountains is the *chinook*, an American Indian word meaning "snow-eater" (Fig. 9-17).

In the winter and early spring, midlatitude cyclones sometimes dump a lot of snow on Colorado cities located east of the Rockies as they pass over those cities following a storm track aimed at the east coast of the United States. As the cyclone moves into the Great Plains, the chinook wind forms and soon blows down into Denver. It is a drying wind because the air contained within it lost most of its moisture on the western side of the Rocky Mountains when it was forced to ascend. As the chinook wind moves downslope on the eastern side of the Rockies, it comes under greater air pressure as it descends, which lowers its relative humidity. Snow is melted quickly when this drying wind hits it. A snow cover two feet thick in Denver might be melted away in one day by a chinook wind.

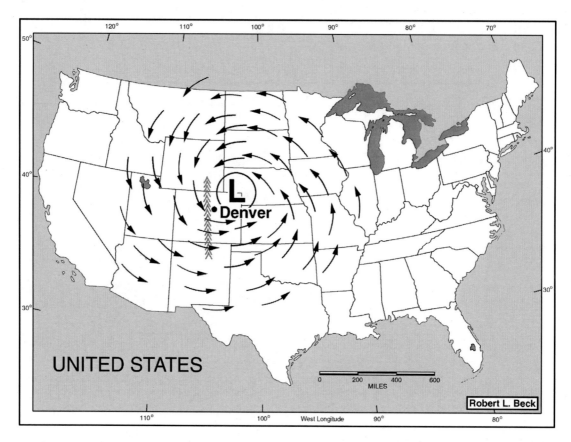

Figure 9-16. Chinook Wind Formation

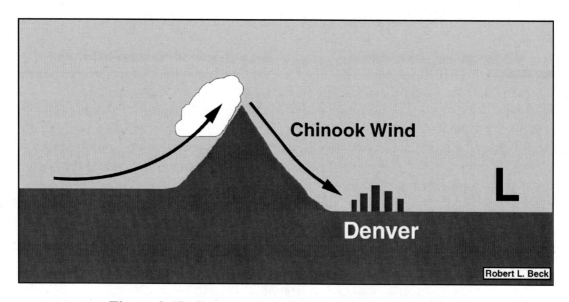

Figure 9-17. Cross-sectional View of a Chinook Wind

The **Santa Ana winds** are downslope winds that occasionally occur in southern California. Similar winds in the European Alps are known as the *foehn winds*. The Santa Ana winds form when a stalled (nonmoving) high pressure cell sits over the Mojave Desert in southern Nevada and southeastern California (Fig. 9-18). Dry air blowing out of the high and down into the California coastal lowlands constitute the Santa Ana winds (Fig. 9-19). Air blows out of a high clockwise in the Northern Hemisphere, so when a high settles over southern Nevada, some of the air naturally blows out of it and into southern California. The Mojave Desert has a high elevation. Air that blows into the lowlands of southern California from the high Mojave Desert is heated as it descends. This further lowers the relative humidity of the Santa Ana winds making them a fire hazard. If wildfires

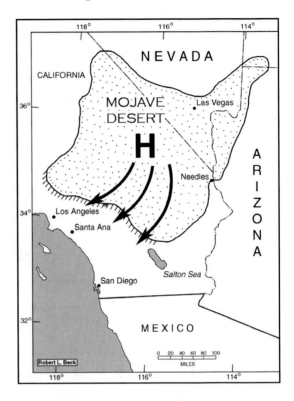

Figure 9-18. Santa Ana Wind Formation

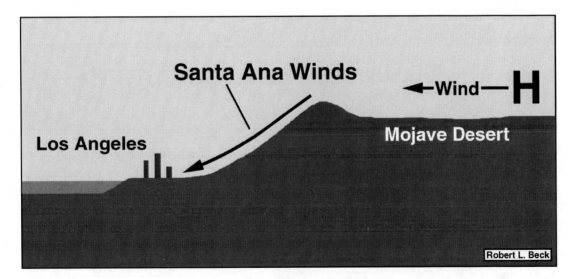

Figure 9-19. Cross-sectional View of the Santa Ana Winds

happen to start in southern California when the Santa Ana winds blow, as they did near San Diego in October 2007, they are almost impossible to put out. The wind fuels the fire; it also it dries out the vegetation making it even more susceptible to fire.

121

Cold air pulled downhill by gravity off an upland area is known as a ***katabatic wind***. Antarctica is the world's coldest, driest, and **highest** continent. It has a high average elevation because about 95% of the continent is covered with a sheet of ice in some places 10,000 feet thick. Cold air sits on this ice sheet and is pulled by gravity over the edge; when this happens the air blows downslope as a katabatic wind (Fig. 9-20). One

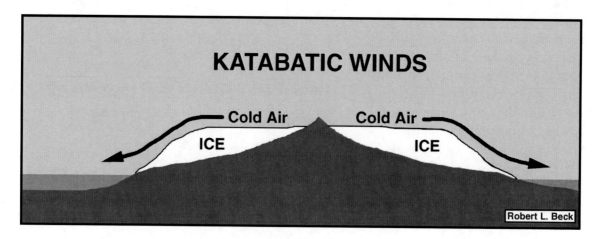

Figure 9-20. Katabatic Winds

who approaches Antarctica from any direction is greeted by windy conditions. Two locally named katabatic winds found in Europe are the ***mistral winds*** and the ***bora winds***. The mistrals are cold winds blowing down into valleys from the Alps, and the bora winds are cold winds blowing down from the high plateaus of southeastern Europe into the lowlands and seas of the Balkans.

Air Masses

An air mass is a large body of air moving as a unit with relatively uniform properties of temperature and moisture distinctively different from the surrounding air. Masses of air exist in the atmosphere just as masses of water exist in oceans and lakes. Air masses are **large**. Some can cover one-half of a continent or maybe one-quarter of an ocean. Air masses **move as a unit.** It is possible to be under the influence of one type of air mass on Monday and be under the influence of a different type on Tuesday. It is also possible to be under the influence of one air mass for weeks at a time. Air masses have similarities of **temperature** and **moisture** within the air mass and dissimilarities of temperature and moisture from the surrounding air. One must understand the concept of air masses and be able to distinguish among a few basic types to comprehend the formation of precipitation along cold fronts and warm fronts attached to midlatitude cyclones, which greatly influence the weather of the midwestern United States.

Temperature and moisture are used to classify air masses into different types. I cover the four basic types of air masses in this course. The matrix shown in Figure 9-21 identifies the four basic types. First, air masses are either cold or hot. If an air mass is

FOUR BASIC TYPES OF AIR MASSES		TEMPERATURE	
		Cold (P = Polar)	**Hot** (T = Tropical)
M O I S T U R E	**D r y** (c = continental)	cP	cT
	W e t (m = marine)	mP	mT

Robert L. Beck

Figure 9-21. Four Basic Types of Air Masses

cold, it originated over a polar area and is designated with a *P*. If it is hot, the air mass originated over a tropical area and is designated with a *T*. Second, air masses are either wet or dry. If an air mass is wet, it originated over a marine area and is designated with an *m*. If an air mass is dry, it originated over a continent and is designated with a *c*. The four basic air masses are: *cP* (dry and cold), *cT* (dry and hot), *mP* (wet and cold), and *mT* (wet and hot). Arctic air masses (*A*) and equatorial air masses (*E*) are two other air mass designations, but they are not discussed in this textbook because they rarely affect Indiana's weather.

Air masses pick up their temperature and moisture characteristics in areas known as *source regions*. Air mass source regions have two essential characteristics: (1) they have extensive and physically uniform surfaces, so areas with irregular topography or mixed land and water surfaces do not form good source regions, and (2) the air must remain over the source region long enough to acquire the temperature and moisture characteristics of the earth's surface, whether land or water. High pressure areas form good source regions because of the general stagnation of the atmosphere in those areas. Low pressure areas have too much mixing of air to be good source regions.

The source regions of the four main air masses that affect the weather of the United States are shown on the map of North America in Figure 9-22. Indiana is almost always under the influence of an mT air mass or a cP air mass—it is either hot and wet in the state or else it is cold and dry. Our mT air masses originate in the Gulf of Mexico and our cP air masses originate in northern Canada. Indiana seldom receives mP air or cT air, for the source regions of these air masses are the Gulf of Alaska and the southwestern deserts of the United States.

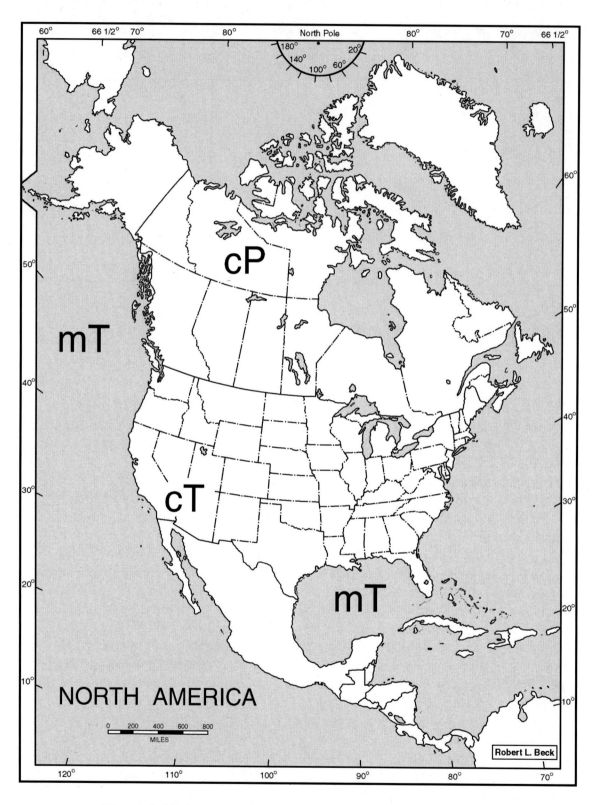

Figure 9-22. Source Regions of North American Air Masses

Figure 9-23. Late Afternoon Sky over Southern Nebraska in the Summer
(Robert L. Beck photo, 2009)

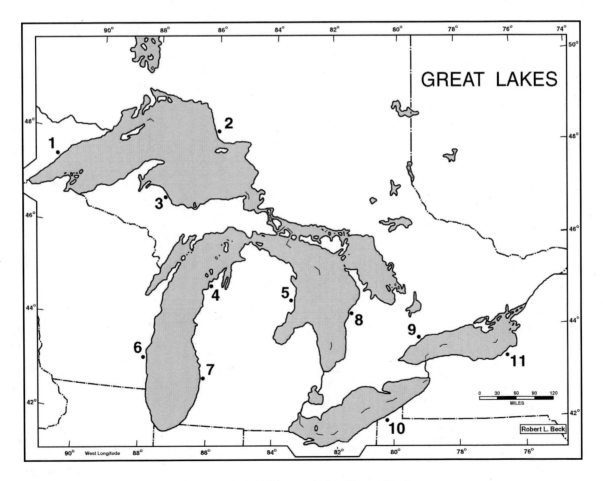

Figure 9-24. Map of the Great Lakes

Module 9 Objectives

You should now be able to:

- Explain why wind is an *advection process*

- Contrast *cyclonic* and *anticyclonic circulations*

- List the three factors governing the speed and direction of wind

- Describe the relationship between *pressure gradient* and *wind speed*

- Describe the air movement in a *convection cell*

- Plot the *world wind belts* on a map of Earth

- List the major wind belts

- Define a *Hadley cell*

- Describe how the *horse latitudes* and the *doldrums* are similar, and also how they are different

- Contrast the *winter monsoon* with the *summer monsoon* in South Asia

- Describe why sea and land breezes occur

- Identify and briefly discuss Earth's major regional and local winds

- List three types of *downslope winds* and describe how they originate

- Define an *air mass*

- Explain why *convection* and *subsidence* are not wind

- Compare and contrast the four major air masses that affect the weather of the United States

"The gentleman calls attention to the good points in others; he does not call attention to their defects. The small man does just the reverse of this." — Confucius

MODULE 10: HUMIDITY

Before beginning the study of precipitation, it is important to consider a few aspects of *humidity*, or the amount of water vapor in the air. The ideas and concepts discussed in this module have a direct bearing on what is covered in Module 11, Precipitation.

Dew Point

A volume of air can only hold a certain amount of water vapor. The amount it holds is a function of its temperature. Warm air can hold more water vapor than cold air; so lowering the temperature of a certain volume of air reduces its ability to hold water vapor. If we keep lowering the temperature of a certain volume, eventually the air is fully saturated. The temperature at which that volume is fully saturated is known as the *dew point*. In the atmosphere, *the dew point is most often reached by lowering the air temperature.*

Expressing Humidity

There are three main ways to express humidity—absolute humidity, specific humidity, and relative humidity. *Absolute humidity* is the weight of water vapor in a given **volume of air**, and it is usually expressed as grams per cubic meter (e.g., 4 grams per m^3). This is the least useful way to express humidity in physical geography, for air volumes are constantly expanding and contracting with changes in air temperature. *Specific humidity* is the weight of water vapor in a given **weight** of air, and it is usually expressed as grams per kilogram. The specific humidity of tropical air is high, for a kilogram of warm air holds a greater weight of water vapor than a kilogram of cold air. The specific humidity of polar areas is therefore low.

Relative humidity, the third way of expressing humidity, is the most commonly used measure of humidity in physical geography. Relative humidity is a ratio between the amount of water vapor in the air and the amount of water vapor the air could hold at its current temperature. For example, imagine a certain volume of air holds 4 grams of water vapor but that it could hold 8 grams of water vapor at its current temperature. That volume has a relative humidity of 50% (4/8 = 0.50). In this example, the numerator of my fraction, 4, is the amount of water vapor in the air and the denominator of my fraction, 8, is the amount of water vapor the air could hold at its current temperature. To repeat:

$$\frac{4}{8}$$

4 = amount of water vapor in the air

8 = amount of water vapor the air could hold at its current temperature.

Measurement of Relative Humidity

A *hygrometer* is any instrument used to measure relative humidity. One type of hygrometer is a *sling psychrometer* (Fig. 10-1), which is constructed by mounting two thermometers onto a plate and then attaching that plate to a handle with a swivel. The bulb of one thermometer is covered with a wet cloth when the psychrometer is used. This thermometer is known as the wet-bulb thermometer. The bulb of the second thermometer is left uncovered, so it is known as the dry-bulb thermometer.

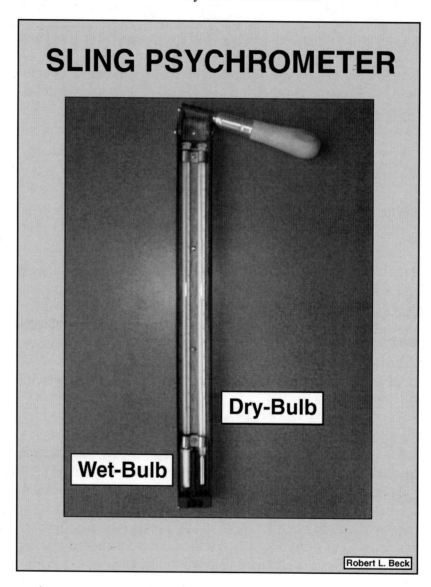

Figure 10-1. Sling Psychrometer
(public domain photo)

To operate the psychrometer, one first dampens the cloth with water, grabs the handle, and then starts slinging the two thermometers through the air. What happens next? Well, the water on the cloth starts to evaporate (remember that evaporation is a

128

cooling process), so the temperature of the wet-bulb thermometer starts to drop, but the dry-bulb temperature remains the same. After you sling the psychrometer for about a minute, you read the temperature of the wet-bulb thermometer and subtract it from the temperature of the dry-bulb thermometer to arrive at a figure known as the ***wet-bulb depression***. You then consult a psychrometric table to find the relative humidity of the air you are measuring. For example, assume that after spinning a sling psychrometer you observe the dry-bulb temperature is 70° and that the wet-bulb temperature is 60°. The wet-bulb depression in this case is 10° (70° – 60° = 10°). By cross-referencing the dry-bulb temperature with the wet-bulb depression on a psychrometric table, such as the simple one shown below, you determine the relative humidity is 55% (Fig. 10-2).

DRY-BULB TEMPERATURE (degrees F)	WET-BULB DEPRESSION								
	4	5	6	7	8	9	10	11	12
	Relative Humidity (%)								
40	68	60	52	45	37	29	22	15	7
50	74	67	61	55	49	43	38	32	27
60	78	73	68	63	58	53	48	43	39
70	81	77	72	68	64	59	55	51	48
80	83	79	75	72	68	64	61	57	54
90	85	81	78	74	71	68	65	61	58

Figure 10-2. Psychrometric Table

What is the relative humidity if the wet-bulb depression is 0°? The relative humidity would be 100%! When there is no evaporation of water from the cloth the wet-bulb temperature does not change, so the air is fully saturated. ***When wet-bulb depressions are low, relative humidities are high; and when wet-bulb depressions are high, relative humidities are low.***

The sling psychrometer has a number of advantages: It is fast, accurate, fun to use, and highly mobile. It can be used in the field to take quick relative humidity readings. But it also has a number of disadvantages: It requires the application of water, it is easily broken, and you have to spin it mechanically. It does not simply indicate the relative humidity of a room by hanging on a wall. These disadvantages lead some people to prefer a second instrument for measuring relative humidity, the ***mechanical hygrometer.***

Early hygrometers used bundles of human hair (but only certain types of human hair) connected to a meter to register changes in relative humidity. A Swiss physicist,

Horace Bénédict de Saussure, constructed the first hygrometer using human hair in 1783. The human hair absorbed water vapor from the atmosphere and expanded or contracted in proportion to changes in relative humidity. Synthetic fibers eventually replaced human hair. Semiconductors, now used in many hygrometers, measure changes in electrical resistance. This resistance is affected by humidity.

Mechanical hygrometers are slow, and they are not as accurate as sling psychrometers, but they are constantly recording the changes in relative humidity and they do not have to be spun. Some people have hygrometers hanging on a wall in their houses.

Changing Relative Humidity

Relative humidity is changed in the atmosphere by either: (1) adding water vapor to the air through evaporation or (2) changing the temperature of the air. In other words, changing either the numerator or denominator of the relative humidity fraction discussed earlier. If a certain parcel of air holds 4 grams of water but it could hold 8 grams, its relative humidity is 50%. If evaporation adds 2 grams of water to that parcel, its relative humidity rises to 75% (6/8 = 0.75). Adding water to the air does not change the ability of that parcel to hold water, but it does change the amount of water in it, raising the relative humidity (Fig. 10-3).

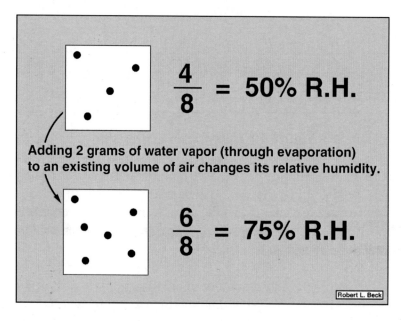

Figure 10-3. Changing Relative Humidity Through Water Vapor Addition

The more common way that the atmosphere changes the relative humidity of a parcel of air is to change its temperature, for this affects the air's ability to hold moisture. Cooling the air by lowering its temperature reduces its ability to hold water, so the relative humidity of that parcel rises. For example, a parcel of air that holds 4 grams of water but could hold 8 grams of water has a relative humidity of 50%; if its temperature is lowered, the parcel contracts, reducing the amount of water it can hold, for it now might only be able to hold 5 grams. The air parcel's relative humidity rises from 50% to 80% because those same 4 grams of water are still in the parcel (4/5 = 0.80) (Fig. 10-4).

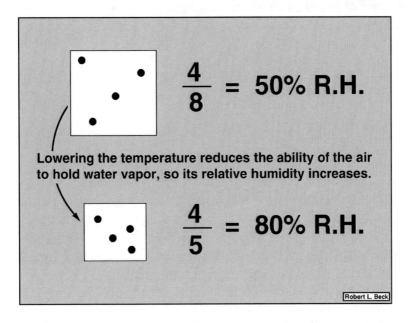

Figure 10-4. Changing Relative Humidity by Lowering the Air Temperature

Heating the air by raising its temperature increases an air parcel's ability to hold water, so its relative humidity falls. Using my same example, if a parcel of air holds 4 grams of water but could hold 8 grams of water, it has a relative humidity of 50%; when its temperature is raised the parcel expands, increasing the amount of water it can hold, for it now might be able to hold 12 grams. Its relative humidity falls from 50% to 33% because those same 4 grams of water are still in the parcel (4/12 = 0.33) (Fig. 10-5).

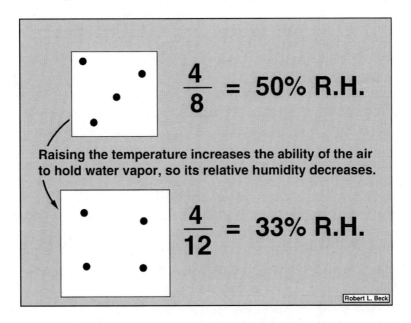

Figure 10-5. Changing Relative Humidity by Raising the Air Temperature

A major point about understanding the formation of precipitation is that, in most instances, ***when the air temperature decreases, relative humidity increases and when the air temperature increases, relative humidity decreases.*** As a general rule, air temperature and relative humidity are inversely related; when one goes up the other goes down.

Daily Changes of Relative Humidity

Like air temperature, relative humidity goes through a fairly recognizable pattern of daily changes, but as mentioned, its pattern is mostly the inverse of temperature changes. Relative humidities are usually lowest when the air temperature is highest, in the middle of the afternoon around 3 PM or 4 PM (Fig. 10-6). Relative humidity starts to increase as the air temperature starts to fall. If the temperature falls during the night to the dew point, then the relative humidity is at 100%. At that point water vapor in the air might begin to condensate onto objects near the ground (such as flowers or grass), or fog might form in the lower part of the atmosphere. Often the dew point is not reached until the lowest temperature of the day is recorded, a few minutes after sunrise.

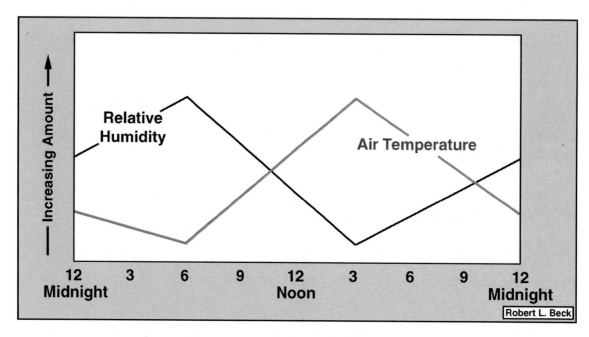

Figure 10-6. Daily Changes of Relative Humidity

The rising of the sun starts to lower the relative humidity as air temperature increases. Relative humidity falls throughout the late morning hours and into the early afternoon, and it reaches its lowest point in the middle of the afternoon (Fig. 10-6). I have described a weather situation for a typical clear day, but clouds and wind can alter the daily pattern of both air temperature and relative humidity. Clouds have a delaying effect concerning daily temperature curves and winds move water vapor over Earth's surface horizontally, which might easily alter the relative humidity of a certain locale.

Fog

Fog is essentially a cloud at the base of the atmosphere consisting of billions of liquid droplets settling toward earth. The drops become larger as they settle, for they collide with smaller droplets not settling as quickly. When the collision takes place, the drops coalesce (fuse together) to form a larger droplet. A 600-foot fog layer settles out in about one hour, so if a relatively thin fog layer persists for many hours new droplets have formed to maintain that layer. There are many specific types of fogs, but they can all be classified into two general categories—evaporation fogs and cooling fogs.

EVAPORATION FOGS

Evaporation fogs form when water vapor is added to the air (Fig. 10-7). A *steam fog* is an evaporation fog that commonly occurs over water bodies in Indiana every autumn. All summer Indiana's lakes and ponds are warmed by the sun. When the cold weather of autumn begins to appear, those water bodies are now reservoirs of heat. During the night and early morning hours, cold air moves over these warm lakes and ponds. The warm water of the pond evaporates water vapor to the atmosphere, but it immediately condenses when it hits the cold air above, for it is quickly cooled to the dew point. From an observer on shore, the pond appears to be steaming as small columns of fog swirl into the air above the water surface (Fig. 10-7).

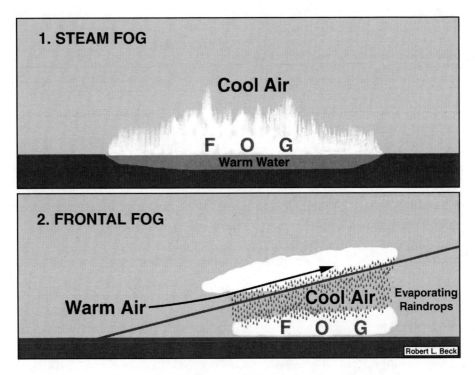

Figure 10-7. Types of Evaporation Fogs

A *frontal fog* is a second type of evaporation fog. These fogs are also known as *continental fogs* because they can cover large areas of Earth's surface. Frontal fogs occur

133

along warm fronts (which I discuss later in the module on precipitation) when warm raindrops evaporate as they hit cold air near Earth's surface. The cold air, however, causes the water vapor from the raindrop to condensate quickly, thus forming the fog (Fig. 10-7). A frontal fog stretched across the central United States, from Ohio to Nebraska, on February 4, 2008. It was positioned just north of a warm front.

COOLING FOGS

Cooling fogs occur more commonly than evaporation fogs, and they form over cold ground surfaces or when air chills as it is forced to rise over a topographic barrier (Fig. 10-8). Perhaps the most common cooling fog is the ***ground fog***, also known as a *radiation fog*. A ground fog forms when Earth's surface becomes cold, which chills the air above it to the dew point producing the fog. This chilling process is known as ***radiation cooling*** (Fig. 10-8).

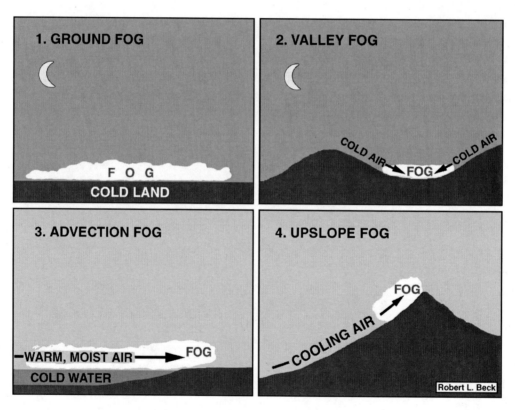

Figure 10-8. Types of Cooling Fogs

In hilly areas, air drainage sometimes produces a ***valley fog*** when cold air settles into river valleys (Fig. 10-8). This type of cooling fog is especially common in the hill lands of southern Indiana, and it often occurs on humid summer nights. Cold air from the hillsides cools the bottomland air to the dew point as it settles in for the evening. I have driven through valley fogs many times. On the hilltops the stars can be seen throughout the clear, night sky, but when you descend into the valley, you can barely see the road because the fog is so thick.

134

Advection fogs form when warm, moist air blows over a cold surface, which then chills the air to the dew point producing the fog (Fig. 10-8). San Francisco is famous for its advection fogs. Cold ocean water produces a fog off the coast, and that fog is drawn inland as the daytime heating begins over the city. The fog is carried inland by a sea breeze.

A final type of cooling fog is the *upslope fog*, which forms when air is cooled to the dew point as it ascends a topographic barrier such as a mountain or hill (Fig. 10-8). Many of Earth's mountainous regions have more or less permanent upslope fogs on their windward sides, or the side of the mountain hit by the wind (Fig. 10-9).

Figure 10-9. Upslope Fog, British Columbia
(Robert L. Beck photo, 1975)

Frost

There are two types of frost—white frost and black frost. When people think of frost they usually have a mental image of *white frost*, which is also known as *hoar frost* or *jack frost*. White frost forms (usually during the night) when the temperature falls to the dew point, which is at or below freezing. Instead of forming dew, the water vapor forms white frost. When the dew point is at or below freezing it is then known as the *frost point*.

Black frost occurs when the temperature falls below freezing without reaching the dew point (frost point). No visible frost is formed, but the air temperature might have fallen low enough to kill your neglected tomato plants still lingering in the garden. For example, no visible frost will be present in the morning if the frost point of the previous night was 26 degrees but the nighttime low temperature only fell to 27 degrees. Black frost is also simply known as *freeze*. Weather stations often announce frost and freeze warnings when cold weather is imminent in the late summer, early fall, and late spring.

There are two main ways to protect temperature-sensitive plants from frost. One way is to select a favorable site for your plants (Fig. 10-10). In Indiana, and throughout most of the eastern United States, people avoid planting temperature-sensitive plants in low-lying areas. You should plant your apple trees on hillsides or hilltops, for as it was mentioned earlier, our first fall frosts and last spring frosts occur in low-lying areas.

Bodies of water also help protect plants from frost, for water holds heat. Michigan is one of the leading producers of cherries in the United States, and most of its cherry orchards are located in a strip of land running north-south just east of Lake Michigan. The westerlie winds carry some of the heat from Lake Michigan into the state of Michigan and help water-modify the climate along the shore. This is the coast that receives the wind, so it is known as the *windward coast* (Fig. 10-10). Across Lake Michigan, in Wisconsin, is the *leeward coast*. It is not water-modified because the winds blow from west to east.

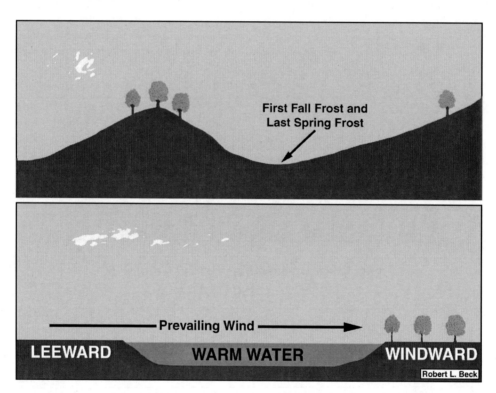

Figure 10-10. Favorable Sites to Protect Crops from Frost

Temperature-sensitive plants greatly benefit when they are placed in windward coasts or surrounded by water bodies. The Great Freeze of 1895 in Florida virtually wiped out the citrus industry in the state, for on February 8th of that year the temperature fell into the teens and remained there for several hours. The orange groves around Keystone City, however, survived the night with no substantial damage. Keystone City, at a slightly higher elevation than the areas around it, is positioned between two fairly large lakes, and many smaller lakes are located nearby. The citizens of the community were apparently so impressed with the attention they received from people all over the state concerning that event that they changed the name of their town to Frostproof.

136

The second way to protect crops from frost is to provide some sort of artificial protection (Fig. 10-11). Covering plants with cloth or paper is one artificial means used to protect plants from frost. The covering helps trap the earth heat around the plant thus preventing that heat from escaping to space during the night (Fig. 10-11). Smudge pots have also been tried, with limited success apparently, to protect crops from frost. Smudge pots are filled with oily substances, which are then set afire. As the fire burns, it generates a thick, heavy, black smoke that is supposed to drift throughout the orchard to act as an artificial cloud, thus again trapping the earth heat and preventing its loss to space (Fig. 10-11 and Fig. 10-12). Any slight wind virtually renders the smudge pot useless, for the smoke simply blows away, letting the earth heat pass to the upper atmosphere, thus chilling, and perhaps killing, the fruit on the trees. Smudge pots generate a lot of air pollution; in many areas their use has been banned.

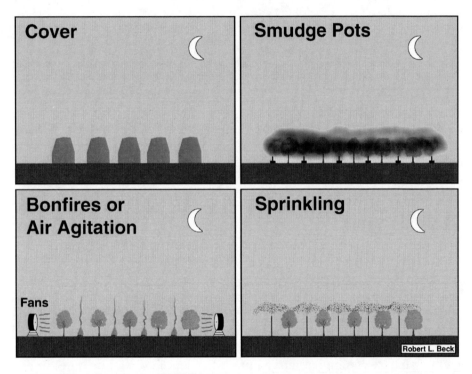

Figure 10-11. Artificial Ways to Protect Crops from Frost

Burners or bonfires have been used by fruit growers to protect their crops. The idea here is not to provide heat for the fruit directly but to heat selected points in the atmosphere so that inversion layers do not form and to reestablish small convection cells (Fig. 10-11). This mixes up the air and keeps the cold air moving around so it will not just settle around the valuable fruit. Agitating the air with fans or helicopters also keeps the cold air moving around, which delays or prevents temperature inversions from developing (Fig. 10-11).

Sprinkling fruit with water is another way to protect it from frost (Fig. 10-11 and Fig. 10-13). Recall that freezing is a heating process, so when water freezes on fruit it releases heat to the environment, which helps raise the air temperature of the orchard. The ice shell around the fruit also insulates it from the cold air in the orchard. Growers have to be careful when sprinkling their fruit with water, for if they allow too much of it to freeze the weight of accumulated ice might devastate the orchard by breaking all the major branches and limbs of the trees.

Fig. 10-12. Smudge Pots in an Avocado Grove, Ventura County, California
(John Brothers photo, 2007)

Fig. 10-13. Water Pipe with Sprinkler Head in an Orange Grove, Central Florida
(Robert L. Beck photo, 1972)

Module 10 Objectives

You should now be able to:

- Discuss why the *dew point* is related to air temperature

- Identify and contrast the three measures of humidity

- Compare and contrast the two instruments used to measure relative humidity

- Distinguish between high relative humidities and low relative humidities using data obtained by a sling psychrometer

- Discuss the two main ways that relative humidity is changed

- Explain how relative humidity is related to temperature and predict what will happen to the relative humidity of a volume of air if its temperature is changed

- Discuss how and why relative humidity changes throughout the day

- List the two types of fog, discuss how they originate, and differentiate among six subtypes of fogs

- Compare and contrast the two types of frost

- Discuss five ways to protect crops from frost

MODULE 11: PRECIPITATION

Water vapor molecules are moved around the atmosphere when the wind blows; they eventually condensate to form cloud droplets, which join together to form raindroplets resulting in **precipitation**, the fourth weather element. Precipitation includes both the liquid and solid forms of water that **fall** from the atmosphere. Rain, snow, hail, and sleet are all forms of precipitation. I once had two Japanese students in a geography class that I taught many years ago. I used the word *precipitation* in their class one day. After class they came up to me and asked what the word *precipitation* meant. I told them that, "precipitation is water that falls from the atmosphere to the earth." They asked why I did not use the word *rain*. I told them that snow, sleet, and hail are also forms of precipitation. They said, "But rain is not snow!" I said, "That's true, but they are both forms of precipitation." They ended the conversation by shaking their heads and saying, "It's a very technical word." I later checked with two Japanese instructors and they both told me, "There is no Japanese word for precipitation." I have never viewed the word the same since.

Formation of Raindroplets

In Module 5 (Atmosphere), I mentioned that gases, liquids, and solids are floating around in the atmosphere. The floating solids are too lightweight to fall, so they remain suspended and consist of such things as pollen, ice particles, dust, minerals, bacteria, viruses, smoke particles, dander, and ash. These solids are vitally important in the formation of precipitation, for they are a surface around which water can condense in the troposphere.

When air reaches saturation, usually by cooling it to the dew point, water vapor molecules begin to condense onto solid objects. At night, when saturation occurs at Earth's surface, condensation surfaces are readily available—dew forms on plants. In the higher levels of the atmosphere, when saturation occurs, water vapor condenses onto any available solid. The floating solids onto which water vapor condenses in the atmosphere are known as **condensation nuclei** (Fig. 11-1).

A cloud droplet is formed when water vapor condenses onto a floating solid object. Cloud droplets are too lightweight to fall. They remain suspended in the atmosphere until hundreds, or even thousands, of them start banding together to form a raindroplet, which is a liquid droplet **falling** from the atmosphere (Fig. 11-2). One raindroplet, composed of hundreds of cloud droplets, is loaded with the solid objects that were at the centers of its cloud droplets. People who wash their cars and then let them stand out in the rain know about this firsthand. After the rainwater evaporates from the car, a thin dirty film covers it. This film is composed of the solids carried out of the atmosphere by the raindroplets.

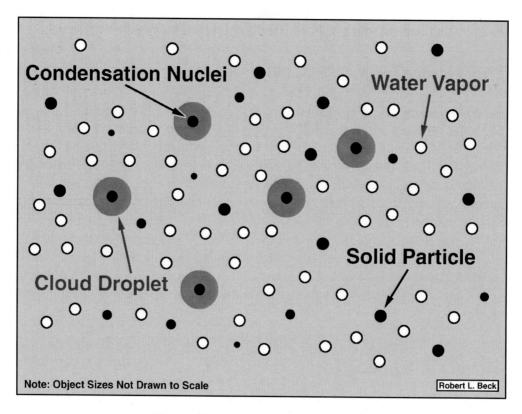

Figure 11-1. Condensation Nuclei

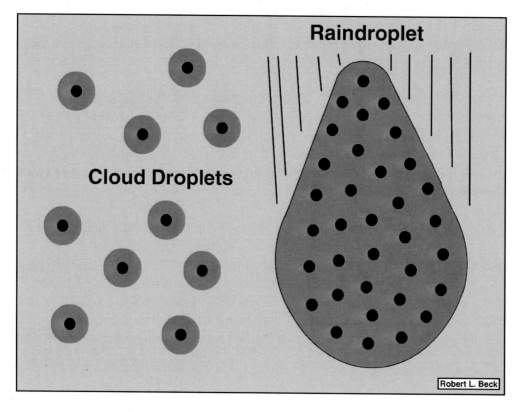

Figure 11-2. Cloud Droplets and Raindroplet

140

Air must be lifted (or caused to rise in some way) to produce precipitation. Air that moves upward produces precipitation; air that moves downward (subsides) produces dry conditions or droughts. Low pressure areas are associated with precipitation because convection occurs at the center of the low. High pressure areas are associated with dryness, because subsidence occurs at the center of the high.

There are four precipitation-producing conditions—convectional precipitation, orographic precipitation, convergence precipitation, and frontal precipitation. I will discuss them next.

Convectional Precipitation

The afternoon summer thundershower is produced by hot, rising air and is known as *convectional precipitation*. Earth's surface, even in central Indiana, is not a flat, featureless plain, for we find hills, valleys, forests, croplands, and other surfaces of various kinds scattered around the state. Some of these surfaces become hot when exposed to the high-angle July sun, but others remain relatively cool. You need to think of the earth's surface as composed of hot areas that are often situated adjacent to cool areas.

When the sun beats down on exposed, dark surfaces in July, the air above such surfaces becomes hot from earth radiation. The hot air eventually starts to rise and when it does it becomes known as a *thermal* (Fig. 11-3). Large birds such as vultures and hawks "ride the thermals," especially in the spring, summer, and fall, as they search for food. Whenever I see a vulture riding a thermal, I look beneath it to the ground surface to

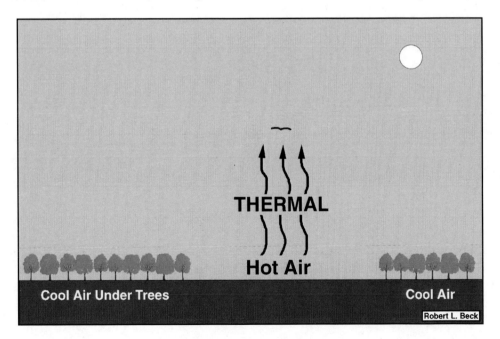

Figure 11-3. Thermal

141

see if I can spot what is producing a thermal lift for the bird. Air desirous of moving up into the troposphere from its original position near the earth's surface is said to be *unstable*. Whenever the weather conditions are right to produce rising air, we have an *unstable atmosphere*, which usually occurs during a summer day. The opposite condition, a *stable atmosphere*, occurs when the surface air does not want to rise and desires to remain in its original position near the earth's surface. Stable atmospheres usually occur during winter nights, especially when a temperature inversion is in place.

Because air pressure inversions do **not** exist in our atmosphere, a parcel of air rising in a thermal always comes under less air pressure, which causes it to expand. The air molecules in that parcel do not collide as frequently with the other air molecules in the parcel, and as a result it cools (Fig. 11-4). The cooling or warming of air by changing its air pressure is known as the *adiabatic process*. The air is not heated or cooled directly,

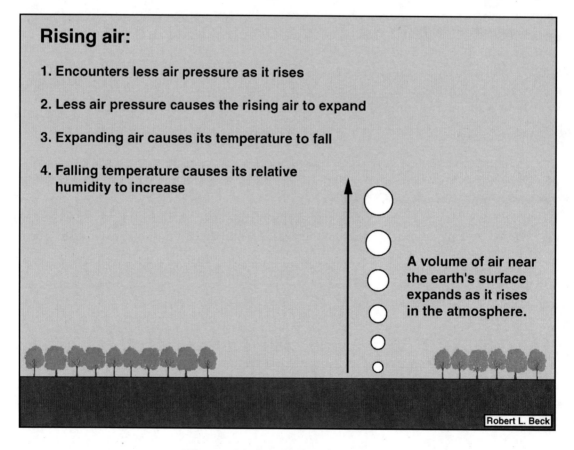

Rising air:

1. Encounters less air pressure as it rises

2. Less air pressure causes the rising air to expand

3. Expanding air causes its temperature to fall

4. Falling temperature causes its relative humidity to increase

A volume of air near the earth's surface expands as it rises in the atmosphere.

Robert L. Beck

Figure 11-4. Adiabatic Cooling

but its temperature changes because its pressure changes. Air that is not fully saturated (relative humidity less than 100%) cools or warms at a rate of 10°C per kilometer (about 5.5°F per 1,000 ft.). This rate of cooling (or warming) is known as the *dry adiabatic rate*. For example, if a rising parcel of air has a surface temperature of 90°F, at 1,000 feet above the surface its temperature will be 84.5°F, and at 2,000 feet it will be 79°F. Using Celsius, if it begins its ascent with a temperature of 35°C at ground level, then at one kilometer its temperature will be 25°C. (Fig. 11-5).

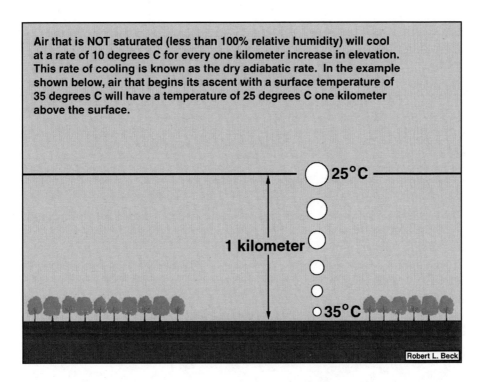

Air that is NOT saturated (less than 100% relative humidity) will cool at a rate of 10 degrees C for every one kilometer increase in elevation. This rate of cooling is known as the dry adiabatic rate. In the example shown below, air that begins its ascent with a surface temperature of 35 degrees C will have a temperature of 25 degrees C one kilometer above the surface.

25°C

1 kilometer

35°C

Robert L. Beck

Figure 11-5. Dry Adiabatic Rate

Hot air at the surface might have a relative humidity of 60%, but as it rises the adiabatic process causes it to cool through expansion, so its relative humidity increases. The relative humidity keeps going up as the air continues to rise—70%, 80%, 90%, and at 100% the dew point has been reached. The elevation in the atmosphere where rising air reaches 100% relative humidity is known as the ***lifting condensation level (LCL)*** (Fig. 11-6). Cumulus clouds start to form as warm air continues to rise up and above the LCL, for the air has reached its dew point so water vapor starts to condense forming cumulus clouds. Cumulus clouds often have flat bottoms, which marks the LCL (Fig. 11-6).

You should now recall that condensation is a heating process, for sensible heat is released to the environment when water vapor turns back into liquid water. When cumulus clouds begin to form, the release of sensible heat slows the rate of adiabatic cooling. Now, instead of cooling at 10°C per kilometer, the air cools at something less than 10°, maybe 8° or 7° or 6°. It now cools at the ***wet adiabatic rate*** (also known as *saturated adiabatic rate*), which is variable and less than 10°C per kilometer (Fig. 11-7).

Cumulus clouds often begin forming in the late morning of a summer day. These clouds grow vertically, for the air inside them is moving up and out (Fig. 11-8). By late afternoon they might develop into cumulonimbus clouds, or towering clouds possibly extending to the upper reaches of the troposphere. Cumulonimbus clouds bring rain and sometimes violent storms; they often have ***anvil heads*** on them because they are so tall (Fig. 11-9). Anvil heads form because the cloud top has extended into the high wind zone bordering the stratosphere. The high winds move the cloud top at a faster rate of speed than the slower winds near the earth's surface. Hail sometimes forms in cumulonimbus clouds and occasionally it is thrown into the anvil head. Convectional precipitation accounts for only about 5% of Indiana's annual precipitation and most of it occurs in the summer.

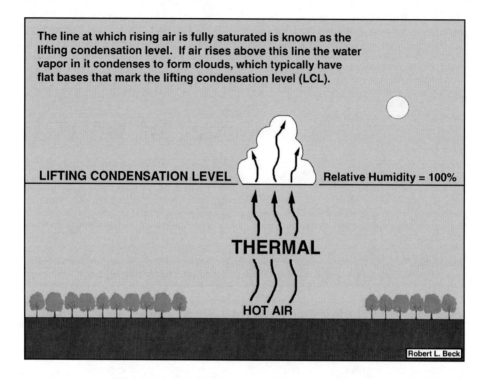

Figure 11-6. Lifting Condensation Level

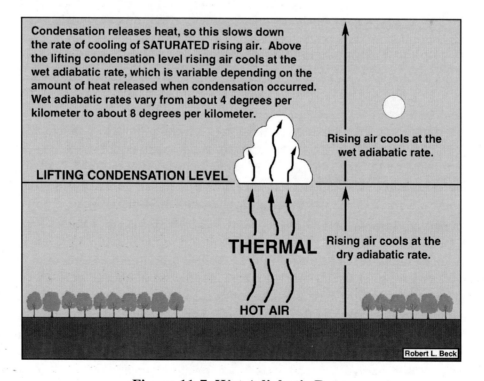

Figure 11-7. Wet Adiabatic Rates

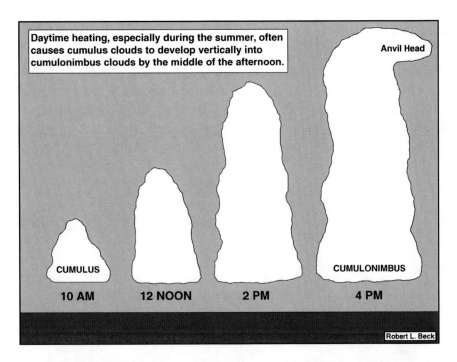

Daytime heating, especially during the summer, often causes cumulus clouds to develop vertically into cumulonimbus clouds by the middle of the afternoon.

Anvil Head

CUMULUS

CUMULONIMBUS

10 AM   12 NOON   2 PM   4 PM

Robert L. Beck

Figure 11-8. Vertical Development of Cumulus Clouds

Figure 11-9. The anvil heads of a thunderstorm approaching Greencastle, Indiana, on June 4, 2011, are highlighted by the sun in this photograph, which was taken in the late afternoon at about 8 PM. This particular storm brought strong winds, heavy rainfall, and a lot of lightning and thunder. It moved from north to south across Putnam County, and it was produced by daytime heating. The high temp. of the day was about 95°F, which is more typical of mid-July than early-June.
(Robert L. Beck photo, 2011)

Orographic Precipitation

Orographic precipitation is produced when air rises over a topographic barrier. Some people define orographic precipitation as related to mountains, but that is not entirely correct, for sometimes even small hills are enough to provide a lift for precipitation to occur. One hilly region in Indiana is an area known as the Crawford Upland, which runs north-south from Crawford County on the Ohio River to Putnam County west of Indianapolis (Fig. 11-10). Interstate 70, between Indianapolis and Terre Haute, crosses

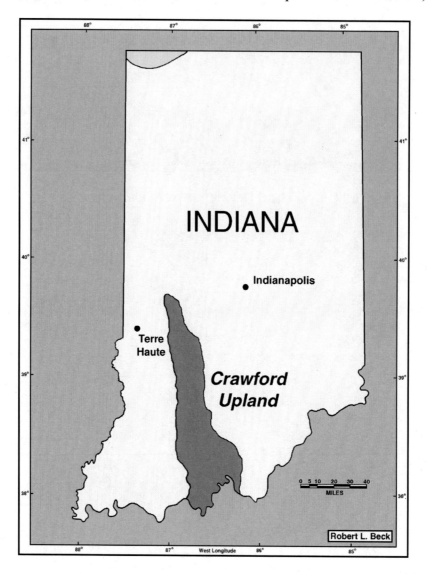

Figure 11-10. Crawford Upland

this hill region (milepost 29 to milepost 44). The elevation of Terre Haute is about 500 feet above sea level, but the elevation of the Crawford Upland is about 800 feet, so there is a 300-foot rise in elevation between Terre Haute (milepost 7) and southern Putnam County (milepost 37). I have driven the interstate from Terre Haute to Indianapolis about 1,200 times in my life, and on many occasions I have seen it raining, sprinkling, or

146

snowing in the Putnam County hills while it was dry in Terre Haute, 30 miles away. The wettest area in all of Indiana is the hill land of the southern part of the state; some of the state's moisture is produced by gentle uplift over these relatively small topographic barriers. The hill land of southern Indiana probably receives about 5% of its moisture from orographic lifting.

The side of a mountain or hill receiving the prevailing wind is known as the *windward side* (Fig. 11-11) As air strikes that side, it rises, which causes it to come under less air pressure, which causes it to expand, which lowers its temperature, which raises its relative humidity, which causes clouds to form at the LCL, which causes precipitation if enough condensation occurs. In other words, as the air rises on the windward side it *cools adiabatically* to help produce orographic precipitation.

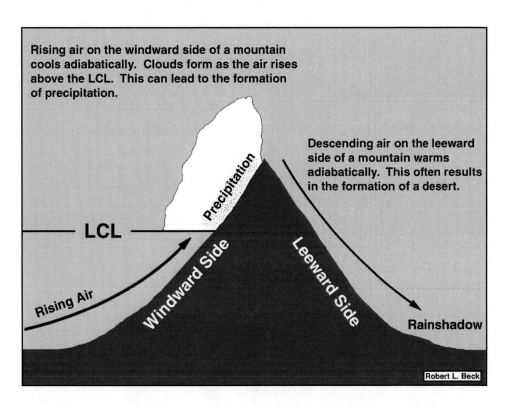

Figure 11-11. Orographic Precipitation

As the air descends on the *leeward side* of the mountain the whole process essentially works in reverse. The air descends, which causes it to come under more air pressure, which causes it to contract, which raises its temperature, which lowers its relative humidity, which causes clear skies, which produce dryness. As air descends on the leeward side, it *warms adiabatically* to help produce dry areas. A few deserts on Earth are located on the leeward sides of mountains and they are known as *rainshadow deserts* (Fig. 11-11).

Find the "Average Annual Precipitation" map of the United States in *Goode's World Atlas* on p. 90. Now find the states of Oregon and Washington on that map (they are named on p. 108). Please observe the western halves of those states receive about 60 to 80 inches of precipitation per year, whereas the eastern halves receive only about 5 to 20 inches per year. This huge difference in annual precipitation is explained by the presence of the Cascade Mountains, which run north-south through the middle of both Oregon and Washington (the Cascade Mountains are shown on p. 110). The Cascade Mountains are in the westerlie wind belt, so storms are driven into them from the Pacific Ocean. The western side of the Cascade Mountains is the windward side with its high amount of precipitation; the eastern side of the Cascade Mountains is the leeward side with its low amount of precipitation. In central Oregon, on the leeward side of the Cascades, is the Great Sandy Desert, which is situated in the western part of the Harney Basin north of Summer Lake (p. 112). The 21st edition of **Goode's World Atlas** labeled the Great Sandy Desert on p. 114, but the 22nd edition does not label it, which I view as a cartographic flaw of the 22nd edition. The Great Sandy Desert is an old name for this dry area of central Oregon, so its name should be included on maps of Oregon even if it is not commonly known by that name today.

Convergence Precipitation

This type of precipitation is mostly found in the low latitudes, especially at the ITC (Intertropical Convergence Zone), where the trade winds converge. Adiabatic cooling results in cloud formation as converging tropical air is forced to rise, and showery precipitation is the result (Fig. 11-12). This type of precipitation is also found in hurricanes and tropical storms when warm, moist air converges from all directions to enter the hurricane or tropical storm. Indiana receives no convergence precipitation from

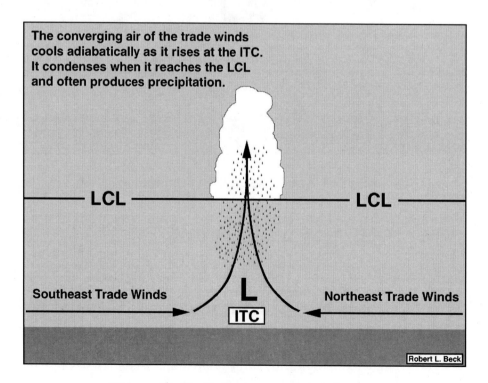

Figure 11-12. Convergence Precipitation

the ITC; however, occasionally we do receive some residual precipitation from a dying hurricane that has moved inland over the southeastern United States. In June 2005 my garden greatly benefited from the 2.5 inches of rain that fell from the remains of Hurricane Arlene; in July 2005 the remains of Hurricane Dennis lingered over central and southern Indiana for about 10 days, producing numerous rain showers and humid conditions; in August 2005 Hurricane Katrina flooded New Orleans, but its dying remains brought 1.2 inches to my yard; and in September 2005 the remnants of Hurricane Rita softened the ground just in time for my autumn planting of flower bulbs by gently dropping 2.7 inches of rain. We received a lot of rain in 2005 from dying hurricanes, much more than we normally do. Most years Indiana does not receive any convergence precipitation.

Frontal Precipitation

Lifting of air along weather fronts is the most important precipitation-producing condition in Indiana and in the United States, so I discuss it in depth. About 80% to 95% of the precipitation that falls on the state each year is caused by air being lifted along, or ahead of, cold fronts or warm fronts attached to *midlatitude cyclones* (mobile low pressure cells). Frontal precipitation is also known as *cyclonic precipitation*.

It has been mentioned many times that air blows into a low pressure system counterclockwise in the Northern Hemisphere. *Buys Ballot's Law* enables one to predict the general location of a low pressure cell (midlatitude cyclone) using only the wind as a guide. This law is useful in the field when no weather instruments are available. I will have at least one question on the next exam that tests your knowledge and ability to use this law. It is easy to use, for all you have to do is stand with your back to the wind and hold out your left arm so that it is positioned at a 90° angle with respect to the wind . . . your left arm is now pointing in the direction of the low (Fig. 11-13). For example, if the wind is blowing from east to west, the low is located to the south. Using Buys Ballot's law in the Southern Hemisphere requires that you hold out your right arm.

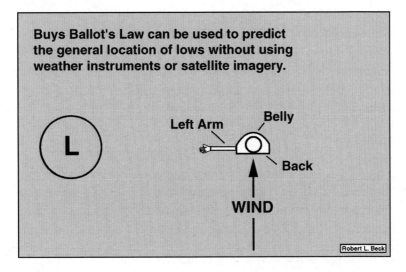

Figure 11-13. Buys Ballot's Law

In what direction is the low pressure cell located if the wind is blowing from northeast to southwest in Indianapolis? Answer is: The low pressure cell is located to the southeast.

There are two main types of cyclones on Earth—**midlatitude cyclones** and **tropical cyclones**, which are more commonly known as *hurricanes* in the United States. Midlatitude cyclones originate in the westerlie wind belt, so the westerlie winds blow them from west to east. A midlatitude cyclone in Nebraska might be moving into Indiana in a couple of days, but a midlatitude cyclone in Virginia has already moved by Indiana. The origin of a midlatitude cyclone is known as **cyclogenesis**, which is loosely translated as *cyclone beginning*.

Cyclogenesis often occurs on the polar front, for the different air temperatures on both sides of the front are capable of producing air pressure variations that give birth to a cyclone. Cyclogenesis can also occur over hot areas of the earth's surface, such as the deserts of the southwestern United States. Hot surfaces, as you should recall, are generally associated with low pressures. Sometimes intense heating of the earth by the sun can result in the formation of a midlatitude cyclone not located on the polar front.

Regardless of where midlatitude cyclones are born, they will be blown by the westerlie winds across the United States generally from west to east (or from southwest to northeast), and their storm tracks converge on New England (Fig. 11-14). A map showing the "Average Tracks of Highs and Lows" was printed in the 21st edition of **Goode's World Atlas** on p. 73, but that map was omitted in the 22nd edition.

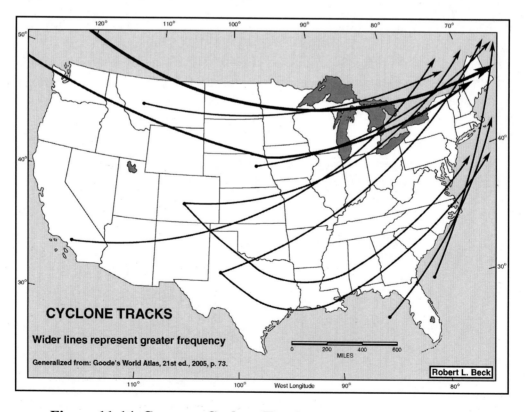

Figure 11-14. Common Cyclone Tracks across the United States

150

Midlatitude cyclones usually pass to the north of Indianapolis, but they might also pass to the south (Fig. 11-14). Whether they pass to the north or to the south is largely a matter of where cyclogenesis occurs. Cyclones that originate in Texas usually go south around; cyclones that originate in the central Great Plains usually go north around; and cyclones that originate in Colorado might go either north or south around Indianapolis. The map also shows that midlatitude cyclones converge on New England most commonly by moving to the northeast along the western side of the Appalachian Mountains. Some of our southern cyclones, however, swing south around the southern edge of the Appalachian Mountains and thence move to the northeast (in the general vicinity of New England) along the eastern side of the Appalachian Mountains. Few cyclones follow the crest of the Appalachian Mountains to converge on New England. The Appalachian Mountains are too short to block a midlatitude cyclone, but they do seem to bifurcate (split into two branches) the tracks of cyclones in the eastern United States.

WIND SHIFTS

One can do a reasonably good job of predicting whether a midlatitude cyclone will pass to the north of the city or to the south by observing *wind shifts*. As the midlatitude cyclone moves east, the winds swirling into it most likely go through a recognizable pattern. Assume that a midlatitude cyclone is located somewhere in the central Great Plains, perhaps in the middle of Kansas, on a Monday. Also assume Indianapolis is receiving a southeast wind trying to blow into that midlatitude cyclone counterclockwise (Fig. 11-15).

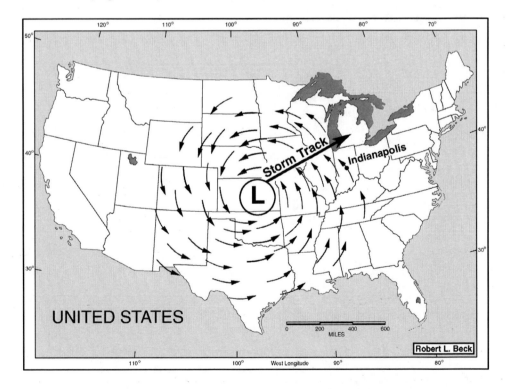

Figure 11-15. Monday Position of a Midlatitude Cyclone

151

Now assume that the cyclone is taking a track north of Indianapolis so that by Tuesday the low is over northern Missouri. The winds in Indianapolis are now blowing out of the south; they have shifted from the southeast to the south (Fig. 11-16).

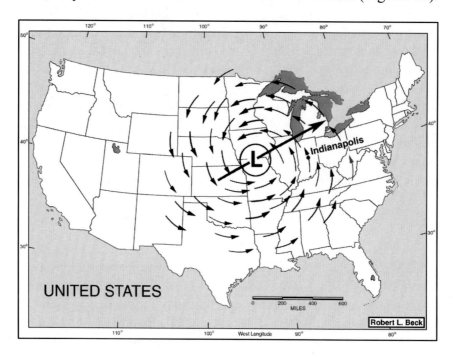

Figure 11-16. Tuesday Position of a Midlatitude Cyclone

On Wednesday, the low is over northern Illinois and the winds in Indianapolis are now blowing out of the southwest (Fig. 11-17).

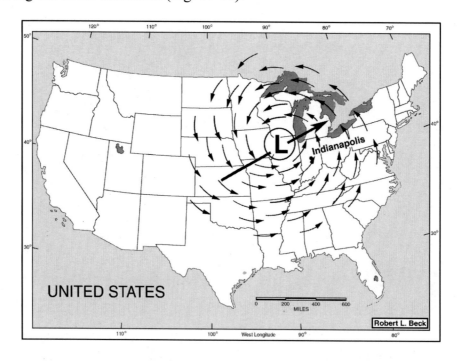

Figure 11-17. Wednesday Position of a Midlatitude Cyclone

On Thursday, the low is over southern Michigan and the winds in Indianapolis are now blowing out of the west (Fig. 11-18).

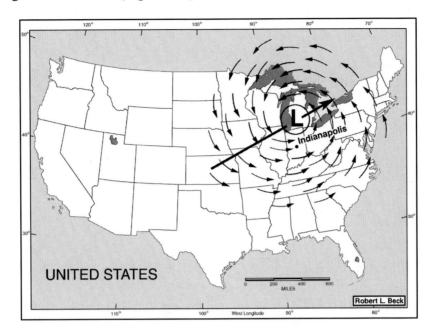

Figure 11-18. Thursday Position of a Midlatitude Cyclone

I will repeat the pattern of shift: southeast, south, southwest, west. Please observe in this example the winds have shifted clockwise; such a shift is known as a *veering wind shift* (Fig. 11-19). If you hear on a morning weather report "the winds are out of the south, but shifting to southwest by evening" then you know a veering wind shift pattern is occurring, and that the low will probably pass to our north.

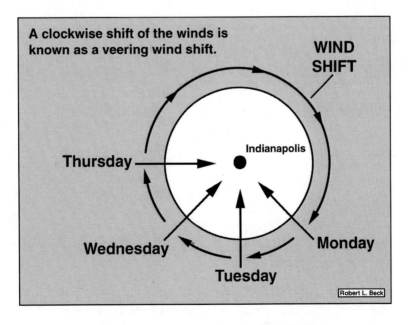

Figure 11-19. Veering Wind Shift

Now assume a midlatitude cyclone takes a southerly route around Indianapolis, as some do. A low in central Arkansas with a storm track aimed at Virginia might give Indianapolis a southeast wind on a Monday (Fig. 11-20).

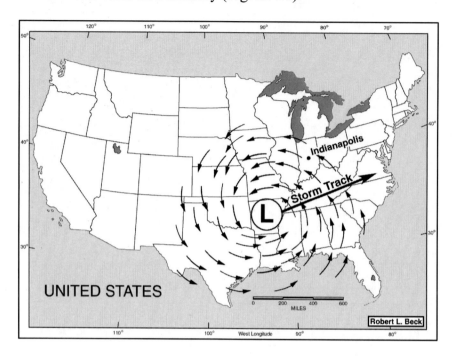

Figure 11-20. Monday Position of a Midlatitude Cyclone

By Tuesday the low is positioned over central Tennessee and the winds in Indianapolis are now blowing out of the east (Fig. 11-21).

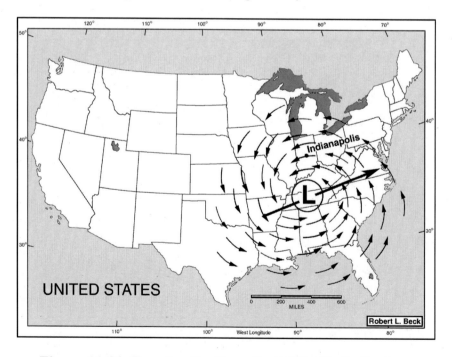

Figure 11-21. Tuesday Position of a Midlatitude Cyclone

154

The low moves to eastern Tennessee by Wednesday and the winds in Indianapolis are now blowing out of the northeast (Fig. 11-22).

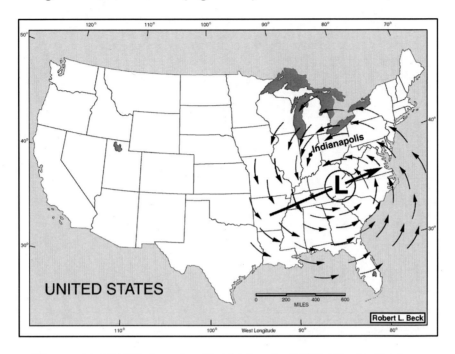

Figure 11-22. Wednesday Position of a Midlatitude Cyclone

On Thursday, the low is over Virginia and the winds in Indianapolis are now blowing out of the north (Fig. 11-23).

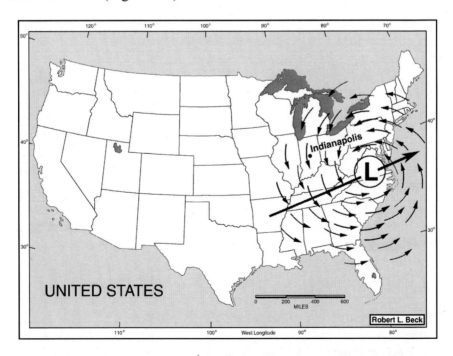

Figure 11-23. Thursday Position of a Midlatitude Cyclone

I will repeat the pattern of shift: southeast, east, northeast, north. Please observe the winds have shifted counterclockwise; this pattern of shift is known as a ***backing wind shift*** (Fig. 11-24). Backing wind shifts tell us the low will probably pass to our south.

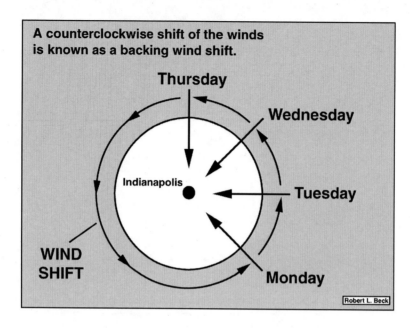

Figure 11-24. Backing Wind Shift

If the wind shifts from the west to the northwest, will the low probably pass to the north or to the south of Indianapolis? Answer is: This is a veering wind shift, so the low will probably pass to the north.

TYPES OF FRONTS

I now go back to the midlatitude cyclone in central Kansas and assume it was born there on the polar front, which I am now showing as a solid, black line (Fig. 11-25). When cyclogenesis occurred, the wind started to blow into the low counterclockwise. The atmosphere is simply trying to reestablish pressure equilibrium by moving air molecules into the cyclone. Some of these air molecules are cold, for they are located on the poleward side of the polar front, and some of them are warm, those on the equatorward side of the polar front. Cold air attempts to enter the cyclone from the northwest and in doing so runs into warm air. Cold air is denser and heavier than warm air, so the cold air simply displaces the warm air by pushing it up. A ***cold front*** is produced when the cold air pushes the warm air up; cold fronts are shown on daily weather maps as blue lines with blue triangles. The cold front in Figure 11-26 is shown as a dark gray line with dark gray triangles. The triangles point in the direction the cold air is moving.

The polar front starts to buckle as the cold front advances into the warm air sector. The warm air undergoes adiabatic cooling as it is lifted by the cold air, so ***cumulonimbus*** clouds often form just ahead of the cold front. These clouds can bring large quantities of rain in a short period of time; they can also bring lightning, thunder, and hail. Hard rains

156

of short duration typify cold front precipitation. A weather station might receive 1 inch of rain in 45 minutes or so. The precipitation band ahead of a cold tends to be narrow

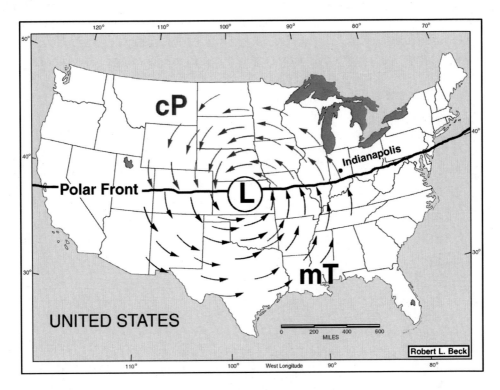

Figure 11-25. Cyclogenesis

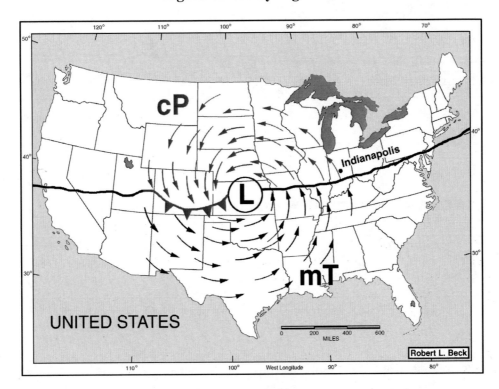

Figure 11-26. Cold Front

157

because the clouds develop vertically. A side profile or cross-section of a cold front is shown in Figure 11-27. The cold front has a steep vertical side where it meets the warm air. Frictional drag of the air in contact with earth objects (such as vegetation, buildings, and topographic barriers) slows the cold front down at the surface, so to a person standing outdoors the cold front passes overhead before it moves through the ground level environment around that person bringing a gust of wind and a change of temperature.

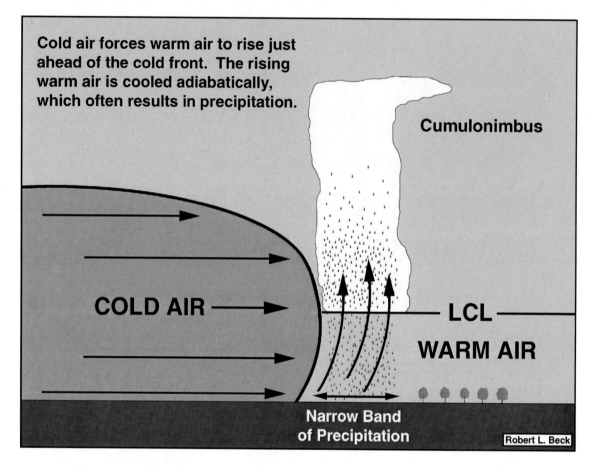

Figure 11-27. Cross-Sectional View of a Cold Front

A cold front typically originates west of the center of a midlatitude cyclone, whereas a ***warm front*** typically originates east of the cyclone's center. Precipitation episodes generated by warm fronts are quite different than those generated by cold fronts, for the structure of a warm front is unlike that of a cold front. Warm fronts are shown on weather maps as red lines with red half-circles. The warm front in Figure 11-28 is shown as a black line with black half-circles. The half-circles point in the direction the air is moving. As you see in the drawing, Indianapolis is north of the warm front, so the city has cP air situated over it even though it has a south wind. Evansville also has a south wind, but mT air is found there.

Warm fronts originate when warm air (which is usually mT air in Indiana) tries to enter the low by spirally into it counterclockwise. This air is almost always blowing into the state from the south or southeast when the warm front is born. As the warm, southern

158

air hits the cold air north of the polar front, it glides over the top of it, for it is too lightweight to displace the heavy, cold air (Fig. 11-29).

Warm air is lifted over the cold air along a gentle gradient, but the rising, warm air still cools adiabatically even though the slope of the warm front is considerably flatter than the slope of a cold front. Clouds develop along a warm front horizontally, and not vertically as along a cold front. These horizontally developed clouds are known as *stratus* clouds, for they have a layered appearance, and they might spread out 200 hundred miles or more beyond the contact of the warm front with the earth's surface (Fig. 11-29). As condensation occurs, the clouds become dark and filled with cloud droplets. When these clouds give the appearance of rain, they are then known as *nimbostratus* clouds, or layered rain-bearing clouds. Precipitation falls from a warm front over a large area because the clouds developed horizontally (Fig. 11-29). Warm front precipitation is characterized by precipitation episodes of gentle rain of long duration. This is the type of rain that falls all day and might bring a total of 1 to 2 inches—a good, soaking rain for the lawn and garden. Because warm air gradually slides over cold air along a warm front, the stratus clouds produced by the rising air are stretched way out over the cold air and often can be seen hundreds of miles away by an observer positioned north of the warm front cloud bank. Precipitation falling from warm front clouds actually falls though cold air before reaching Earth's surface (Fig. 11-29).

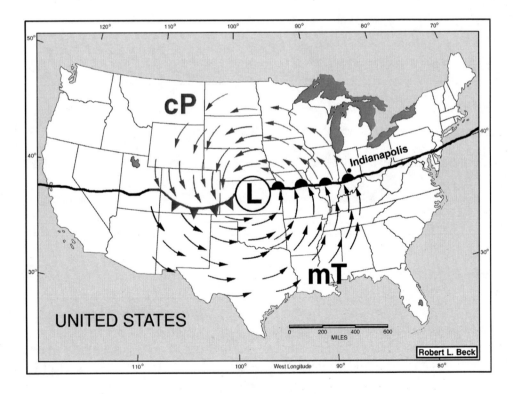

Figure 11-28. Warm Front

Warm fronts sometimes bring large snowfall episodes to Indiana and the eastern United States in the winter, especially in February. One can do a pretty good job of predicting heavy precipitation patterns simply by projecting the track a cyclone will take and estimating whether or not a place will receive warm front precipitation. My hometown of Minden, Nebraska, receives large amounts of warm front precipitation if the low is positioned over southeastern Colorado. If the low is over Arkansas, southern Indiana is likely to receive abundant snowfall. Central Indiana often gets hit with heavy snowfall when a low is positioned over southern Missouri. Such a storm struck central Indiana on February 13, 2007—Indianapolis received about 10 inches of snow mixed with sleet and freezing rain. IUPUI cancelled classes for two days. I was digging out on Valentine's Day, and it was difficult to do so because the sleet and freezing rain produced a two-inch layer of ice, which was covered with eight inches of snow. Whenever I travel during the winter, I try to remain apprised of the position of the low; if it looks like it will be over southern Missouri or Arkansas, I prepare for icy conditions and heavy snow in central Indiana.

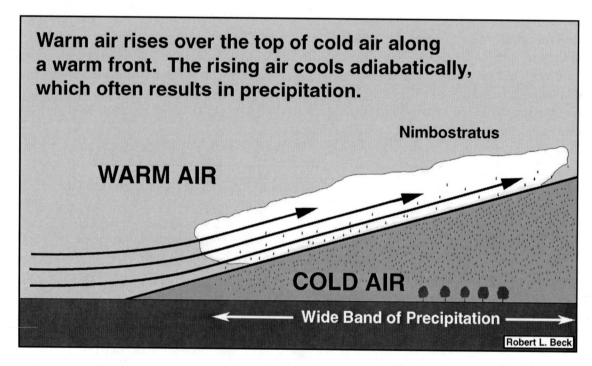

Figure 11-29. Cross-Sectional View of a Warm Front

As cold fronts move, they actively displace the warm air during their advance. Eventually they sweep around the southern flank of a midlatitude cyclone (in the northern hemisphere) and run into the warm front (Fig. 11-30). When a cold front runs into a warm front, the collision produces an *occluded front*, which is shown on weather maps as a purple line with alternating purple triangles and half-circles. The occluded front in Figure 11-31 is shown as a black line with alternating black triangles and half-circles.

The midlatitude cyclone is nearing the end of its life cycle when occlusion occurs. The low stalls and precipitation might fall in the same place for a couple of days as the low dissipates. Occlusion usually does not occur over Indiana, but in May 2006 occlusion did occur here. We had cold, damp weather for about a week. It certainly delayed the ripening of the fruit on my cherry trees. Occluded fronts are much more common in the northern and northeastern states than they are in the Midwest. Occlusion also commonly occurs over the Atlantic Ocean offshore of the eastern United States.

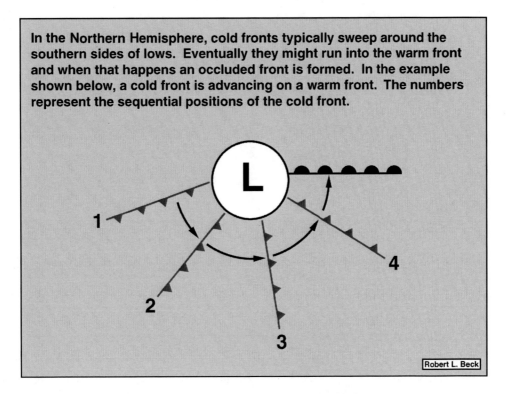

Figure 11-30. Cold Front Movement

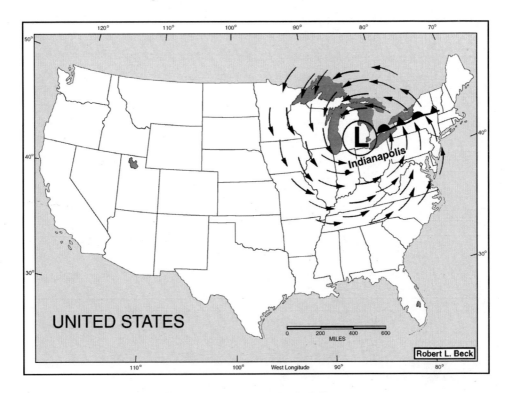

Figure 11-31. Occluded Front

161

Module 11 Objectives

You should now be able to:

- Describe the formation of *raindroplets*

- Differentiate between a *stable atmosphere* and an *unstable atmosphere*

- Compare and contrast *convectional precipitation*, *orographic precipitation*, *convergence precipitation*, and *frontal precipitation*

- Discuss the *adiabatic process*

- Use the dry adiabatic rate to compute temperature changes in the atmosphere

- Compare and contrast the *dry adiabatic rate* with the *wet adiabatic rate*

- Use *Buys Ballot's law*

- Differentiate between *veering wind shifts* and *backing wind shifts*

- Compare and contrast *cold front precipitation* and *warm front precipitation*

Practice Exercise: Match the points on the map with the following five phrases:

_____ mT air   _____ nimbostratus clouds   _____ east wind

_____ cold air   _____ cumulonimbus clouds

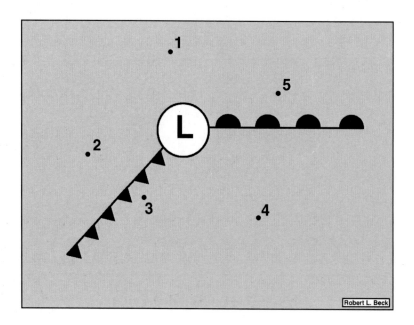

MODULE 12: SEVERE STORMS

In this module I briefly examine four types of severe storms—thunderstorms, squall lines, tornadoes, and hurricanes. All of them are produced by **low pressure systems** and not high pressure systems. A great many people have the mistaken notion that high pressure systems produce severe storms.

Thunderstorms

Thunderstorms form when warm air rises in an ***unstable atmosphere***, which, as you know, typically occurs during a summer afternoon when the base of the atmosphere has become hot. Three stages characterize the life cycle of the thunderstorm. The first stage is the ***cumulus stage***, which results in the formation and vertical development of cumulus clouds. Updrafts of rising air are found within the clouds, and substantial amounts of latent heat are released to the atmosphere as condensation occurs (Fig. 12-1).

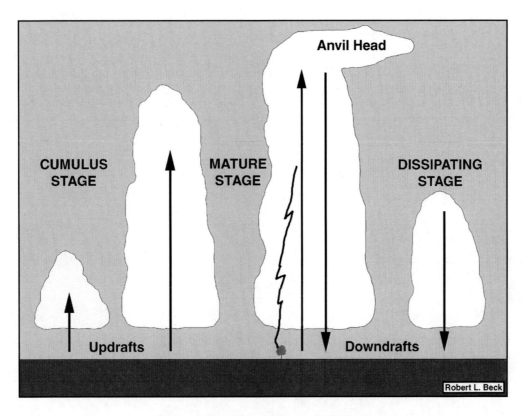

Figure 12-1. Thunderstorm Stages

Lightning and thunder announce the second stage of the thunderstorm—the ***mature stage*** . . . the most intense stage of the thunderstorm. During this stage precipitation starts to fall, and as it does it starts to evaporate, chilling the air in the cloud. The chilled air becomes heavy and starts to sink creating a downdraft. The cumulus cloud has become a cumulonimbus cloud with both updrafts of warm air and downdrafts of

163

cool air within its boundaries. An updraft of warm air adjacent to a downdraft of cool air is known as a **storm cell** (Fig. 12-1).

The **dissipating stage** is the third and final stage of the thunderstorm. Downdrafts of cool air are now found throughout the cloud, so the storm is deprived of the warm, moist, rising air it needs to maintain itself. In essence, the cool, heavy, descending air extinguishes the fire that built the storm in the first place (Fig. 12-1).

Squall Lines

When a cold front approaches, one or more lines of storms might arrive before the storm associated with the cold front itself appears. These narrow bands of thunderstorms that precede cold fronts by dozens or hundreds of miles are known as **squall lines**. Squall lines are also known as *pseudo-cold fronts*, because they give every appearance of being a cold front to an observer in the field.

Squall lines are initiated when downdrafts occur in cumulonimbus clouds along the cold front. These downdrafts, when strong enough, can force warm, moist air to rise in advance of the front producing a squall line. The first squall line can produce a second squall line so that waves of thunderstorms might strike a place before the actual cold front moves through, maybe many hours later (Fig. 12-2).

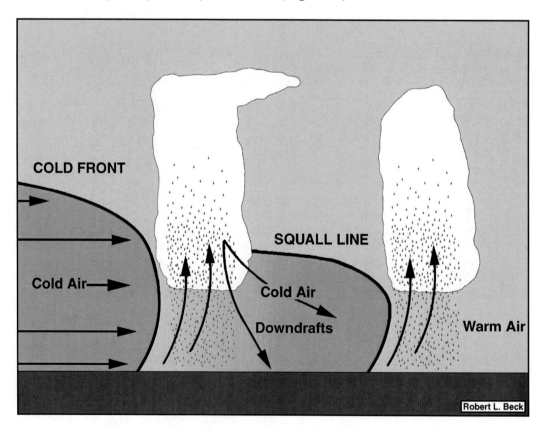

Figure 12-2. Squall Line

164

Tornadoes

Tornadoes are severe storms with intensely low pressures and extremely steep pressure gradients, which explains why these storms have the world's highest wind speeds, 250 to 300 mph. Winds usually converge on the tornado counterclockwise in the Northern Hemisphere, but some clockwise circulations have been observed.

Tornadoes typically originate along squall lines ahead of advancing cold fronts, but severe thunderstorms can also produce them. Once a tornado forms in the United States, it tends to follow the squall line or cold front on a path trending from the southwest to the northeast. Whenever tornado weather threatens, you should always first observe the southwestern sky, for over 80% of all major tornadoes recorded in Illinois from 1919 to 1969 moved from the southwest to the northeast (Fig. 12-3).

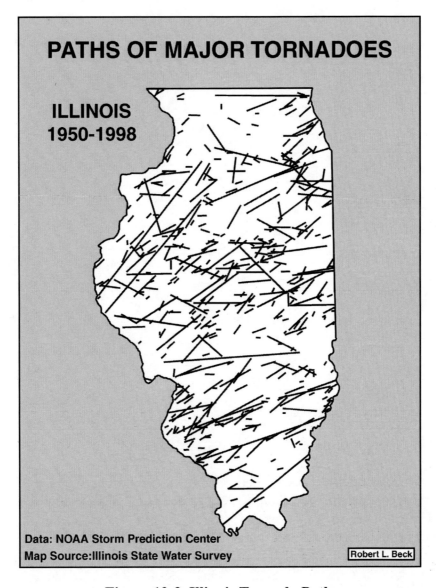

PATHS OF MAJOR TORNADOES

ILLINOIS 1950-1998

Data: NOAA Storm Prediction Center
Map Source: Illinois State Water Survey

Robert L. Beck

Figure 12-3. Illinois Tornado Paths

The exact procedure by which tornadoes form is not fully understood. Many explanations of tornado formation have been developed over the years. One of the leading explanations involves the formation of a *mesocyclone* by a column of horizontally rotating air that is tilted into a vertical column by the strong updrafts of a thunderstorm. Tornadoes sometimes descend from the rotating cloud wall of the mesocyclone.

The average length of a tornado path is about 4 miles. The Tri-State tornado that occurred on March 18, 1925, had the longest path on record, 219 miles. It began in southeastern Missouri, was on the ground all the way across southern Illinois, and terminated near Princeton, Indiana (Fig. 12-4). Over 700 people were killed by this tornado, and it ranks as the worst tornado disaster in U.S. history. Official records, which were not established until the 1950s, rank the Alabama tornados that struck in April 2011 as the worst tornado disaster.

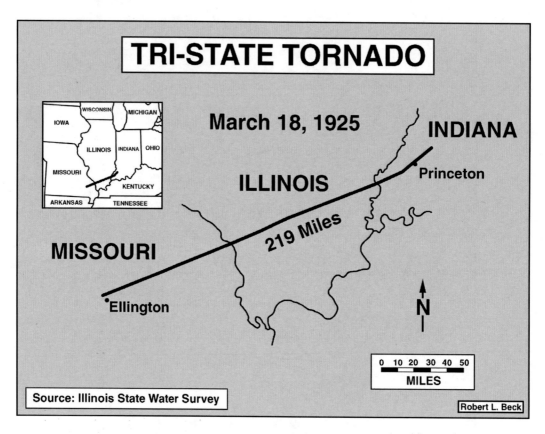

Figure 12-4. Tri-State Tornado

Tornadoes occur on every continent except Antarctica, but the overwhelming majority of them originate in the United States. There are no major mountain ranges in the eastern United States preventing mT air from the Gulf of Mexico from colliding with cP air from northern Canada. When cyclogenesis occurs along the polar front, which is usually positioned west-to-east across the United States, warm air clashes with cold air as both are drawn into the midlatitude cyclone, sometimes producing tornadoes.

The season of tornado formation in the eastern United States has a definite geographic pattern (Fig. 12-5). Northern Florida and the southerly areas of the Gulf Coast states receive many of their tornadoes in January and February[2]; Arkansas, the northerly areas of the Gulf Coast states, and the southeastern states receive most of their tornadoes in March; the Southern Plains, Missouri, Kentucky, and the lower Midwest (including central and southern Indiana) receive most of their tornadoes in April and May; and the Northern Plains and the Great Lakes states receive most of their tornadoes in June and July. This pattern reflects the migration of the polar front, which is tied to the migration of the SSP. More tornadoes originate over North America as the continent is warming up (February – July) than cooling down (August – January).

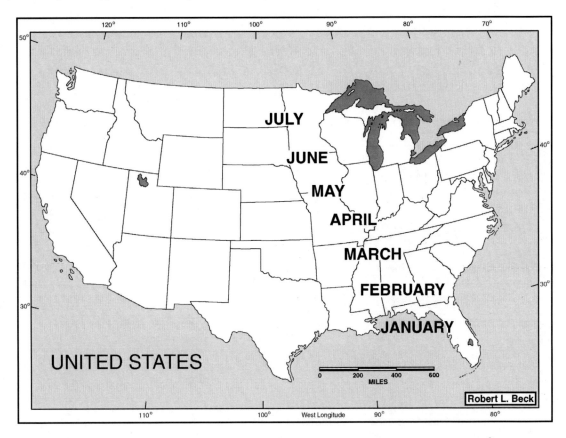

Figure 12-5. Month of Tornado Frequency in the Eastern U.S.[2]

Texas has more tornadoes on an annual basis than any other state, but this is expected given its large size. When the size bias is removed and we look at the number of tornadoes by state per thousand square miles then Florida and Oklahoma are usually ranked first and second. Indiana is usually third. The "tornado alley" of Oklahoma and Kansas receives a lot of national attention because a good share of the nation's tornadoes form in this area, but a smaller and much less known "little tornado alley" extends across the plains of central Illinois and central Indiana.

---

[2]Florida and the southeastern states also receive many tornadoes generated by hurricanes in the late summer and fall. The map shown in Figure 12-5 does not take that fact into account. The map shows tornado frequency associated with the polar front.

Hurricanes

Hurricanes are intense low pressure storms that form in the trade wind belts, so meteorologists call them *tropical cyclones* to distinguish them from the low pressure storms that form in the westerlie wind belts, the midlatitude cyclones. Tropical cyclones are known by different names in different areas of the world. In the Caribbean and the United States we call them *hurricanes*; in East Asia they are known as *typhoons*; in the Indian Ocean and Australia they are known as *cyclones*; in the Philippines they are known as *baguios*; and in parts of Australia they have been called *willy willys*.

Hurricanes do not form on the Equator or within about 5 latitudinal degrees of it. The lack of a Coriolis effect on the Equator and the weak Coriolis effect on both sides of it prevent air from converging to allow cyclogenesis to occur. The areas where hurricanes originate are located from about 5° to 15° North and South Latitudes. There are eight hurricane formation areas on Earth (Fig. 12-6).

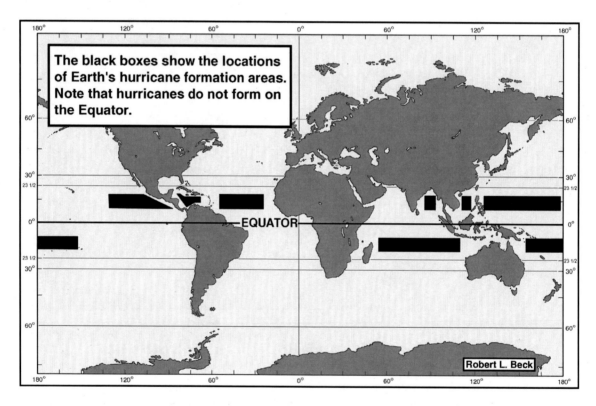

The black boxes show the locations of Earth's hurricane formation areas. Note that hurricanes do not form on the Equator.

Robert L. Beck

Figure 12-6. Hurricane Formation Areas

A tropical storm becomes a hurricane when its wind speeds exceed 74 mph and they begin when an *easterly wave* starts to initiate convergence of tropical air. In the Northern Hemisphere, like midlatitude cyclones, winds spiral counterclockwise as they converge on the hurricane. In the Southern Hemisphere they spiral clockwise. Once a hurricane forms, the trade winds blow it from east to west, so hurricanes have fairly recognizable paths (Fig. 12-7).

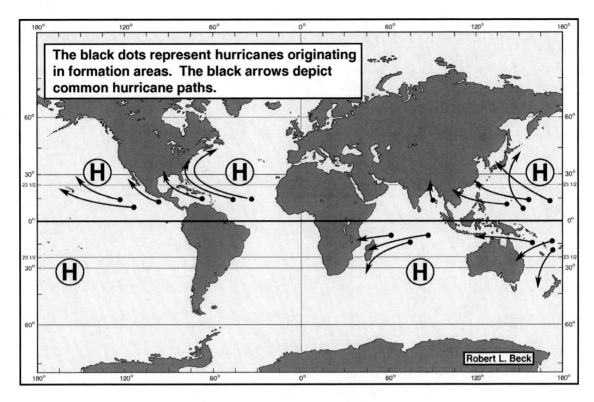

Figure 12-7. Hurricane Paths

Hurricanes often move around the western sides of subtropical high pressure cells (Fig. 12-7). When this occurs, they start to move poleward and might eventually enter the westerlie wind belt, which will cause them to move from west to east just like a midlatitude cyclone. A movie released a few years ago, *The Perfect Storm*, showed a hurricane in the Atlantic Ocean rounding the western side of the Bermuda High to merge with a midlatitude cyclone in the North Atlantic Ocean. The westerlie winds had blown the midlatitude cyclone into the Atlantic Ocean from North America.

Latent heat, stored in the water vapor of converging air, provides the energy needed to keep hurricanes alive. As humid air rises in a hurricane it is cooled adiabatically to the dew point, which brings condensation. Sensible heat is released to the atmosphere when condensation occurs. This fuels the hurricane because the just released sensible heat enables the air to continue to rise, which causes even more condensation and the release of even more sensible heat. Hurricanes rapidly lose their strength when they pass over either cold water or land, for they are deprived of the large quantities of water vapor (containing latent heat) needed to sustain their lives.

The center of a hurricane is known as "the eye." The most powerful storms in the hurricane occur in the eyewall clouds surrounding the eye, but the eye itself is an area of clear weather. Bands of storms surround the eyewall clouds and they extend outward for about 150 miles or so. Places that are directly hit by hurricanes might have to suffer through four or five lines of storms before the eye appears and then another four or five lines of storms before the hurricane passes (Fig. 12-8).

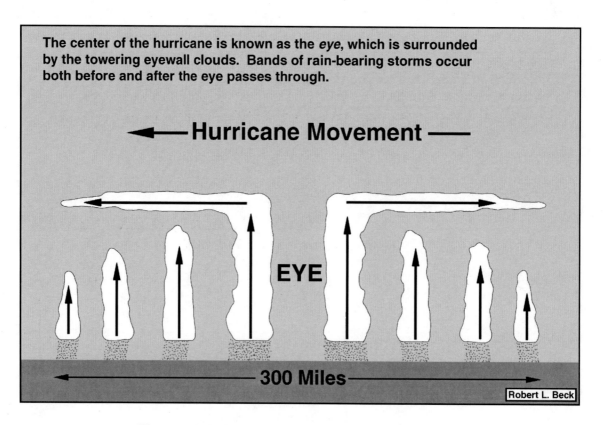

The center of the hurricane is known as the *eye*, which is surrounded by the towering eyewall clouds. Bands of rain-bearing storms occur both before and after the eye passes through.

Figure 12-8. Cross-sectional View of a Hurricane

Module 12 Objectives

You should now be able to:

- Describe the three stages of a thunderstorm

- Compare and contrast *squall line storms* with *cold front storms*

- List at least seven characteristics of tornadoes

- Discuss why more tornadoes form in the United States than anywhere else on Earth

- Describe the geographic pattern of the season of tornado formation in the eastern United States

- Explain why tornado paths in the United States typically trend from the southwest to the northeast

- Identify which state has the most tornadoes on a yearly basis and explain why this is the case

- Discuss why hurricanes do not form on the Equator

- Describe why hurricanes tend to follow relatively predictable paths

- Identify the source of energy needed to keep a hurricane alive and explain how that energy source fuels the hurricane

- List at least seven characteristics of hurricanes

Practice Exercise: Using colored pencils, draw the approximate position of the polar front in the eastern United States on this map for February, April, and June.

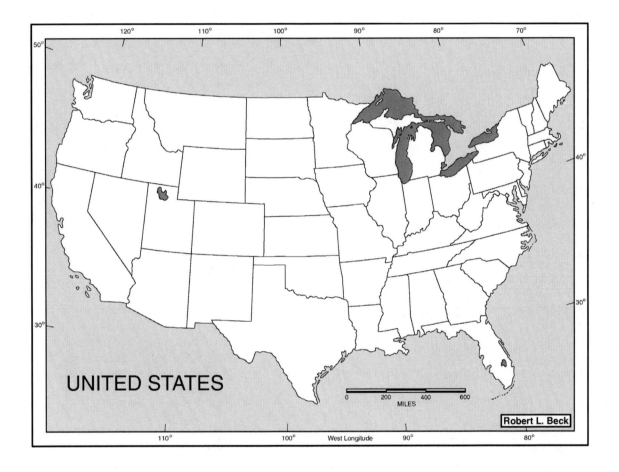

****

"I have read many definitions of what is a conservationist, . . . but I suspect that the best one is written not with a pen, but an axe." — Aldo Leopold, ***A Sand County Almanac***, 1949.

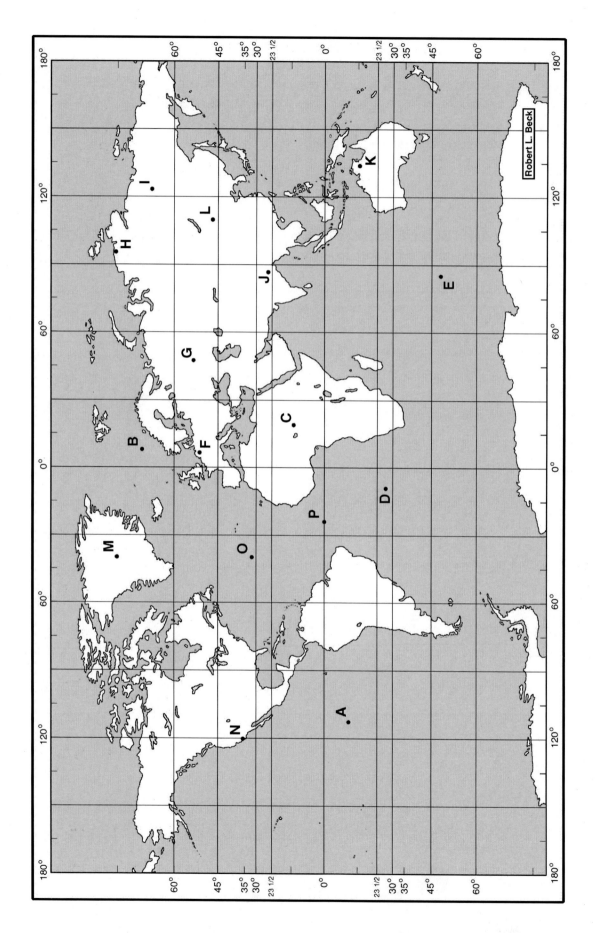

MODULE 13: HYDROSPHERE

Water is one of the most important substances in our lives. Our bodies, for example, are mostly composed of water. Understanding the distribution of water helps one to understand the distribution of different life-forms, such as vegetation. The excess or lack of water certainly plays a major role in influencing the types of plants one finds growing in any particular area of Earth's surface. Even in my own small yard, different plants grow in different spots partially because of variations in soil wetness.

The distribution of the world's climates is strongly influenced by the distribution and movement of water. Ocean currents move energy around in seawater, and latent heat is redistributed around the globe through the movement of water vapor. Water is vital to life on Earth and also in understanding many of the patterns studied in physical geography.

Global Water Storage

I like to begin the study of water by identifying the major containers that store Earth's water. What are these containers? Where is water stored on Earth? Of course, most of Earth's water is stored in the *oceans*, which account for about 97% of Earth's water. The original oceans are thought to have been composed of freshwater, but with time weathered minerals from the earth's rocks have settled in the oceans making them salty.

Glaciers, ice caps, and snowfields hold about 2% of Earth's water, so they rank second behind the oceans in water storage. Antarctica holds most of Earth's freshwater. There is about twice as much freshwater in Antarctica as in all other freshwater sources on Earth combined. Many people underestimate the size of Antarctica. Cartographers often remove Antarctica from maps, and others have the attitude it is unimportant because there are no permanent populated places on it (research centers do not count as populated places). Antarctica encompasses an area of 5,000,000 square miles covered with an ice sheet nearly 10,000 feet thick in places. The United States, by comparison, has an area of only about 3,600,000 square miles. Imagine traveling from southern Florida to northern Alaska over an ice sheet similar to the one found in Antarctica. One can begin to comprehend the amount of water in Antarctica when viewed in those terms. The Greenland ice sheet, the Northern Hemisphere's largest, is quite small when compared to Antarctica. In my opinion, Antarctica will become an increasingly important water source as Earth starts to run out of freshwater. Arab countries have long experimented with the possibilities and practicalities of towing icebergs to the dry Middle East.

Water stored in *groundwater aquifers* is the third most important water storage container. An aquifer is a zone of water-bearing rock. Water enters an aquifer from percolating down through the soil or from lateral migration via an underground route. Many cities in Indiana, including Indianapolis, get all or part of their drinking water from groundwater aquifers.

Lakes and ponds, both fresh and salt, are the fourth leading water storage container. Freshwater lakes have a constant inflow and outflow of water, but saltwater lakes, such as Great Salt Lake in Utah, only have streams flow into them—no streams flow out of them, so the salts carried into the lake by the river accumulate.

A lot of water is stored in the soil. ***Soil water*** is stored in clay minerals, in organic matter, in pore spaces, and in humus (partially decomposed organic matter). *Soil water* does not mean the same thing as *groundwater*, for a person does not drill a well and pump water out of the soil. Soils cover a large portion of Earth's surface, and some of them are deep, so they store an abundance of water. I usually ask my traditional lecture classes to prepare a list of Earth's major water storage containers. About one-half or more of them fail to include soil water in their lists.

Stream water is water confined to a channel flowing to a lower level under the influence of gravity. Water might enter the stream from a precipitation event, from a lake, from an underground source, or from running off the surface. Water flowing in the Amazon River is stream water, but so is the water flowing in Fall Creek in Indianapolis. A detailed discussion of streams is presented in Module 24.

Atmospheric water includes cloud droplets, raindroplets, water vapor, and the various icy forms such as snow and hail. Water has a short stay in the atmosphere. It might be there only for a few minutes or for a couple of days before it condenses and precipitates out. Of course water is constantly entering the atmosphere, through evaporation, from a variety of sources. Condensation nuclei, as discussed earlier in Module 11, play a vital role in helping liquid water enter and leave the atmosphere.

Finally, plants and animals store water in their bodies. Some plants, and animals, have the ability to store large quantities of water—certain cacti and camels are two good examples. Goats can live in an even drier environment than camels, for although a camel can store a lot of water it must drink a large volume when dehydrated. Goats can get almost all the water they need by simply eating plants. Water in plants and animals is essential for good health, for water helps cycle nutrients and minerals throughout the body and it helps certain animals, such as humans, expel waste and regulate body temperature through the act of sweating. Water stored in the biosphere is known as ***biological water***.

There are eight major water storage containers on Earth, and there are many minor containers such as water stored in canned foods, automobile radiators, municipal water towers, and various other containers devised by humans. People disagree as to the rank order of the major containers, but the order presented above is the order we will use in this course.

To transfer large quantities of water from one container to another requires a process of some sort, which links the two containers. For example, to transfer water from the ocean to the atmosphere requires a process, which, in this case, is evaporation. To transfer water from a lake to an animal requires a process—ingestion (drinking). To transfer water from the soil to the ground requires a process—percolation. Atmosphere to stream—precipitation. Stream to lake—runoff. Soil to plant—absorption. And so forth.

Hydrologic Cycle

The water cycle is just one of many cycles in the natural world. Others include the carbon cycle, the phosphorous cycle, the nitrogen cycle, and the oxygen cycle. The water cycle is important to us not only because we consume a lot of water as individuals but also because it is an energy flow system—when you move liquid water and water vapor around Earth you also move heat around.

The oceans cover about 71% of Earth's surface and the continents and islands account for only about 29%, so the oceans are a good place to begin a discussion of the hydrologic (water) cycle. *Evaporation* is usually considered the first step in the water cycle (Fig. 13-1). The oceans absorb large amounts of solar radiation, and as a result the tropical areas of the oceans evaporate huge quantities of water.

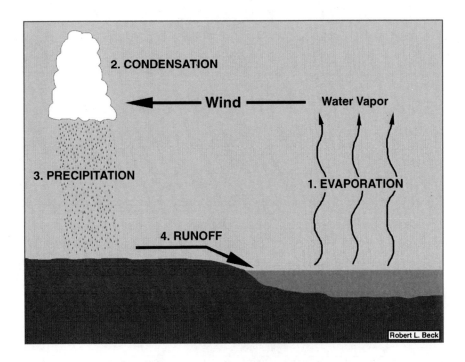

Figure 13-1. Hydrologic Cycle

Water vapor from oceanic environments is carried inland over the continents by the winds. The cooling of water vapor causes *condensation* to occur, the second step in the water cycle, and clouds form as a result.

If enough condensation occurs in a cloud, it starts to form *precipitation*, the third step. Rain, snow, sleet, or hail falls from the cloud to the earth. Once there it might (1) percolate down into a groundwater aquifer, (2) evaporate, or (3) run off the land and go back into the ocean to begin the cycle all over again. *Runoff* is the fourth step in the hydrologic cycle.

I have presented a simple and basic hydrologic cycle to illustrate its main components. The complete water cycle is much more complicated than this.

Ocean Currents

Everyone who takes an introductory physical geography course should be introduced to Earth's major ocean currents. A good place to begin is by studying the *gyres*, which are the circular motions of the ocean situated beneath the subtropical high pressure cells (Fig. 13-2). The centers of the gyres are positioned at about 30° latitude in both hemispheres. In the Northern Hemisphere the gyres circulate clockwise and in the Southern Hemisphere they circulate counterclockwise, so they circulate just like the diverging air of the high pressure cells above them.

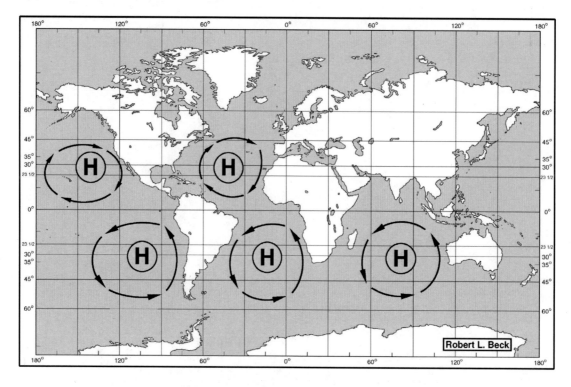

Figure 13-2. Gyres

Ocean currents are classified as either *warm currents* or *cold currents*. Do not assume, however, that a warm current is warm with respect to your body. In the Second World War the Germans found that if a pilot was shot down over the warm current off the west coast of Norway, he would be dead in about 20 minutes from exposure to the ocean water. Currents are warm or cold depending on (1) where they originate, (2) their direction of flow, and (3) how they compare in temperature to adjacent landmasses. In general, a current is warm if it originates in the tropics and flows poleward, and a current is cold if it originates in a polar area and flows equatorward (Fig. 13-3). A current flowing poleward originating in the middle latitudes is warm, but a current flowing equatorward originating in the middle latitudes is cold. You should now be able to classify the numbered currents on Figure 13-3 as either warm or cold.

Ocean currents pulling away from continents cause deep ocean water to rise, thus replacing the surface water moving out to sea. This process is known as *upwelling,* and it mostly occurs off the western coasts of landmasses. One of the classic places where this happens is off the coast of Peru. The Peru Current moves out into the Pacific Ocean and away from the coast of South America, so deep ocean water rises (upwells) to replace the water moving away from the landmass. Upwelling stirs up sediments that otherwise collect at the bottom of the ocean. These sediments contain plant nutrients, so plant populations are generally large in areas where upwelling occurs. This helps produce sizable fish populations in the same area. Fishing is traditionally an important economic activity in countries where upwelling occurs along their coasts.

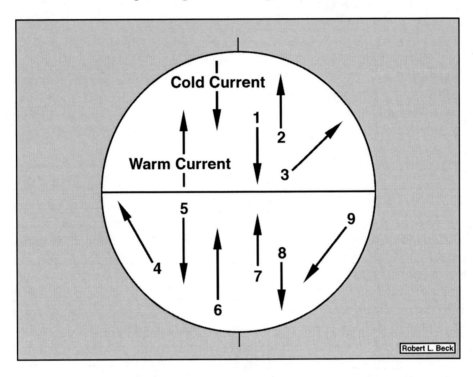

Figure 13-3. Cold Currents and Warm Currents. Which of the numbered currents are cold and which are warm?

The "Annual Precipitation and Ocean Currents" map depicted in ***Goode's World Atlas*** on pp. 36–37 shows the principal surface currents of the world's oceans; so do the maps on pp. 282–286. I use these maps to identify the major currents. You should be following along on the maps as I go through the currents, but first try to identify the gyres in each ocean and note their direction of flow. Please note there are some discrepancies between the sets of maps. For example, the West Australian Current on page 286 is labeled red, which is the color used to identify warm water currents. The West Australian Current is actually a cold water current so it should be labeled blue. Another discrepancy concerns the Canary Current off the northwestern coast of Africa. This cold water current is properly labeled on page 284, but on page 36 the map mixes warm water and cold water. A third problem (on page 285) concerns the Benguela Current off the southwestern coast of Africa. This cold water current is named for Benguela, Angola. Please now find this city and note the red arrows (warm water) offshore. These arrows should be blue. Discrepancies such as these are common on world maps showing ocean currents. The information presented next is what we will be using in this course.

SURFACE CURRENTS OF THE WORLD'S OCEANS

I want to finish this module by identifying the principal **surface** currents of the world's oceans, for they are the ones that greatly influence the world pattern of climate. Subsurface currents, which I will not be discussing, play an important role in the world distribution of temperature and moisture. Subsurface currents and their relationships with surface currents are studied in detail in oceanography courses.

I start with the ***North Equatorial Current*** and the ***South Equatorial Current***, two warm water currents that flow from east to west on both sides of the Equator in the Atlantic Ocean, Indian Ocean, and Pacific Ocean. These currents are driven by the trade winds. In the Atlantic Ocean the South Equatorial Current is cleaved by the nose of Brazil so that part of it turns to the south, where it is known as the ***Brazil Current***. The other part of the South Equatorial Current is deflected so that it flows along the north coast of South America, thence into the Caribbean Sea, and thence into the Gulf of Mexico through the Yucatan Channel (the body of water between Cuba and Mexico).

Warm water exits the Gulf of Mexico through the Straits of Florida as the ***Gulf Stream***, a strong current pushed by the westerlie winds across the Atlantic Ocean in the direction of Europe. About halfway across the Atlantic Ocean it becomes known as the ***North Atlantic Drift***, a warm water current that strikes the western coast of Europe and eventually enters the Arctic Ocean off the coast of Norway. The climate of western Europe is much milder than expected (given its latitude) because of the tropical energy contained in the North Atlantic Drift.

Along the eastern side of the Bermuda High (the subtropical high pressure cell in the North Atlantic Ocean) air blows equatorward. This drives the surface water beneath it to produce the ***Canary Current***, a current that originates in the middle latitudes off the northwestern coast of Africa. This cold water current begins as a branch of water spiraling off the warm water North Atlantic Drift, but the Canary Current flows equatorward and it is much colder than the hot Sahara Desert, which borders it to the east. The Canary Current, named for the Canary Islands, flows into the North Equatorial Current, and that current flows along, but to the east of, the Lesser Antilles Islands to merge with the Gulf Stream just off the eastern coast of Florida.

Three cold water currents flow out of the Arctic Ocean. They are: (1) the ***Greenland Current*** (between Iceland and Greenland), (2) the ***Bering Current*** (between Alaska and Russia), and (3) the ***Labrador Current*** (between Labrador and Greenland). The Greenland Current is labeled as the East Greenland Current on the maps shown in ***Goode's World Atlas***. The Bering Current is not depicted very well, nor is it labeled; it flows equatorward out of the Arctic Ocean and through the Bering Strait along the eastern side of Asia, where an extension of it eventually turns into the cold water ***Kamchatka (Oyashio) Current***, which also is not labeled. The Kamchatka Current flows south all the way to Hokkaido, the northern major island of Japan. The Bering Current and the Kamchatka Current are not labeled on the maps, but they are shown as the blue arrows just east of the Kamchatka Peninsula on p. 37 and p. 282.

Cold water constantly circulates around Antarctica as the *West Wind Drift*, a current driven by the Southern Hemisphere's westerlie winds from west to east. There are no major landmasses at the latitudes where the West Wind Drift flows, so it is perhaps the world's most regular current in terms of lacking major undulations. The subtropical high pressure cell in the South Atlantic Ocean helps pull some of the cold water from the West Wind Drift equatorward along the west coast of southern Africa to form the cold water *Benguela Current*, which eventually merges with the South Equatorial Current.

Ocean currents in the Pacific Ocean, with one exception, mirror the pattern of ocean currents in the Atlantic Ocean. The Pacific Ocean's South Equatorial Current is cleaved by the Solomon Islands in the western Pacific Ocean so that part of it flows poleward along the eastern coast of Australia as the warm water *East Australian Current* (*Goode's World Atlas*, p. 37 and p. 282). The poleward blowing winds curving around the western side of the subtropical high pressure cell in the South Pacific Ocean help push the East Australian Current to the south. However, the equatorward blowing winds of the same high pressure cell help pull cold water from the West Wind Drift equatorward along the western coast of South America to form the cold water *Peru Current*, which is also known as the *Humboldt Current*, named for a famous European explorer of South America, Alexander von Humboldt. The Peru Current is the Pacific Ocean equivalent of the Atlantic Ocean's Benguela Current and it merges with the South Equatorial Current just as the Benguela Current does.

In the North Pacific Ocean, the North Equatorial Current is deflected by the Philippines to curve poleward around the western side of the Hawaiian (California) High to form the warm water *Japan Current* (also known as the *Kuroshio Current*), the Pacific Ocean's equivalent of the Gulf Stream. The Japan Current is pushed from west to east by the westerlie winds, and it turns into the warm water *North Pacific Drift* in the middle of the Pacific Ocean, but this current is not labeled on the maps in *Goode's World Atlas*. The North Pacific Drift hits the west coast of the United States, where it cleaves to form the equatorward flowing cold water *California Current* and the poleward flowing warm water *Alaska Current*, which also is not labeled. The shape of Alaska's coastline keeps the warm water of the North Pacific Drift (and its poleward extension, the Alaska Current) confined to the Gulf of Alaska, so it does not enter the Arctic Ocean as does the North Atlantic Drift.

The circulation pattern in the South Indian Ocean is similar to those of the South Atlantic Ocean and the South Pacific Ocean. The subtropical high pressure cell in the South Indian Ocean helps pull cold water equatorward off of the West Wind Drift to form the cold water *West Australian Current*, which merges with the South Equatorial Current near the Tropic of Capricorn (p. 37). The South Equatorial Current flows to the west in the Indian Ocean to hit the east coast of southern Africa, where one branch cleaves to form the poleward flowing warm water *Agulhas Current* between Madagascar and Africa. The other branch is turned by the Horn of Africa so that it heads toward India as the warm water *Southwest Monsoon Current*. The reversing wind patterns of the South Asian monsoons also change the direction of water flow in the Indian Ocean, for during the winter the Southwest Monsoon Current reverses itself to become the warm water *Northeast Monsoon Current*. This reversed ocean current in the Indian Ocean is shown as a dashed red line in the 21st edition of *Goode's World Atlas* on p. 21, but it has been omitted in the 22nd edition.

I plan to have a lot of questions about ocean currents on the next exam. You need to know their names, in what ocean they are found, their direction of flow, what sides of the continents they affect, whether they are warm or cold, what wind belt they are related to, in which hemisphere they are located, if they originate by flowing off another current, and the names of their equivalent currents in the other oceans.

Module 13 Objectives

You should now be able to:

- Identify Earth's eight major water storage containers

- List the four steps of the *hydrologic cycle*

- Draw 21 major ocean currents on a world map, name them, show their direction of flow, and classify them as being either a warm water current or a cold water current

- Discuss how the direction of flow of Earth's major ocean currents is related to Earth's wind and pressure belts

Practice Exercise: Draw the 21 major ocean currents on this map using colored pencils. Identify the cold currents with a blue pencil and the warm currents with a red pencil. Show their direction of flow with arrows. Use *Goode's World Atlas* and the material presented in this module to complete the exercise.

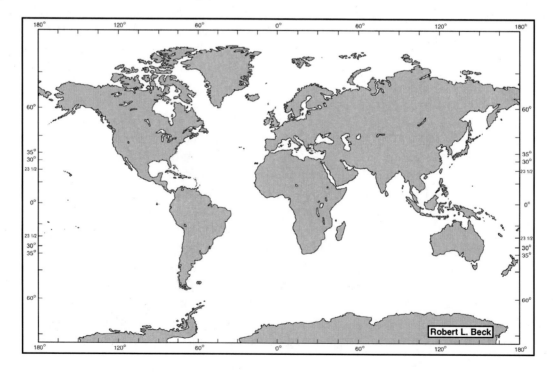

MODULE 14: INTRODUCTION TO CLIMATE

I always begin the study of physical geography with Earth–sun relationships, for they greatly influence Earth's weather. Understanding the basics of weather (and water) is necessary before studying climate, which plays a huge role in influencing the distribution of Earth's vegetation, which is one of the genetic factors of soil formation. There is a common phrase used by physical geographers, "climate-vegetation-soil." In other words, one should **not** study soil until he or she knows something about vegetation, and one cannot fully comprehend the world distribution of vegetation until he or she knows something about climate; but to understand climate it is necessary to know a lot about weather, and to understand weather one must study Earth–sun relationships. Many geographic patterns one finds in nature come down to variations in sun angle.

Difference between Weather and Climate

People often use the words *weather* and *climate* as if they mean the same thing, but they are **not** synonymous, so the words should never be used interchangeably. Weather and climate in many instances are the opposites of each other. Weather is a **short-term** condition of the atmosphere, whereas climate is **long-term** weather. Weather affects our lives because it forces us to make daily decisions such as what type of clothing to wear; climate forces us to make long-term decisions such as what type of house to build. Weather is something we **experience with our senses**, we walk outside to see and feel the weather; climate is something we **experience with our minds**, for we do not walk outside and feel the climate. Weather is something that **exists**; climate is an **abstract idea**, so some people argue it does not exist. The study of weather is known as *meteorology* and the study of climate is known as *climatology*.

I have met people in my life who insist that climate, being an abstract idea, is irrelevant and that weather is the only thing that really matters. In my opinion, such people are quite ignorant. I have found that to be a good climatologist you first have to be a good meteorologist. In other words, the study of meteorology might lead one to pursue a higher level of understanding in the field of climatology. A good meteorologist, on the other hand, might not know anything about climatology and might not even care to.

Climate Controls

All the factors that operate together to produce a climate are known as the *climate controls*. Explaining why different areas of Earth have similar or dissimilar climates requires that all controls be examined. The ancient Greeks classified the world's climates into three types—the torrid climate, the temperate climate, and the frigid climate (Fig. 14-1). To the ancient Greeks there was only one control, *latitude*. The torrid climate was hot because it was located in the tropics and subtropics, the temperate climates were mild because they were in the middle latitudes, and the frigid climates were cold because they were located in the polar areas. Latitude is an important control, for it is directly related to sun angle, length of daylight, and air temperature, but it is only one of seven major climate controls. Latitude is an important beginning point to explain the world's distribution of climates, but the other six controls also need to be considered.

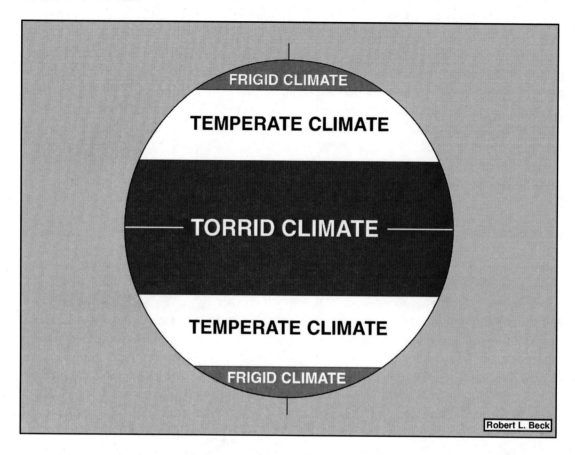

Figure 14-1. Climate Classification Using the Ancient Greek System

The *ocean currents* influence the distribution of climates. It was mentioned in the last module that northwestern Europe has a mild climate because the North Atlantic Drift transports heat from the tropics to moderate its climate. Latitude alone, then, will not explain why northwestern Europe has such a mild climate, for one needs to add that second control, ocean currents, to begin to explain why northwestern Europe has such a mild climate in a latitude the ancient Greeks would consider to be frigid. Ocean currents influence the world distribution of air temperature and humidity. Marine (maritime) air masses also originate over them.

Moisture sources is a third climate control. Condensation and precipitation will not occur in large amounts if there is no water around. The best moisture sources are the tropical gulfs and seas of the world's oceans, but large lakes are good moisture sources, too. Places near the centers of continents (and far away from a moisture source) would be much wetter if a moisture source were located nearby.

Places near the ITC or the polar front are likely to be wetter than places far away from them, even if they are located at the same latitude. Therefore, *proximity to rain-producing systems* is a fourth climate control. A tropical station always near the ITC is likely to be much wetter than a tropical station far away from the ITC. The same idea holds true for the middle latitudes and the polar front. Midlatitude cyclones often originate and move along the polar front, so if a station is always near the polar front its chances of receiving rain are much better than a station far away from the polar front.

Topography is a fifth climate control. It is an important one, for it influences both the pattern of temperature and the distribution of moisture. Temperatures generally decrease as one increases in elevation, so the tall mountains on Earth have distinctive climate zones ringing the mountain largely based on temperature differences. But mountains also block the flow of air causing moisture to precipitate out heavily on the windward sides while producing deserts on the leeward sides. One cannot explain the climate patterns of Oregon and Washington, for example, without considering the role the Cascade Mountains play.

The whole pattern of *atmospheric circulation* is a climate control. Whether or not a city is situated in a wind belt or a pressure belt will have a major influence on its type of climate. Indianapolis, being located in the westerlie wind belt, receives storms that migrate to the east. The city would be considerably drier if it were constantly under the influence of a high pressure cell. San Francisco would have a much different climate if the winds blew from the east and not from the west.

Land and water is the seventh, and last, climate control. Stations located in the middle of a continent have land-dominated climates that bring extremes of temperature, but stations located on the windward side of an ocean are water modified, so their climates are milder than those in the interior.

Different combinations of the climate controls produce different climates around Earth. We cannot explain the climate of Indiana, for example, by only considering latitude. We are located in the interior of North America, so we have cold winters and hot summers. We are usually near the polar front, so a midlatitude cyclone influences our weather about every six or seven days. No mountains block the flow of air from our principal moisture source, the Gulf of Mexico, located several hundred miles away. We are in the middle latitudes, so we have reasonably high sun angles in the summer but fairly low sun angles in the winter. All these controls, working together, produce Indiana's climate.

To understand the world distribution of climates requires one to think constantly about how the climate controls interact. It is easy to list them out and briefly describe them, but it is an entirely different matter to synthesize their interactions mentally.

Köppen Climatic Classification System

Wladimir Köppen, a German **botanist**, published his first climatic classification system in 1918. His system was based on the idea that climate, being abstract, cannot be seen directly, but that it can be seen in the vegetation of an area. Köppen's climate boundaries are therefore designed to match vegetation boundaries, so people who teach physical geography often use vegetation terminology to define climate regions.

The original Köppen Climatic Classification System was later modified by Köppen himself and again by Geiger, one of Köppen's students. World climate wall maps published in Germany today list the author as Köppen–Geiger, but most people simply call Geiger's revisions as *modified Köppen*.

An American geographer, Glenn T. Trewartha, simplified and further modified the Köppen–Geiger system. His system, usually referred to as *Trewartha-modified Köppen*, is shown in the 21st edition of *Goode's World Atlas*, but the 22nd edition reverts back to the Köppen–Geiger original, which I view as a major flaw of the 22nd edition. *Goode's World Atlas* is published in the United States, so I believe it should use Trewartha's enhancements. I produced a map in May 2011 as a substitute for the climate map included in the 22nd edition. My map is a generalized version of Trewartha's map; a black-and-white line drawing of it is shown in this textbook on both page 211 and page 212. I recommend students color one copy (with pencils or pens) using my color original shown online (http://www.iu.edu/~g107/mod16/World Climate Regions.jpg). My map is based on the *Trewartha-modified Köppen* system, but I have simplified Trewartha's original map and I have altered it slightly by adding some minor regional boundaries to enhance the teaching presentation of this book. I will be using my map and the *Trewartha-modified Köppen* system to discuss the world distribution of climate regions in Modules 15 to 19; students should be constantly referring to my *World Climate Regions* map (p. 211 or p. 212) as I move through the various climate regions. Please keep in mind my map is based on Trewartha's map, so it does not exactly match the "Climate Regions" map shown in the 22nd edition of *Goode's World Atlas*.

The Köppen system, or its many variants, is the most widely used climatic classification system on Earth today. Virtually every introductory physical geography textbook published in the United States has at least one chapter devoted to it. I believe every student who studies physical geography should be exposed to it. The system itself has a number of faults, so some people believe it is outdated and should be ignored, but it is so widely used that not to teach it in an introductory physical geography class leaves a big gap in a student's knowledge about the discipline.

The Köppen system is an *empirical system* in that it uses the measurable features of temperature and moisture to establish climate boundaries. It is not a *genetic system*, so it makes no attempt to discover the origins (genesis) of a climate. This also leads to criticism of the Köppen system, for people who seek a genetic explanation of climate look on empirical systems as merely classification exercises with no higher goal than classification itself. I disagree with those people, for through the study of the Köppen system one begins to understand both the global patterns of climate and the global patterns of vegetation. It is also truly geographic in that it brings together weather variables in a spatial framework.

Köppen Climate Groups

Köppen used the capital letters of *A, B, C, D*, and *E* to establish his major climate groups. Each group was then subdivided into individual climates. As a highly general model, the arrangement of the climate groups on Earth is related to latitude (Fig. 14-2).

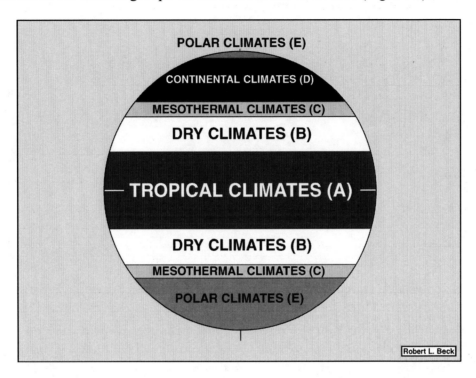

Figure 14-2. Latitudinal Model of the Köppen Climate Groups

Please observe the A climates circle Earth near the Equator, so they are known as the ***tropical climates***; the B climates are largely situated in the subtropics (on both sides of the A climates), so they are known as the ***dry climates***; the C climates are situated poleward of the B climates, so they have mild climates that are not too hot nor too cold, and they are therefore known as the ***mesothermal (middle temperature) climates***; the D climates, only found in the Northern Hemisphere poleward of the C climates, are the land-dominated ***continental climates*** of the middle to high latitudes; the E climates are located at both poles, so they are known as the ***polar climates***.

Africa matches the Köppen model fairly well (*World Climate Regions* map, p. 211). Observe the A climates are found on the Equator, the B climates are on both sides of the A climates, and the C climates are found poleward of the B climates on both the northern and southern tips of the continent. There are also a couple of exceptions to the general model. For example, a B climate is found at the Equator in eastern Africa, where an A climate should theoretically be located; and a C climate is found between an A climate and a B climate south of the Equator. Overall, however, Africa does extend from C to C (Fig. 14-3). Please also see the African climate cross-section models on pages 243–245 of this textbook; you should be continually referring to these African cross-section models as I move through the A, B, and C climates (Mods. 15, 16, and 17).

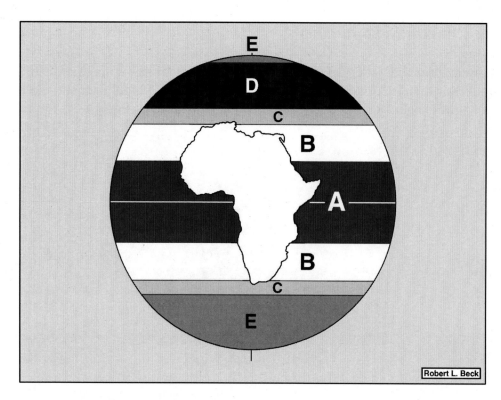

Figure 14-3. Africa Superimposed on the Köppen Climate Group Model

Please now view the "Climate Regions" map in ***Goode's World Atlas*** on page 30 and observe the boundary line between the C climate and the D climate in North America goes though southern Indiana. The map shows all land just north of the Ohio River in both Indiana and Ohio is in a C climate region. It also shows that Indianapolis is in a different climate region than Evansville. According to the map, Evansville has a C climate and Indianapolis has a D climate—Evansville has the same type of climate as Orlando, Florida; Charleston, South Carolina; Houston, Texas; Atlanta, Georgia; and New Orleans, Louisiana. Is not this absurd! How dare someone devise a climatic classification system that lumps Evansville with these subtropical U.S. cities. People do not say, for example, "I'm going to Evansville for spring break next year because it has a warm, subtropical climate!" One can now begin to understand why some people despise the Köppen system and its variants, including the Trewartha-modified Köppen system. It is not accurate, or is it?

My response to such criticisms is that (1) the only area in Indiana where one finds water moccasins (poisonous snakes commonly found in water areas in the southeastern United States) is in the southwestern part of the state near Evansville; (2) the only area in the state where we find old, highly weathered, and poor soils (ultisols) such as those found in Georgia is in the counties bordering the Ohio River, especially Crawford County; (3) the only area of the state where we find bald cypress growing in the state (a tree common to the lower Mississippi River valley of Louisiana and Mississippi) is in the lower Wabash Valley near Evansville; and (4) the only area where we find tobacco production in the state (a crop most closely associated with Kentucky and North Carolina) is in the counties bordering the Ohio River (Fig. 14-4). On the one hand, it is easy to be critical of the Köppen system, for it does have its faults, but on the other hand there are many distributions in the natural world that closely match Köppen's boundaries. I like the Köppen system, even with its problems, so we will be using it in this course.

Fig. 14-4. Tobacco Field in Southern Indiana
(Gage Brogan photo, 2006)

Defining Climate Regions

The word *region* is perhaps the single most controversial word used in the discipline of geography, for this word implies that within the region there is a uniformity, or sameness, that sets the region off from other regions around it. It might seem easy to plot a regional boundary. Do you not just have to locate them on a map?

The boundaries between climate regions shown on maps in atlases seem to be fixed, accurate, and precise; would not a large publisher such as Rand-McNally want to make sure it is offering a good product? Well, climate boundaries are not as precisely defined as they seem to be, for they are defined using average positions of isotherms based on at least 30 years of weather data.

The boundary between the C and D climates in Indiana and the eastern United States is based on the average position of certain January isotherms (Köppen uses the $-3°C$ (26.6°F) isotherm, but Trewartha uses the 32°F (0°C) isotherm). In the past 100 years there have been cold winters when the defining isotherm lay far to the south of Indiana, in Tennessee. There have also been warm winters when the defining isotherm lay far to the north, in northern Michigan. The average position of the defining isotherm, however, runs east-to-west through southern Indiana between Evansville and Indianapolis, so that is where it is placed on climate maps. It is important to bear in mind the boundaries between climates are really transition zones. The whole state of Indiana

187

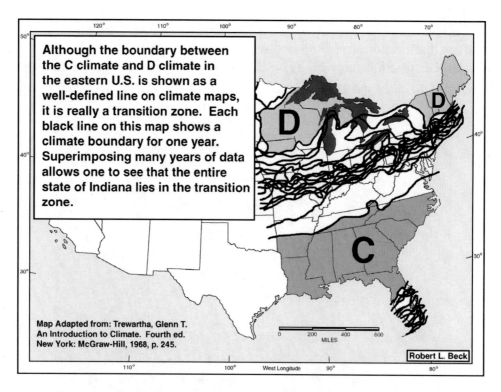

Although the boundary between the C climate and D climate in the eastern U.S. is shown as a well-defined line on climate maps, it is really a transition zone. Each black line on this map shows a climate boundary for one year. Superimposing many years of data allows one to see that the entire state of Indiana lies in the transition zone.

Map Adapted from: Trewartha, Glenn T. An Introduction to Climate. Fourth ed. New York: McGraw-Hill, 1968, p. 245.

Robert L. Beck

Figure 14-5. Climate Boundaries in the Eastern United States

lies in a transition zone between the C climate of the southeastern states and the D climate of the northern states (Fig. 14-5). Southern Indiana normally has a C climate, as defined by Köppen, and northern Indiana normally has a D climate, but some winters of the past saw Indiana experience weather that, using data for only one year, would have placed the whole state in either the C climate region or in the D climate region. Regions are useful when communicating certain ideas to people, but often their boundaries are not exact, and the placement of the boundaries is largely a matter of opinion.

Module 14 Objectives

You should now be able to:

- Describe the difference between *weather* and *climate*

- List, and briefly discuss, Earth's seven major climate controls

- Discuss the *Köppen Climatic Classification System* and identify its basis

- Describe the difference between an *empirical system* and a *genetic system*

- List the five major Köppen climate groups, name them, and draw their locations on a globe

- Discuss why it is so difficult to draw a regional boundary on a map accurately

MODULE 15: TROPICAL CLIMATES

In this module I begin to examine the world climate and vegetation regions, not only to describe where they are but also to explain why they are located where they are. **Please read this module slowly!** Further, you must **constantly** be referring to my *World Climate Regions* map, p. 211, to understand what I am saying. This module serves as a model for Modules 16, 17, 18, and 19.

The tropical climates, in the Trewartha-modified Köppen system, are designated with a capital *A*, and the average temperature of their coldest month is greater than 64.4°F, which is normally rounded up to 65°F. These climates are found in the wet, low latitudes, so they are also known as the ***tropical rainy climates***.

The tropical climates are colored red or pink on my *World Climate Regions* map shown online (http://www.iu.edu/~g107/mod16/World Climate Regions.jpg). They are mostly located between 20° N. Lat. and 20° S. Lat., with their center being positioned on the Equator. They are either (1) wet all year, (2) receive ITC precipitation at the time of the high sun, or (3) receive precipitation from the trade winds or monsoon winds. There are two main tropical climates—the ***tropical rainforest climate*** (also known as the wet equatorial climate) and the ***tropical savanna climate*** (also known as the tropical wet and dry climate).

Tropical Rainforest Climate

The tropical rainforest climate is designated as either an ***Af climate*** or an ***Am climate,*** and it is colored red on my *World Climate Regions* map presented online. The *A* means that the average temperature of the coldest month is greater than 65°F and the *f* means "full-year precipitation," so there are no prolonged dry seasons; but in some Af climates rainfall does lessen enough to produce a short dry season of one or two months. By contrast, the Am climates have a period of very heavy precipitation followed by a period of diminished precipitation, which might extend over several months producing drought-like conditions. The Am climates are coastal tropical rainforest climates, and their precipitation is generated from either the trade winds or seasonal monsoon winds. The *m* refers to "monsoon." Usually about 70 to 80 inches of rain per year falls in the tropical rainforest climates. The ITC is principally responsible for this precipitation abundance, but convectional thunderstorms contribute to the overall total. Many weather stations in Af climates near the Equator experience a *double maximum of precipitation*—once when the ITC is moving north and again when it is moving south.

The tropical rainforest climates have hot temperatures throughout the entire year. The difference in average temperature between the warmest month and the coldest month is often only about 5°F. Daily temperature ranges, the temperature difference between the daily high and daily low, average about 10°F to 25°F. It is often said, therefore, that "night is the winter of the tropics."

Graphs showing the average temperature and moisture characteristics of a weather station are known as **climographs** . . . 17 of them are lined up horizontally on the bottom of the "Climatic Regions" map in *Goode's World Atlas*, pp. 30–31. The curving or sinuous line near the top of a climograph shows the pattern of temperature from January through December. The black bars extending upward from the base of the climograph depict rainfall totals per month. For example, the Af climograph shows weather data for Singapore, a city positioned at the southern tip of the Malay Peninsula (its location is shown on page 31 at 1° N. Lat., 104° E. Long.). Please observe that the average January temperature of Singapore is about 27°C (81°F) and that its average January precipitation is about 21 centimeters (precipitation values are listed to the far right), which is about 8.3 inches.

The temperature curve of Singapore is almost flat, which graphically reinforces the fact that tropical rainforest climates have uniformly hot temperatures throughout the year. High monthly rainfall totals are found in Singapore; at least 15.2 centimeters (6 inches) of precipitation falls every month of the year, so there are no dry seasons. You should be examining the climographs as we move though all other climates of Earth.

The Af and Am climates (*World Climate Regions,* p. 211) are found in the Amazon Basin of South America, the Congo Basin of central Africa, and throughout the islands of southeast Asia. They are also shown as coastal strips in Central America, the Caribbean Islands, Brazil, West Africa, Madagascar, southwestern India, and mainland Southeast Asia.

Tropical rainforest, of course, is the natural vegetation of the tropical rainforest climate. Broadleaf evergreen trees dominate the composition of this forest type (Fig. 15-1). Their leaves are wide to catch as much solar radiation as possible and they remain green the entire year. You should now go to the "Natural Vegetation" map in *Goode's World Atlas*, pp. 42–43, and observe that broadleaf evergreen trees (labeled B) are found roughly in the same areas as the tropical rainforest climate. Another characteristic feature of tropical rainforest vegetation is the presence of climbing vines ***(lianas)*** rooted in the ground.

Figure 15-1. Tropical Rainforest, Queensland, Australia
(Rick Bein photo)

190

The floor of the tropical rainforest is poorly lit, so there is relatively little undergrowth; however, areas in the tropical rainforest that do receive a lot of light (such as the edges of the rainforest and along major streams) have dense undergrowth, which is known as *jungle*. The Am climate has a brief dry season, which causes a few trees to shed their leaves (tropical deciduous trees). Jungle is found in these areas, too.

The tropical rainforest climate has both high temperatures and high humidities the entire year. Soils found in such climates have had almost all their plant nutrients leached out of them by the abundant precipitation. The world's poorest soils (oxisols) are found in the tropical rainforest climates of South America and Africa (*Goode's World Atlas*, pp. 44-45). The lush vegetation tricked many people from Europe and the United States into thinking that the tropical rainforest climate must have excellent soils. Attempts to clear and farm the rainforest using agricultural practices that work well in Indiana almost always fail in tropical rainforest soils. They simply require too much fertilizer to sustain agricultural production.

Shifting cultivation is an agricultural practice used by native peoples who live in tropical rainforest environments. This involves clearing a small patch of the rainforest, through the use of machete and fire, and then cultivating crops in it (Fig. 15-2). The ash from the fire acts as a temporary fertilizer helping the crops to grow. The patch is abandoned after a couple of years in crop production (Fig. 15-3). The rainforest will reclaim the patch, and soon trees will be growing there once again. This type of farming is also known as *slash and burn agriculture*. It is often viewed as a wasteful practice by people not familiar with rainforest environments, but it is considered to be a sustainable agricultural practice if an adequate amount of time (50 years or so) occurs between burnings. If a rainforest plot is slashed, burned, farmed, abandoned, and then slashed again only a few years later not enough time would have elapsed for the natural environment to restore fertility to the area. Overuse of a rainforest environment quickly depletes the soils of plant nutrients whether it is overused by a foreigner or a native.

Figure 15-2. Rainforest Clearing, Amazon Basin, Brazil
(Rick Bein photo)

The warm temperatures and abundant precipitation, while producing the world's poorest soils, also produce the world's most diverse ecosystems. It has been estimated that in one square mile of the tropical rainforest one might count as many as 3,000 different species of trees. Contrast this with the high latitude, boreal forests of Canada, where only about 40 tree species are found from one side of the country to the other.

Figure 15-3. Abandoned Plots, Amazon Basin, Brazil
(Rick Bein photo)

Tropical Savanna Climate

The dominant tropical savanna climate is the *Aw climate,* and it is colored pink on my *World Climate Regions* map. The world's rarest climate, the *As climate*, is also a tropical savanna climate and it, too, is colored pink. I mentioned earlier that the tropical savanna climate is also known as the ***tropical wet and dry climate***, for unlike the tropical rainforest climate, which has full-year precipitation, the tropical savanna climate has a period of wetness followed by a period of drought. The *A* again means that the average temperature of the coldest month is greater than 65°F and the *w* means "winter drought" or "dry winter," so the rainy period in this climate occurs during the summer at the period of high sun.

To be precise quantitatively, but which in practice is often ignored cartographically, Trewartha defined the *w* as applying to a situation in which the six summer months (May–October) have 10 times as much precipitation as the six winter months (November–April). The *As* climate has a summer drought, but in the *s* climate (dry summer) the six winter months must not only receive 3 times as much precipitation as the six summer months, but also in this climate the annual precipitation must be less than 35 inches with the driest month receiving less than 1.2 inches. The *w* and the *s*, therefore, are not defined using the same numeric criterion. In both cases, the high degree of exactness concerning classification is difficult to remember and viewed as cumbersome. Can you easily remember what I just said concerning the *w* and the *s*?

192

Points 1 and 2 on the South Asia maps (pp. 113–114) are two of the few places on Earth where an As climate occurs. Which monsoon brings them rain?

Many people, including me, prefer the simpler, but less precise, qualitative phrases of "winter drought" or "dry winter" to indicate a station has a dry period in the winter regardless if it fits Trewartha's definition exactly. For example, Homestead, Florida, which is situated in a major producing area of winter vegetables, is located south of Miami and it is depicted as an Aw climate in both *Goode's World Atlas* (22nd edition, p. 30) and on my *World Climate Regions* map (p. 211), which is based on the Trewartha-modified Köppen system. To be classified as an Aw climate in the Köppen system, which is presented in *Goode's World Atlas* (22nd edition) a station must have at least 10 times the amount of precipitation in the wettest summer month as in the driest winter month. Homestead's wettest summer month is August with 9.2 inches, and its driest winter month is December with 1.6 inches (Fig. 15-4), so it does not meet the requirement for inclusion as an Aw climate even though it clearly has a dry winter relative to its wet summer. This is an example of why many geographers prefer the qualitative phrase "dry winter" instead of adhering to exact data collected by weather instruments leading to burdensome classification systems. I do use precise quantitative divisions to separate world climates into the major groups (A, C, D, and E), but I also use inexact qualitative phrases to break down the major groups into subgroups such as Af, Aw, As, and many others.

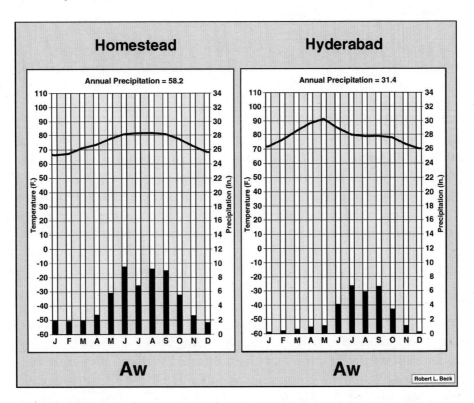

Figure 15-4. Climograph of Homestead, Florida (left), and Hyderabad, India (right). Both of these climates in this book are assumed to be Aw climates even though they do not meet all requirements to be included as such by both Trewartha and Köppen.

193

It is sometimes difficult to distinguish between the Aw climate and the Am climate using only climographs. The principal differences between them relate to the amount of precipitation and the length of the dry season. Am climates typically receive a lot more precipitation than Aw climates and they often have a shorter dry season. If one examines a climograph and notices huge precipitation bars concentrated together in one season of the year, the climate in question is probably an Am climate, not an Aw. Precipitation is less and the dry season is usually quite lengthy in the Aw climate, but some Aw climates do have relatively short dry seasons and a lot of precipitation compared to others. A further difference concerns their locations. Am climates tend to occur in coastal climates because they receive copious precipitation from the trade winds or monsoon winds. Aw climates tend to occur in inland locations with their rainfall generated by the ITC. Precise separation of these two climates is somewhat tricky, for they tend to grade into each other. I am personally not so concerned about using precise measurements to establish regional climates boundaries . . . it is more important to understand the general pattern of where climates occur and to attempt to explain why that pattern exists. Geographers use temperature and precipitation data as best as they can to set climate boundaries, but many do not worry about the exact locations of the climate boundaries on maps, for the boundaries represent broad transition zones and not precise lines. The climate controls mentioned in Module 14 interweave in countless ways to produce Earth's distinctive climates, so to fret about trying to define climate regions precisely in a scientific manner to portray them accurately on maps has the potential to make dull what should otherwise be an interesting topic.

The tropical savanna climate (Aw) is characteristically located poleward of the tropical rainforest climate (Af) in both hemispheres. Observe on my *World Climate Regions* map (p. 211) that an Aw climate region in South America is found (1) in Colombia and Venezuela (north of the Amazon Basin) and (2) in central and southern Brazil (south of the Amazon Basin). The same pattern holds in Africa on both sides of the Congo Basin. It also holds true in Southeast Asia, but in this case the Aw climate regions are situated in mainland Southeast Asia and northern Australia (map, p. 211).

Alternating wet and dry seasons characterize the tropical savanna climates, for they are situated between the wet tropical rainforests and the dry subtropical deserts. Rain is produced by the ITC, which settles over these climates in the high sun period (summer). Drought is produced by a subtropical high pressure cell usually positioned over the nearby subtropical desert. During the low sun period (winter), the high pressure cell migrates in the direction of the SSP and as a result settles over the tropical savanna climate. For example, in Africa locate the point 10° S. Lat., 20° E. Long. on p. 31 in *Goode's World Atlas*. Observe it is situated in an Aw climate region. Now locate that same point on the "January Pressure and Predominant Winds" map on p. 34. You should note that in January, which is the southern hemisphere's high sun period, a low pressure (the ITC) is positioned over that point, so in that month one expects large amounts of rainfall. If you now find the point on the "July Pressure and Predominant Winds" map on p. 35, you will observe it is now under the influence of a high pressure cell (as indicated by the blue color). July is a winter month in the southern hemisphere, so the point will now have drought conditions, hence the Aw (winter drought) designation.

Savanna is the natural vegetation of the Aw climate and it consists of a mixture of tall grasses and fire-resistant trees (Fig. 15-5). The savanna is where the large herd animals of Africa congregate . . . so do the predators that kill them. Lions and other big cats hunt wildebeest, zebras, gazelles, and antelopes in Africa's savanna region (Fig. 15-6). Africa's savanna is said to have a "parkland" appearance, mostly dominated by grassland with scattered clumps of trees, especially flat-topped acacia trees that have a distinctive silhouette. The vegetative environment consisting of a mixture of grasses and trees known as *savanna* is technically found only in the tropics and subtropics, but some naturalists have applied the word, most inappropriately, to similar environments in the middle latitudes. I have seen, for example, publications in which the author is discussing

Figure 15-5. Savanna Herbivores, Southern Africa
(Rick Bein photo)

Figure 15-6. Lion, Savanna Predator
(Rick Bein photo)

the savannas of Indiana. What? An environment consisting of a mixture of grasses and trees in the middle latitudes is known as a *woodland*, not a savanna.

When the ITC is overhead in the summer the grasses and trees of the savanna prosper, for there is an abundance of sun and rain, but plants and animals suffer when the subtropical high settles over the savanna during the low sun (winter) period. Grasses dry out, water holes dry up, and animals struggle to survive (Fig. 15-7). At this time the

Figure 15-7. Savanna in the Dry Season, Sudan
(Rick Bein photo)

vegetation is susceptible to fire, and if one happens to get started it might ravage huge areas before it burns itself out. Fires have been associated with the tropical savanna climate for such a long time that the trees living there have become fire-resistant through natural evolution processes (Fig. 15-8).

The ancient Phoenicians, who were skilled mariners, viewed huge fires burning in interior Africa as they sailed along the coast thousands of years ago. Some of these fires were probably set by humans for a variety of reasons, including hunting. The use of fire is perhaps the first major human impact on Earth's natural environment. Modern people often view ancient people as living in harmony with the environment, but there is a lot of evidence to suggest this was not the case.

You should now be able to discuss when the wet and dry periods occur in southern Vietnam, northern Australia, and the southern tip of Florida. These three areas all have Aw climates, so they have winter droughts. The rainy season in southern Vietnam and the southern tip of Florida occurs during the high sun period from May to October (to verify this check the "Average Precipitation" map on p.35 in *Goode's World Atlas*). Australia, being in the southern hemisphere, has its high sun period from November to April; therefore, its Aw climate receives abundant precipitation during that time (to verify this check the "Average Precipitation" map on p. 34). When it is wet in southern Vietnam and the southern tip of Florida, it will be dry in northern Australia; when it is dry in southern Vietnam and the southern tip of Florida, it will be wet in northern Australia (check both precipitation maps on pp. 34–35 to verify).

Figure 15-8. Fire in the Savanna, Brazil
(Rick Bein photo)

Module 15 Objectives

You should now be able to:

- Use temperature data to differentiate A climates from the C, D, and E climates

- Compare and contrast the two main types of *tropical climates*

- Differentiate between the *w* and the *s* in the Köppen system

- Discuss the geographic distribution of the tropical climates and explain why they are located where they are

- Describe a *climograph*

- Discuss the precipitation patterns of the tropical climates and relate the patterns to the types of natural vegetation found in the tropical climates

- Use the climate map in *Goode's World Atlas* to predict the month or season of precipitation of the A climates shown on the map

- Draw the locations of the tropical climates on a world map

- Briefly describe the major characteristics of savanna vegetation

Practice Questions: Which one of these climographs is **not** a tropical climate? Why not? Which one is a tropical rainforest climate? Which one is a tropical savanna climate? Which one is an Am climate?

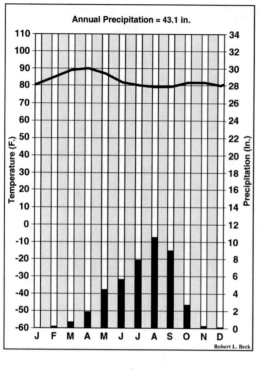

1

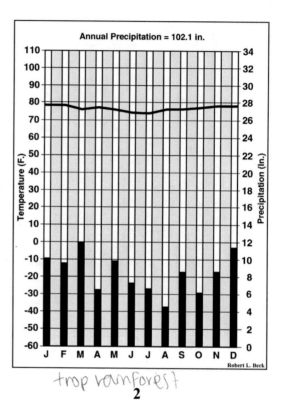

trop rainforest

2

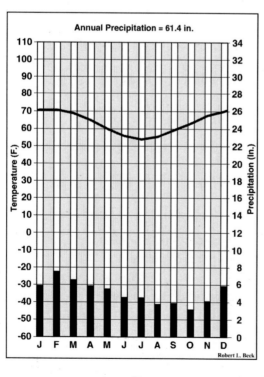

3

Annual Precipitation = 99.5 in.

Am **4**

198

Practice Exercise: Construct a climograph using the data and graph shown below. What type of climate does this climograph show? What is its natural vegetation? Where on Earth is it located?

	J	F	M	A	M	J	J	A	S	O	N	D
TEMP.:	83	82	83	83	80	78	78	78	82	84	85	84
PRECIP.:	13.3	13.2	10.7	4.7	0.4	0.0	0.1	0.2	0.7	2.6	6.1	9.1

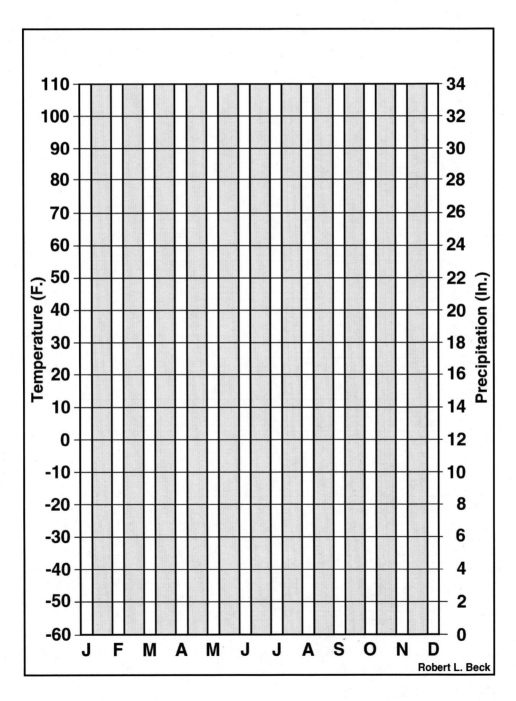

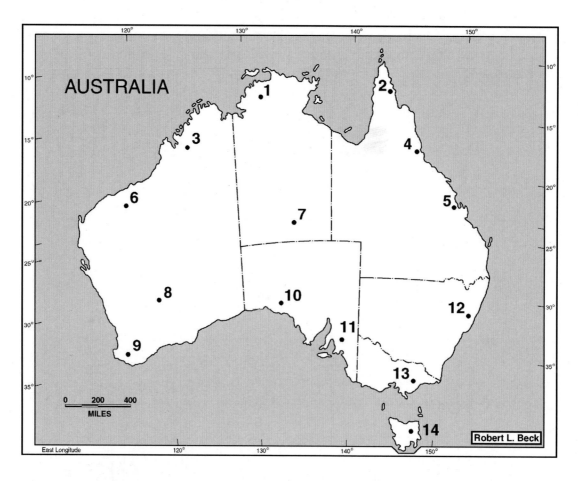

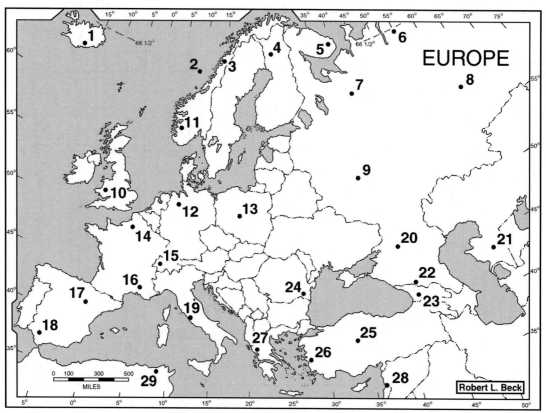

MODULE 16: DRY CLIMATES

The dry climates, as you know, are designated with a capital **B**. These include both the arid and semiarid areas of Earth. The arid areas (deserts) are designated as a **BW** and the semiarid areas (steppes) are designated as a **BS** (*World Climate Regions* map, p. 211). Both deserts and steppes are defined by a formula, which we will not be using in this course, that includes both precipitation and temperature data. In both climates, however, potential evaporation exceeds precipitation. In the A, C, D, and E climates precipitation exceeds evaporation. The BW climates are colored orange on my *World Climate Regions* map (http://www.iu.edu/~g107/mod16/World Climate Regions.jpg) and the BS climates are colored yellow. The map also shows the letters **h** and **k** next to either a BW or a BS. The **h** stands for "hot" and the **k** for "cold," but more specifically the **h** refers to a situation in which every month of the year averages above 32 degrees F. By contrast, a **k** indicates at least one month will be below freezing.

The first geographic pattern you should note concerning dry climates is that **steppes surround deserts.** This pattern is thoroughly logical, for obviously a desert is found at the heart of an arid area, and as you move outward in all directions the climate gets a little wetter until you reach a point where it is too wet to be a true desert, so you enter a steppe (Fig. 16-1). Examine the B climates in Australia and observe that the BS surrounds the BW. The same pattern holds true all over Earth, but in a few places, where seacoasts or mountains are involved, the BS does not completely surround the BW.

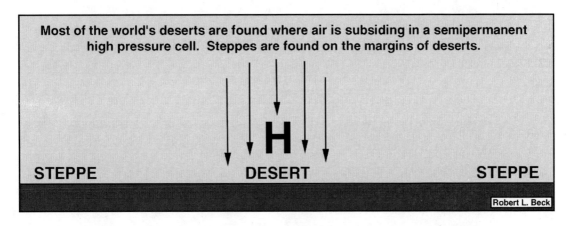

Figure 16-1. Geographic Relationship of Steppes to Deserts

Desert Climates

There are four main types of deserts. I now examine the geographic distribution of the desert climates and explain why they are located where they are. All four types of deserts are designated **BW**.

You already know that subsiding air in a high pressure cell produces droughts, so by far the most common type of desert on Earth are the **subtropical deserts** found at about 20° to 30° north and south latitudes. The largest desert on Earth, the Sahara Desert in Africa, is of this type (Fig. 16-2). Observe on my *World Climate Regions* map, p. 211, (and also on the "Land Cover" map of Africa in *Goode's World Atlas*, p. 255) that the 25° N. Lat. line goes through the middle of the Sahara. The Arabian Desert in the Arabian Peninsula and the Thar Desert in northwestern India are also subtropical deserts positioned at about 25° North Latitude.

The Sonoran Desert, on the boundary between the United States and Mexico, is a subtropical desert, but it is positioned at about 30° N. Lat. So is the Negev Desert of southern Israel (Fig. 16-3).

Figure 16-2. Sahara Desert, Sudan
(Rick Bein photo)

Figure 16-3. Negev Desert, Southern Israel
(Robert L. Beck photo, 1971)

In the Southern Hemisphere one finds the Great Victoria Desert, the Gibson Desert, the Great Sandy Desert, the Tanami Desert, and the Simpson Desert in western Australia (*Goode's World Atlas*, p. 274); the Kalahari Desert in southern Africa (p. 255); and the Atacama Desert along the west coast of South America (p. 160) all positioned from about 20°–30° S. Lat. In general, the locations of the world's subtropical deserts are highly predictable geographically. Nearly all of them are positioned in the same latitude zone and are situated beneath a subtropical high pressure cell for much of the year.

Not all deserts are positioned at 20° to 30° latitude. What other factors can explain why certain areas are deserts and other areas are not? A second factor, and one we have already studied in Module 11, is topography. Mountains block the flow of air creating ***rainshadow deserts*** on their leeward sides. The world's classic rainshadow desert is the Patagonian Desert in southern Argentina (*Goode's World Atlas*, p. 160). The center of this desert is located at about 45° S. Lat., a latitude that should be wet, for it is situated in the Southern Hemisphere's westerlie wind belt. Being in the westerlie wind belt, however, means the western side of the Andes Mountains is the windward side, so southern Chile receives abundant precipitation, whereas southern Argentina is dry (examine the variation of precipitation in southern South America on the "Annual Precipitation" map on p. 161, *Goode's World Atlas*).

Cold ocean currents flowing through tropical areas produce narrow coastal deserts that extend inland a few dozen miles. Cold ocean water chills the air above it so that it is highly stable and absolutely refuses to rise, and rising air is necessary to produce precipitation. These deserts are found on the western sides of landmasses in tropical areas and are known as ***west-coast deserts***. Observe in southwestern Africa, adjacent to the Benguela Current, that a thin strip of desert extends northward along the coast. This is the Namib Desert, and it is mostly located in the country of Namibia (*Goode's World Atlas*, p. 255). The Atacama Desert in South America extends northward along the coast to about 5° S. Lat. The cold water Peru Current is offshore the entire length of the Atacama, which is the world's driest desert. Arica, Chile, is the world's driest city, and it is located in the Atacama Desert just south of the Peru border (*Goode's World Atlas*, p. 168). People live there because valuable copper deposits are located nearby and because Arica serves as a port for landlocked Bolivia (a transport line connects Arica with La Paz, Bol.).

The ***interior deserts*** are the fourth type of desert and are dry because they are far removed from a moisture source. The three large interior deserts on Earth are located in Asia and are designed ***BWk***, so they are cold deserts. The Turkestan Desert surrounds the old Aral Sea, which was a shallow body of water and not a significant source of moisture. The Gobi Desert and the Takla Makan are two interior deserts located in western China (their exact locations can be found on the map on pp. 222–223, *Goode's World Atlas*). These three deserts are located at about 40° to 45° N. Lat., so they are situated in the westerlie wind belt. Moisture from the Atlantic Ocean has a hard time reaching central Asia because of the distances involved, and air that might be drawn into these deserts from the Indian Ocean or Pacific Ocean is blocked by high mountains. The United States has a small interior desert in the Intermontane region of the West. The Red Desert near Rock Springs, Wyoming, has a BWk climate.

The natural vegetation of desert climates is known as ***xerophytic vegetation***, which consists of plants adapted for life and growth with a limited water supply (Fig. 16-4). Xerophytic vegetation has developed survival mechanisms that limit transpiration losses and provide for the storage of water inside the plant. Many xerophytic plants are covered with thorns or spikes, which helps protect the plant from thirsty animals seeking water (Fig. 16-5).

Figure 16-4. Xerophytic Vegetation, Southern Arizona
(Robert L. Beck photo, 1987)

Figure 16-5. Saguaro Cactus, Xerophytic Plant of the Sonoran Desert
(Robert L. Beck photos, 1987)

Practice Exercise: The climographs of four northern hemisphere B climates are shown below. One is a BWh, one is a BWk, one is a BSh, and one is a BSk. Match the climographs with their appropriate designations.

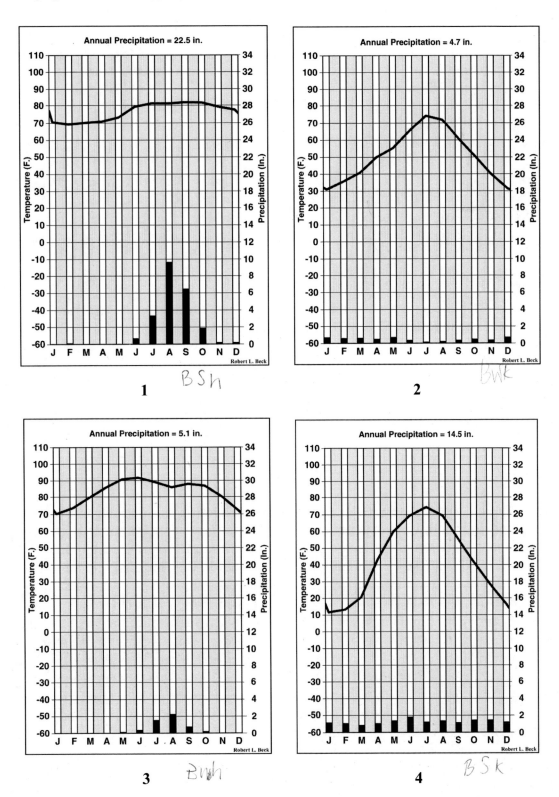

1   BSh

2   BWk

3   BWh

4   BSk

205

Steppe Climates

The steppe climates, **BS**, are a little more complicated geographically than the deserts. We still have the same four factors operating, so one can find subtropical steppes, rainshadow steppes, west-coast steppes, and interior steppes (BSk). But there is a fifth type of steppe—the tropical steppe. I mentioned earlier that **steppes surround deserts**. I suggested you examine the continent of Australia to observe the BS climate surrounding the BW. Now note if you travel from the center of Australia's BW climate and proceed poleward that you pass through a BS climate before reaching the coast. This BS climate is located at 30° S. Lat., so it is a *subtropical steppe*, but if you travel equatorward from the center of the BW climate, you again encounter a BS climate before reaching the coast. This steppe is located at about 18° S. Lat., so it is a *tropical steppe*. The same pattern occurs in Africa. Observe that if you travel poleward from the center of the Sahara Desert, you hit a subtropical steppe before reaching the Mediterranean Sea and that if you travel equatorward you hit a tropical steppe before reaching 0° (Fig. 16-6). In other words, subtropical deserts are surrounded by steppes, but more specifically **two** steppes that differ in their latitudinal positions with regard to the desert. Both subtropical steppes and tropical steppes are designated **BSh**.

Tropical steppes have different precipitation patterns than subtropical steppes. The tropical steppe equatorward of the Sahara Desert receives precipitation from the **ITC in the summer.** This is shown in the climograph of N'Djamena, Chad, which receives almost all of its precipitation (over 22 inches) in the summer months of May through October (Fig. 16-6). Virtually no rain falls in N'Djamena in the winter months from November through April. The lack of precipitation in the winter is explained by changing air pressure, for the semipermanent high pressure cell residing over the Sahara Desert shifts to the south with the migration of the SSP into the southern hemisphere. N'Djamena is therefore dry in the winter months because it is dominated by high pressure.

The subtropical steppe poleward of the Sahara Desert, as represented by the climograph of Tripoli, Libya, does not receive moisture from the ITC, for obviously the ITC does not pass through the Sahara Desert to bring it rain. Rather, the subtropical steppe receives its moisture from **midlatitude cyclones in the winter**. The climograph of Tripoli (Fig. 16-6) shows this concept nicely, so does the climograph of Banghazi, Libya, depicted in *Goode's World Atlas* on p. 30. Drought conditions occur in both Tripoli and Banghazi during the high sun period of the summer when temperatures are high. In this case the semipermanent high pressure cell over the Sahara Desert shifts to the north with the migration of the SSP into the northern hemisphere. Tripoli and Banghazi are therefore dry in the summer months because they are dominated by high pressure.

The steppes north (poleward) and south (equatorward) of the Sahara Desert are both designated BSh, but they have different patterns of precipitation because they have different moisture sources. The tropical steppe, as represented by N'Djamena, receives precipitation from the ITC, but Tripoli and Banghazi receive precipitation from mid-latitude cyclones. Khartoum, Sudan, in the Sahara Desert, has a desert climate (BWh).

Only about six inches of precipitation falls in Khartoum in a calendar year, and virtually all of it falls in July, August, and September when the ITC is not too far away (Fig. 16-6).

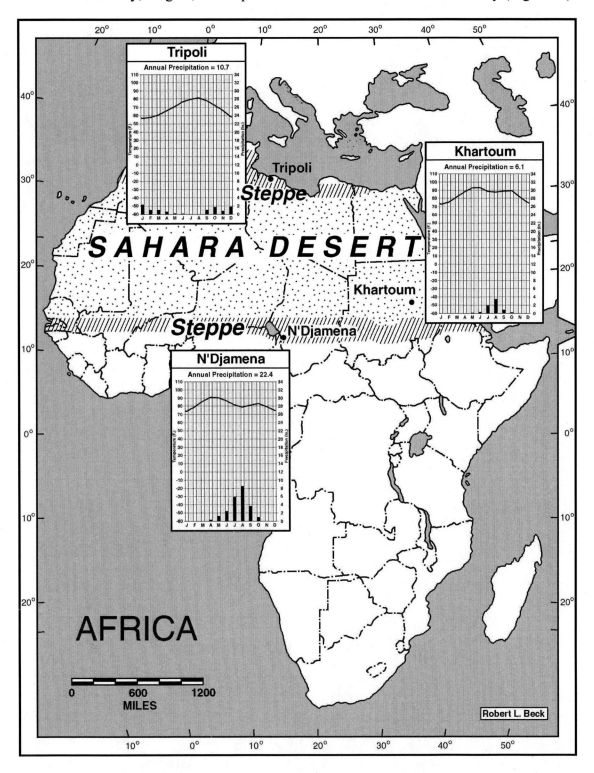

Fig. 16-6. Dry Climates of North Africa

207

The natural vegetation of steppe climates generally consists of short grasses often mixed with short, shrublike trees that grow singly or in small clumps. The word **steppe** is a Russian word that means "short grassland." Many trees in certain tropical steppes are covered with thorns to protect themselves from browsing animals; ***thornforests*** are mixed with short grasses in some BS climate regions. The Gran Chaco region of South America ("Vegetation" map, p. 161, ***Goode's World Atlas***) is an area dominated by thornforests, and much of it is situated in a tropical steppe climate.

One of the most famous steppe regions on Earth is an area in Africa known as the ***Sahel***, which is an Arab word meaning "coastline." Now normally we think of a coastline as separating an ocean, sea, or lake from a landmass. It is also possible, however, to think of the Sahara Desert as a "sea of sand," so the word does make sense if perceived differently from its traditional land–water usage. The Sahel is the tropical steppe (BSh) positioned equatorward of the Sahara Desert (Fig. 16-7). It is situated between the BWh climate of North Africa and the Aw climate of central Africa (*World Climate Regions*, p. 211). It is labeled on the "Land Cover" map of Africa in ***Goode's World Atlas***, p. 255.

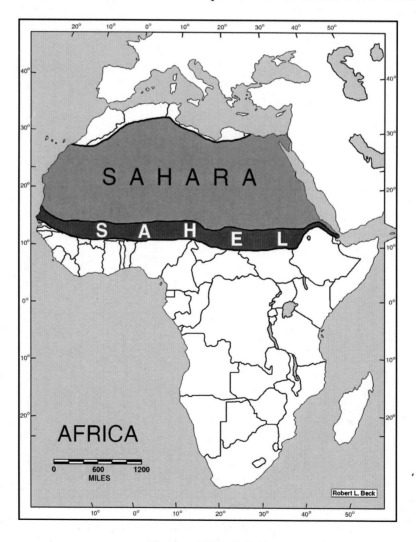

Figure 16-7. Sahel

The Sahara Desert has been slowly expanding to the south and moving into the Sahel over the past several dozen years. This process is known as ***desertification*** . . . the process by which land turns into a desert. Why is the Sahara Desert expanding? Is it a natural process or one caused mostly by humans? Or is it both a natural and a human-accelerated process? If it rains in the Sahel, the rain is generated by the ITC during the high sun period (summer). There is some evidence that the ITC is not moving as far north as it did many years ago; this seems to suggest that maybe this is a natural process. On the other hand, humans might have contributed to the expansion of the Sahara by causing large numbers of animals, cattle and goats in particular, to overgraze the short grasslands of the Sahel. Once the land is overgrazed, it is much easier for the wind to move soil and sand particles allowing the Sahara to expand.

Interior steppes, like interior deserts, are far removed from a moisture source. In the middle latitudes such steppes are designated as ***BSk***, for their winters are bitterly cold. The BSk climate in North America's Great Plains extends poleward from the United States into southern Canada (*World Climate Regions* map, p. 211). An extensive interior steppe is also found around the Turkestan Desert in Central Asia and throughout much of Mongolia and parts of China, around the Gobi Desert (*World Climate Regions* map, p. 211). ***Short grasses*** constitute the native vegetation of the interior steppes, which are perhaps the world's most famous herding and ranching regions (Fig. 16-8).

Figure 16-8. Steppe Grassland, Western Nebraska
(Robert L. Beck photo, 1990)

The world's best soils, the mollisols (discussed in Module 26), are found in BSk climate regions. The grass cover and the dry climate help give them a high degree of fertility. The mollisols in the steppe grasslands of North America, southern Ukraine, northern China, and Argentina are outstanding producers of wheat, which is a plant harvested for its seed milled to manufacture flour used to make bread, pasta, cakes, and cookies. Please observe that the distribution of wheat production (***Goode's World Atlas***, p. 59) correlates strongly with the distribution of the BSk climates (and also the BSh climates in Pakistan, India, and Australia). Wheat is produced in the C and D climate regions, but the best wheat (hard wheat to produce bread flour) comes from the BSk.

Module 16 Objectives

You should now be able to:

- Discuss the geographic relationship between *desert climates* and *steppe climates*

- List the four main types of deserts

- Differentiate between the *h* and the *k* in the Köppen system

- Draw the locations of Earth's major deserts and steppes on a world map

- Explain why the world's deserts are located where they are

- Discuss the precipitation patterns of the steppe climates and relate the patterns to the types of natural vegetation found in the steppe climates

- Use the *World Climate Regions* map (p. 211) to predict the month or season of precipitation of the steppe climates shown bordering the BWh climates

Practice Exercise: Which of the following two climographs is a tropical steppe and which is a subtropical steppe? Both climographs represent stations in the Northern Hemisphere.

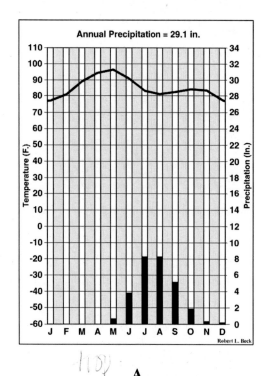

A

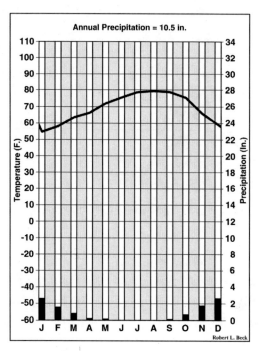

B

210

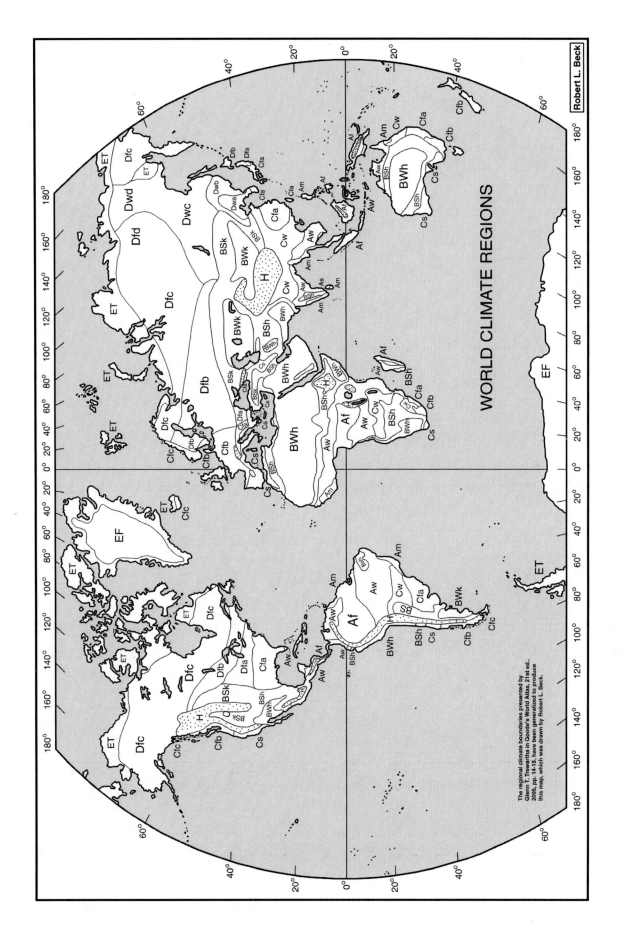

WORLD CLIMATE REGIONS

Robert L. Beck

The regional climate boundaries presented by
Glenn T. Trewartha in Goode's World Atlas, 21st ed.,
2005, pp. 14-15, have been generalized to produce
this map, which was drawn by Robert L. Beck.

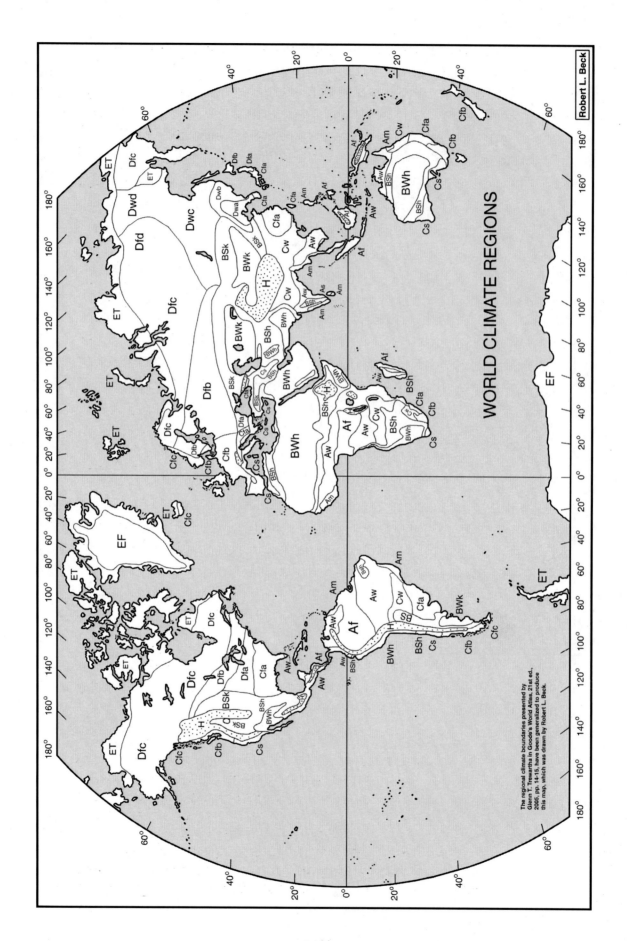

WORLD CLIMATE REGIONS

The regional climate boundaries presented by
Glenn T. Trewartha in Goode's World Atlas, 21st ed.,
2005, pp. 14-15, have been generalized to produce
this map, which was drawn by Robert L. Beck.

Robert L. Beck

212

MODULE 17: MESOTHERMAL CLIMATES

The mesothermal climates in the Trewartha-modified Köppen system are designated with a capital *C*, and the average temperature of their coldest month is less than 65°F but greater than 32°F (Köppen used −3°C (26.6°F)). The coldest month is a "middle temperature," so it is neither extremely cold nor extremely hot. The mesothermal climates are located in the wetter areas of the subtropics and in the lower middle latitudes; they are normally positioned poleward of both the A and B climates. There are four C climates.

Humid Subtropical Climate

The humid subtropical climate is one of the world's major climates and it is a big producer of food. On the *World Climate Regions* map presented in this textbook (p. 211) it is designated as a Cfa, and it is colored light green on my *World Climate Regions* map shown online (http://www.iu.edu/~g107/mod16/World Climate Regions.jpg). The *C* means that the average temperature of the coldest month is less than 65°F but greater than 32°F; the *f* means "full-year precipitation" so there are no dry seasons (at least as a long-term average); and the *a* means a "hot summer" with the hottest summer month averaging above 72°F.

Cfa climates have a predictable geographic location, for they are always found on the eastern side, and especially the southeastern corners, of continents. We have a Cfa climate region in the southeastern corner of the United States (*World Climate Regions* map, p. 211), but there is also a Cfa climate in the southeastern corner of South America, the southeastern corner of Africa, the eastern side of Australia, and the eastern side of Asia. All these areas have warm ocean currents offshore and, with the exception of Australia, are positioned at about 30° to 35° latitude. There are even two minor Cfa climate regions in southeastern Europe.

Precipitation in the Cfa climates is produced by midlatitude cyclones and in some cases by hurricanes (tropical cyclones). In any case the precipitation is cyclonic in origin. ***Subtropical forest***, which is highly diverse geographically, is the native vegetation of the humid subtropical climates (Fig. 17-1). *Evergreen trees*, especially pines in the southeastern United States, are found in these forests, but so are ***deciduous trees***, which shed their leaves annually to conserve energy, to conserve water, and to protect the plant from cold temperatures. Plants native to Cfa climates in other areas of the world, such as soybeans from China, have been introduced into the southeastern United States with good results. Other plants, however, have been a disaster. One such plant is ***kudzu***, native to the humid subtropical climate of Japan and Korea, that has taken over large areas of the American South by spreading its vines over trees, poles, fences, wires, and buildings, including houses (Fig. 17-2). Kudzu spread rapidly after its introduction into the United States in 1876, for it had few enemies here that would inhibit or prevent its explosive growth. It was introduced as an erosion control plant and also because it is a legume, so it adds nitrogen to the soil via nitrogen-fixing bacteria in its root system. Conservation workers in the 1930s viewed it as a "miracle vine," but by the 1950s people began to realize it was a threat to native trees by enveloping them thereby depriving them of light.

Summers are hot and humid in Cfa climates. If you know what it is like living in Alabama, Mississippi, Georgia, or even southern Indiana in the summer, then you know what it is like living in southeastern China—hot, humid, nasty, and bug infested. The winters, on the other hand, can sometimes be fairly cold, but usually they are mild when compared to the climates of the continental interiors. Spring is the most enjoyable season of the year, but autumn can be nice, too.

Figure 17-1. The subtropical forest in the southeastern United States includes a diverse mixture of evergreen trees, deciduous trees, and water-tolerant trees such as bald cypress (right). Pines are a common tree in the Southeast due to the sandy soil.
(Robert L. Beck photos)

Figure 17-2. Kudzu Growing Over Trees in Northern Mississippi
(Robert L. Beck photo, 2000)

Atlanta, Georgia, is positioned near the heart of the humid subtropical climate region of the southeastern United States. Its coldest month, January, has an average temperature of about 43 degrees, which makes it too cold to be an A climate and too warm to be a D (Fig. 17-3). Its 50 inches of precipitation is spread out over the year, so there are no dry seasons on a long-term average. Of course droughts can, and do, occur, but they do not show up when weather data is averaged over a period of 30 years. The abundance of precipitation coupled with a hot July of 80°F gives Atlanta a Cfa designation. Louisville, Kentucky, also has a Cfa climate, but it is situated near the northern edge of the region as indicated by its 33°F average January temperature. The boundary between the Cfa climate region and the Dfa climate region is located somewhere in Indiana between Louisville and Indianapolis, for Indianapolis has an average January temperature of 27 degrees, which makes it a D climate. The climographs of Atlanta and Louisville are highly similar, but Louisville does have a cooler winter and less precipitation because it is farther removed from the Gulf of Mexico moisture source.

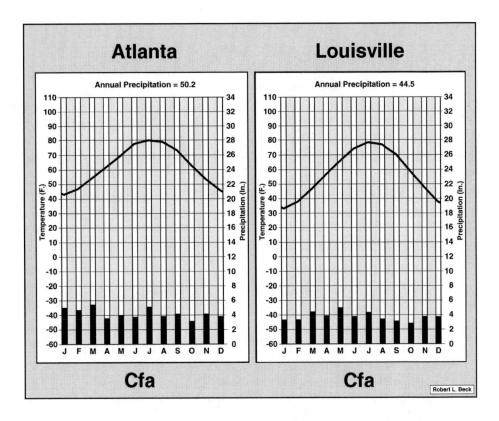

Figure 17-3. Climographs of Atlanta, Georgia, and Louisville, Kentucky

Both Atlanta and Louisville receive most of their precipitation from weather fronts attached to midlatitude cyclones. Atlanta, however, is much more likely to receive convergence precipitation from dissipating hurricanes because it is nearer the sea and because its latitude puts it closer to the Atlantic Ocean's hurricane belt than Louisville, which is positioned several hundred miles inland from both the Atlantic Ocean and the Gulf of Mexico.

215

Mediterranean Climate

If you now jump to the opposite corner of the continent, the southwestern corner, one finds a totally different climate. In this corner is what many people consider to be the world's finest climate, the Mediterranean, which is designated as a *Cs* climate (Csa and Csb). Again, the *C* means that the average temperature of the coldest month is less than 65°F but greater than 32°F. The *s* means "summer drought." The Mediterranean climates are colored dark green on my online map.

The coastal areas of southern California are in the southwestern corner of the United States (*World Climate Regions* map, p. 211), so they are on the opposite coast from the Cfa climates of the southeastern United States. Now find the Mediterranean climate of central Chile (in South America). Observe it is on the opposite coast from the humid subtropical climates of northern Argentina and Uruguay. The Cs climate in southwestern Africa is on the opposite coast from the Cfa climate in southeastern Africa. Even the world's largest Cs climate region, around the Mediterranean Sea in southern Europe and North Africa, is on the opposite side of the Eurasian landmass from the humid subtropical climate region of eastern China. The Cs climates are typically positioned at about 35° to 38° latitude, and all, except for the lands bordering the Mediterranean Sea, have cold ocean currents offshore.

Physical geographers commonly describe the Mediterranean climate as having "summer drought and winter rain." But why does it have a summer drought and why does it rain in the winter and not all year-round? You know the world pressure belts migrate with the direct rays of the sun. So when the SSP (subsolar point) moves north, the pressure belts move north, and when it moves south, the pressure belts move south. The periods of rainfall and drought in the Cs climates are produced by these pressure belt migrations.

In June and July, when the SSP migrates to its maximum northern position, the Northern Hemisphere's subtropical high pressure cells (the California High and the Azores High) settle over the Cs climate regions of North America and Europe, producing droughts. Observe on the Csa climograph for Athens (***Goode's World Atlas***, p. 31) that the time of **maximum temperature** (June and July) is also the time of **minimum precipitation.**

The migration of the SSP causes the ITC to migrate in response. In January, the ITC is looping south over southern Africa; the subtropical high pressure cells are drying up the Sahara and Kalahari Deserts; and midlatitude cyclones are generating rain in all of Europe and the coastlands bordering the Mediterranean Sea in southwestern Asia and northern Africa (Fig. 17-4). By July, the ITC has shifted to the north and is positioned south of Africa's Sahara Desert in the Aw climate region just north of the Equator (Fig. 17-4). The push of the ITC to the north causes the Azores High to shift to the north, so it settles in over northern Africa and the Mediterranean Sea, which brings dry conditions to southern Europe in the summer by preventing access to the lands bordering the Mediterranean Sea by rain-producing midlatitude cyclones. Northern Europe, however, continues to receive rain in the summer because the Azores High does not migrate far enough north to block the flow of midlatitude cyclones to most of France, the British Isles, Scandinavia, Germany, and areas to the east. Northern Europe is not subjected to the summer drought as is southern Europe, so Northern Europe has abundant precipitation all year (see Dublin climograph, *Goode's World Atlas,* p. 31).

In December and January, when the SSP migrates to its maximum southern position, the Northern Hemisphere's subtropical high pressure cells shift to the south. This allows midlatitude cyclones to bring precipitation to all of Europe in the winter. The high pressure cell that brought dryness to Athens in the summer now weakens and shifts to the south, which allows midlatitude cyclones to dampen the winter weather. Please now examine the "Average Precipitation" maps in *Goode's World Atlas* (pp. 34–35) to see that coastal Turkey, Italy, Spain, and southern California are all wetter in the winter than they are in the summer.

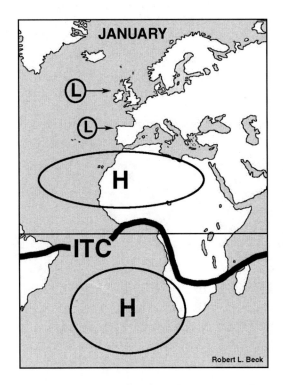 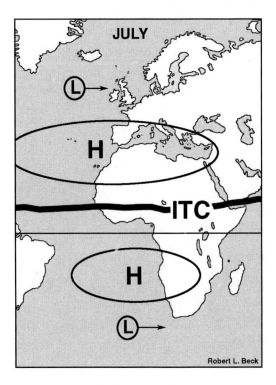

Figure 17-4. Approximate Positions of Highs and Lows over Africa and Europe in January and July

The Mediterranean climates in the Southern Hemisphere are just like the Mediterranean climates in the Northern Hemisphere in that they have "summer drought and winter rain." Please keep in mind, however, the beginning of summer in the Southern Hemisphere occurs in December, and the beginning of winter occurs in July. The shift of the pressure belts north in July enables midlatitude cyclones to bring rain to the southern tip of Africa at that time (Fig. 17-4). The area around Cape Town is dominated by a subtropical high pressure cell in its summer (January), so little rain falls there as a result. Midlatitude cyclones bring rain to Cape Town in its winter (July). Like the areas bordering the Mediterranean Sea, Cape Town has summer drought and winter rain, so it, too, has a Cs climate and is indicated as such on my *World Climate Regions* map, p. 211. You should now be able to tell me which month, January or July, is one of central Chile's wettest months. Of course it is . . . July!

The natural vegetation of the Mediterranean climate, to survive, has to be able to withstand a high sun drought. This is opposite of what most vegetation on Earth has to endure, for most of the world's climate regions receive precipitation year-round or they receive precipitation at the time of the high sun. Vegetation in the Mediterranean climates has developed a number of survival strategies to live through the high sun drought.

Sclerophyll is the natural vegetation of Mediterranean climates (Fig. 17-5). This word can be broken down into two components: *sclero-* (hard) and *-phyll* (leaf). Hard leaves help prevent the loss of water through pore spaces in the leaf. The leaves are also covered with a waxy coating further preventing loss of water. Many sclerophyll species have an extensive root network used to find water deep underground or they have the capability to store water inside the plant for long periods of time—corks are made from the bark of the cork tree (a tree found in Mediterranean climates), which helps hold water inside the tree. Water is also stored inside grapes, a vine crop commonly found in Mediterranean climate regions. Olive trees have a long life, so they spend their energy surviving and not growing.

Figure 17-5. Chaparral, Sclerophyll Vegetation, Southern California
(Tim Brothers photos)

Winter wheat, another Mediterranean crop, has a survival strategy different from any of those I have listed. Gardeners know that you plant corn, peas, beans, potatoes, cucumbers, radishes, carrots, and many other crops in the spring and that you harvest these crops in the summer or fall. Winter wheat has an opposite life cycle, for you plant winter wheat in the fall and harvest it in the spring (Fig. 17-6). Winter wheat is the raw material used to make flour from which bread is made. This crop has evolved a life cycle different from our other common crops because it relies on the wet winter for growth. It is in seed during the hot, dry summer.

218

When I mention "bread, wine, and olives," what do you think of? You should be thinking of Italian cuisine! Every time I get to this part of the course, I start to get hungry. The foods we eat are tied, in many respects, to the climates in which they were first domesticated and grown. Wine and bread are two symbols of Christianity, so it was perfectly natural for the Spanish to carry winter wheat and grapes to the Mediterranean climate regions around the earth where they settled. Today, important wine-producing regions are found in the Cs climate regions of southern California, central Chile, southern and southwestern Australia, coastal South Africa, and southern Europe.

Figure 17-6. Winter Wheat, Central Kansas
(Robert L. Beck photo, 1993)

Marine West Coast Climate

I began this module by starting with the humid subtropical climate, which is found on the southeastern corners of continents; next I moved to the Mediterranean climate, which is found on the southwestern corners of continents; now I move to the marine west coast climate, which is typically found **poleward** of the Mediterranean climate. Marine west coast climates are designated as *Cfb* or *Cfc*. Once again, the *C* means that the average temperature of the coldest month is less than 65°F but greater than 32°F; the *f* means "full-year precipitation," the *b* means a "cool summer," and the *c* means a "cool, short summer" with less than four months over 50°F. Except for Europe, the marine west coast climates cover relatively small areas of Earth; they are colored a medium green on my online map (http://www.iu.edu/~g107/mod16/World Climate Regions.jpg).

Northwestern Europe has the largest marine west coast climate on Earth, for the lack of a major north-south mountain range along the coast allows marine (maritime) air to moderate the climate for several hundred miles inland. The Coast Mountains in Canada and the Cascade Mountains in the United States confine the marine west coast of North America to a narrow strip along the coast. Water vapor carried inland by the westerlie winds would be precipitated out over a much larger area if the Cascade Mountains did not exist. Two cities in Washington nicely demonstrate this concept. Glenoma and Yakima are both at about the same latitude and altitude (800' vs. 1,100'), and they are only 80 miles apart (Fig. 17-7). If these cities were located in Europe they would each be receiving approximately 30 inches of precipitation per year, but in the United States they are separated by the Cascade Mountains, which concentrates precipitation on the windward side facing Glenoma. The leeward side is so dry that the area around Yakima has a B climate. The same situation occurs in South America, with the Andes Mountains confining the marine west coast to a narrow strip along the coast of southern Chile. Both South Africa and Australia have Cfb climates, but they are mainly related to elevation and not to coastal positions. Finally, marine west coast climates are found in Tasmania and New Zealand.

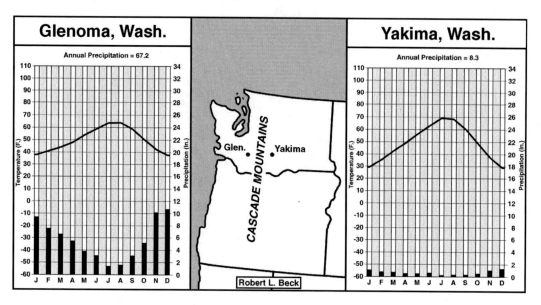

Figure 17-7. Orographic Effect in Influencing Climate Patterns

In many respects the Cfb climate is similar to the Cfa climate (Fig. 17-8). Both have large amounts of annual precipitation, both have mild winter temperatures, both receive most of their precipitation from midlatitude cyclones, and both have forests as their natural vegetation. The big difference between the two climates is the summer temperature. The summer temperature of the humid subtropical climate (Cfa) is hot, whereas the summer temperature of the marine west coast (Cfb) is cool. Montgomery, Alabama, is a hot, sweltering city in the summer; Vancouver, British Columbia, is cool and mild (Fig. 17-8).

The Cfb gives way to the Cfc in the higher latitudes as the summers become much cooler and shorter (*World Climate Regions* map, p. 211). Cfc climates are rare; warm ocean currents moderate the temperature of the Cfc to keep its coldest month above freezing, while also limiting the length of the summer and holding its temperature down.

Marine west coast climates are situated in the westerlie wind belts. Midlatitude cyclones are mostly responsible for the generation of their precipitation, and it is fairly evenly distributed throughout the year; however, a city with a Cfb climate positioned near a Cs climate region (as is Seattle, Washington) normally receives a diminished amount of precipitation in the summer months due to the influence of the nearby high pressure cell.

Forests constitute the natural vegetation of the Cfb climates, but the forest types are variable due to the big differences in precipitation that fall in the various marine west coast climates. Huge amounts of precipitation fall on the marine west coast climates in North America and South America because of the blocking effect of the mountains. The forest composition in these areas is quite different from the forest composition of northwestern Europe, which has a much drier Cfb climate. Some geographers refer to the forest of North America's marine west coast climate as **midlatitude rainforest**, for it is dominated by evergreens living in an environment dripping with precipitation at almost all times.

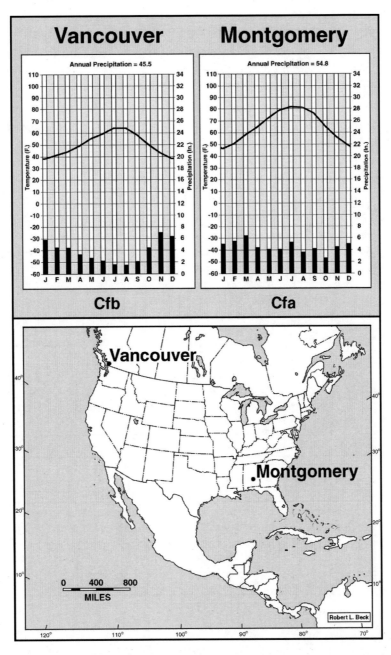

Figure 17-8. The main difference between the Cfa climate and the Cfb climate is the summer temperature. Summers in Cfb climates are much cooler than in Cfa climates.

Subtropical Savanna Climate

The climate that does **not** fit very well in the Trewartha-modified Köppen system is the *Cw* climate, the subtropical savanna climate. Many geographers, including me, normally consider this climate to be a latitudinal extension of the Aw climate. Compare the climographs of Varanasi, India, with Timbo, Guinea (***Goode's World Atlas***, pp. 30–31). It is easy to see that their temperature and moisture characteristics are similar—lots of high sun rain, high temperatures throughout the year, and a pronounced winter drought. The only real difference between the two is that Varanasi has a slightly cooler winter, one in which the temperature falls below 65°F. For practical purposes the Cw climates in southern Africa, India, and southern South America can be grouped with the Aw climate; many geographers simply ignore the Cw climate in these areas and lump it with the Aw when constructing world climate maps. The Cw climate is colored olive green on my *World Climate Regions* map shown online.

One of the world's largest cities, Sao Paulo, Brazil, has a Cw climate (Fig. 17-9). Its coldest month, July, averages about 59°F, so it is too cold to be classified as an A climate. It has a noticeable dry period in the winter, which leads one to classify it as a Cw. This dry period is not a true drought, for even its driest month has almost 1.5 inches of precipitation. Sao Paulo has a Cw climate, but the city is only about 150 miles south of Brazil's Aw climate region. If Sao Paulo were located 150 miles to the north its coldest winter month would average above 32°F, which would make it an Aw climate. As mentioned, the Cw climate region in Brazil can be perceived as a latitudinal extension of the Aw climate region . . . Sao Paulo is a nice example of this.

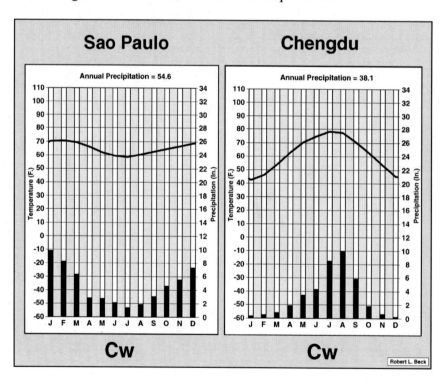

Figure 17-9. Two cities with a Cw climate, but in different hemispheres.

The Cw climate in East Asia (mostly China) is a different story. Here the Cw climate is marginal to the humid subtropical climate (the Cfa of eastern China) on three sides. As one moves inland away from the coast, the precipitation pattern changes so that winter drought characterizes the inland and southern fringe of the Cfa climate, turning it into a Cw climate. This concept is demonstrated with the climograph of Chengdu, China (Fig. 17-9). Chengdu receives very little rain from November through March, so it has a noticeably dry winter. Its coldest month, however, is about 42°F, so it is too cold to be classified as an A climate and too warm to be classified as a D climate. Chengdu has a Cw climate and its climograph makes it easy to see why (Fig. 17-9).

The Cw climate on the northern flank of China's Cfa climate is positioned equatorward of China's Dw climate, which is the characteristic climate of Manchuria (northeastern China) and North Korea. This Cw climate can be viewed as a southerly extension of north China's Dw, which is dry in the winter due to the cold air blowing out of the Central Siberian High. The Cw climate between the Cfa and the Dw in eastern China is thus a transitional climate between the dominant humid subtropical (Cfa) on the eastern coast and the dry winter humid continental climate (Dwa) of the northeast, which is the climate type found in the vicinity of Beijing.

Manchuria

****

Practice Exercise: Two climographs are shown below. Which one is the C climate?

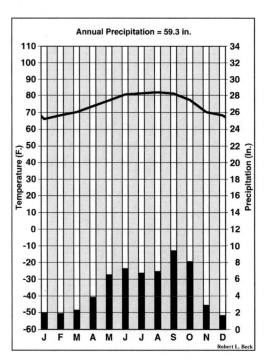

X

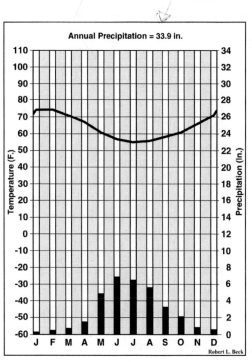

Y

223

Climographic Transect

Climographs of cities along the west coast of North America are shown in the map to the right. The climograph of San Diego (bottom) certainly shows it to be either a Cs climate or a BSh, for in the six month period from the beginning of May to the end of October the city only receives 1.06 inches of precip. During the winter, from November to the end of April, the city receives over 9.5 inches. San Diego most definitely has a summer drought and winter rain.

As one moves north along the coast the summers become progressively less dry, but still there is a noticeable lack of precipitation in the summer months. Even Prince Rupert, with over 100 inches of precipitation annually, has a diminished occurrence of precipitation in the summer.

At some point along the coast the dry summer Mediterranean climate turns into the marine west coast climate (Cfb). Seattle has a dry summer relative to its winter, but its summer is not nearly as dry or prolonged as the coastal cities of southern California. Coastal Oregon and even southern Washington are positioned in the transition zone between the classic Mediterranean climate as represented by San Francisco and the classic marine west coast climate as represented by Prince Rupert.

The C climate is left behind by the time one reaches Juneau. The average temperature of its coldest month is below 32 degrees, which makes it a D climate. It has full-year precipitation, which makes it an *f*, and its warmest summer month is only about 57 degrees. Further, it only has three summer months over 50 degrees, which makes it a Dfc, not a Dfb.

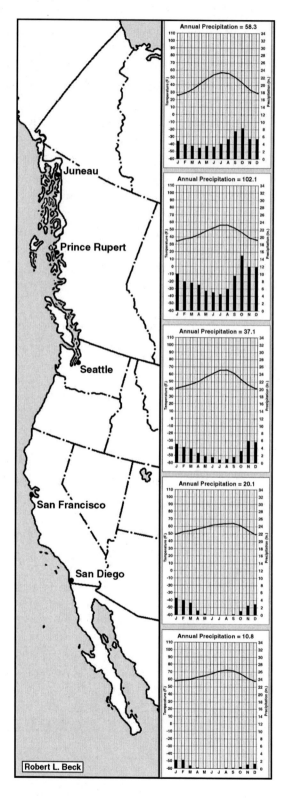

224

Practice Exercise: The climographs of four Northern Hemisphere C climates are shown below. One is a humid subtropical climate, one is a Mediterranean climate, one is a marine west coast climate, and one is a subtropical savanna climate. Which one is which?

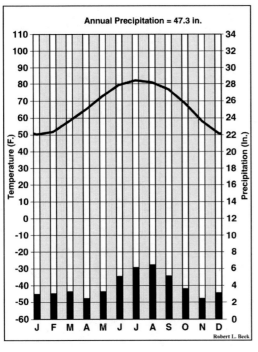

CFA

1

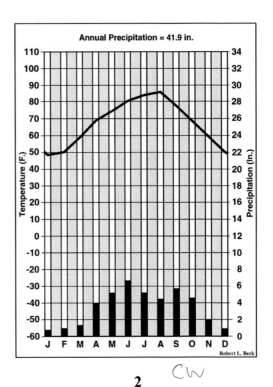

CW

2

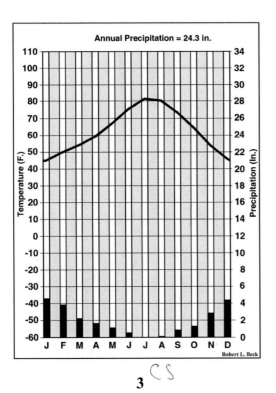

CS

3

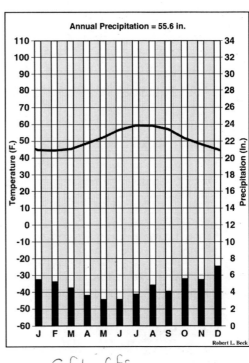

Cfb, Cfc

4

Climograph of Cherrapunji, India— the second wettest place on Earth.

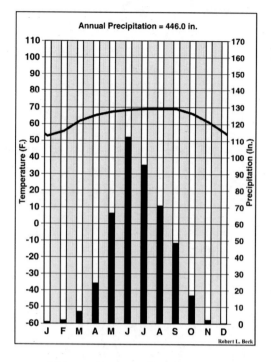

Annual Precipitation = 446.0 in.

What climate type is it?

Is this a C climate? If so, which C is it? If not, why not?

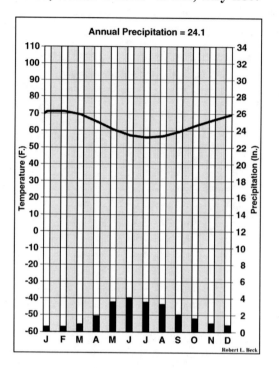

Annual Precipitation = 24.1

Z

Module 17 Objectives

You should now be able to:

- Use temperature data to differentiate C climates from the A, D, and E climates

- Compare and contrast the four main types of *mesothermal climates*

- Discuss the geographic distribution of the mesothermal climates and explain why they are located where they are

- Discuss the precipitation patterns of the mesothermal climates and relate the patterns to the types of natural vegetation found in the mesothermal climates

- Describe the major differences among the four C climates

- Use my *World Climate Regions* map, p. 211, to predict the month or season of precipitation of the C climates shown on the map

- Draw the locations of the mesothermal climates on a world map

- Describe a *climographic transect*

226

MODULE 18: CONTINENTAL CLIMATES

The continental climates are middle to high latitude climates found only in the Northern Hemisphere. Köppen originally called these climates the *cold snow-forest climates*. Trewartha identifies them as *microthermal climates*. I prefer to use the term *continental climates*, for they are land-dominated climates with temperature extremes.

The continental climates are designated with a capital *D*. The average temperature of their coldest month is less than 32°F and the average temperature of their warmest month is greater than 50°F. They are colored blue on my *World Climate Regions* map (http://www.iu.edu/~g107/mod16/World Climate Regions.jpg). In the traditional Köppen system the coldest month of the D climates had to be less than 26.6°F (−3°C), but Trewartha changed this to 32°F. Geographically, the D climates are situated over landmasses and are positioned poleward of the B and C climates. There are two main continental climates.

Humid Continental Climate

The northern two-thirds of Indiana, including the city of Indianapolis, is located in the humid continental climate region. We have a land-dominated climate in central Indiana— winters are cold and summers are hot. Anyone who has lived in Indiana also knows the state receives a fairly large amount of annual precipitation and that humid weather conditions often prevail, especially in the summer.

The average January temperature of Indianapolis is about 27°F, which is less than 32°F; and the average July temperature is about 77°F, which is greater than 50°F. These two conditions mean that the city has a D climate. Indianapolis receives too much rain to be classified as a B climate; it is too cold in the winter to be classified as either an A or C climate; and it is too warm in the summer to be classified as an E climate.

Humid continental climates are designated as *Dfa*, *Dfb*, *Dwa*, or *Dwb*. The letters *a*, *b*, *f*, and *w* have the same meanings as in the other climates I have discussed. To refresh your memory I will list them again: *a* = hot summer, *b* = cool summer, *f* = full-year precipitation, and *w* = winter drought.

The humid continental climate of Indiana and much of the midwestern United States is a Dfa, but as one moves north the summers become cooler, so it turns into a Dfb. The same pattern occurs in eastern Europe. A Dfa climate is found in Romania and northern Bulgaria, but with increasing latitude into Ukraine and Russia the summers become cooler, hence the Dfb throughout much of western Russia (*World Climate Regions* map, p. 211).

A different situation occurs in eastern Asia, for the Central Siberian High forms in the winter as Asia becomes extremely cold. This high pressure cell blocks the flow of

227

midlatitude cyclones across Asia, and it also means that bitterly cold air blows out of central Siberia into eastern Siberia, northern China, and North Korea. Dry conditions prevail when air is blowing from the land to the sea, so a pronounced winter drought occurs in the humid continental climate of eastern Asia. These dry winter humid continental climates are designated Dwa and Dwb. Please now compare the climographs of Indianapolis and Beijing (Fig. 18-1). Both cities are at about the same latitude and have approximately the same temperature curve, but Beijing has a prominent winter drought. Beijing is too wet to be classified as a B climate, so it is a D climate due to its cold January temperature and hot July temperature; however, Beijing does not have the relatively uniform annual distribution of precipitation as does Indianapolis. Both cities have a humid continental climate, but the winter drought makes Beijing a Dwa climate, not a Dfa.

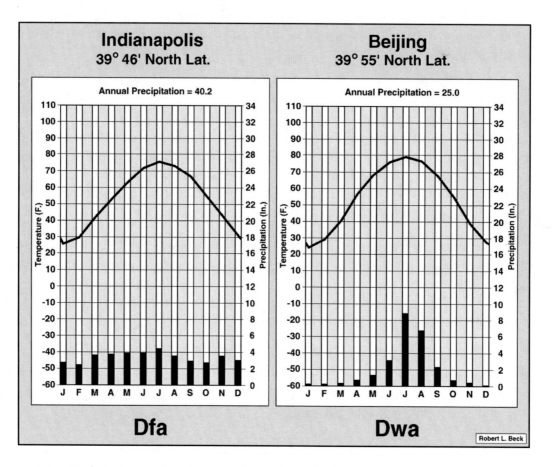

Fig. 18-1. Climograph Comparison of a Dfa Climate and a Dwa Climate

Broadleaf deciduous forest, also known as the ***midlatitude deciduous forest***, is the natural vegetation of Indiana's Dfa climate (Fig. 18-2). Oaks, hickories, beeches, and maples are four of the most common trees in the state. As one moves north into Michigan, and into the Dfb climate region, a ***mixed forest*** of needleleaf evergreen and broadleaf deciduous trees constitute the natural vegetation. The natural vegetation of Earth's humid continental climate regions is either broadleaf deciduous forest or a mixed forest of broadleaf deciduous and needleleaf evergreen.

Figure 18-2. Midlatitude Deciduous Forest, Central Indiana
(Robert L. Beck photo, 2006)

Subarctic Climate

By area, Russia is the world's largest country, and Canada is number two. I mention this because in both countries the subarctic climate region accounts for more than 50% of the area of each country; the subarctic climate is one on the world's largest climate regions.

Subarctic climates are designated as ***Dfc, Dfd, Dwc,*** or ***Dwd.*** The *c* means a "cool, short summer" with less than four months over 50°F; the *d* means a "cool, short summer with a very cold winter." The coldest month in the *d* climate is below −36°F. The other letters are the same as before.

Observe on my *World Climate Regions* map (p. 211) that in North America the zonation of the D climates from south to north is as follows: Dfa, Dfb, Dfc. As one proceeds north from Indiana, the summers become increasingly cooler and shorter, so this is reflected in the lettering nomenclature. The same pattern occurs in eastern Europe and western Asia: Dfa, Dfb, Dfc. The Dfd climate, which is poleward of the Dfc in Asia, is not shown on Trewartha's map in the 21st edition of ***Goode's World Atlas***, but I have indicated its approximate position on my *World Climate Regions* map. In eastern Asia the sequence is: Dwa, Dwb, Dwc, Dwd. I know these letters might seem confusing, but they do have a clear pattern based on temperature changes with increasing latitude.

The subarctic climates have the world's largest temperature ranges. Verkhoyansk, in Russia, has an average July temperature of 60°F, a little cool but really not too bad; its average January temperature is −58°F, a little warmer than Antarctica but really, really cold. Its annual temperature range is 118°. The map of "Average Annual Temperature Range" in ***Goode's World Atlas***, p. 33, shows the subarctic climate region of eastern Siberia to have the world's largest temperature ranges. The map is also interesting because it shows that tropical climates have small temperature ranges. The average annual temperature range in Indianapolis is only about 50 degrees, for our average July temperature is 77°F and our average January temperature is 27°F. Indianapolis, though, has a large annual temperature range when compared to cities in the southern United States and along the west coast of North America (***Goode's World Atlas***, p. 33).

The natural vegetation of the subarctic climate is a forest type known as ***taiga***, which consists of needleleaf trees such as pines, hemlocks, spruces, and firs (Fig. 18-3). Most taiga species are evergreen trees, but in eastern Siberia the winters are so cold that even some needleleaf trees shed their leaves (such as the larch tree), so they are classified as needleleaf deciduous trees. Trees in the taiga grow slowly and they do not grow very high, only about 40 feet at most. At the northern edge of the taiga the growing season is so short that trees grow only a few feet high.

Figure 18-3. Taiga, Yukon Territory
(Robert L. Beck photo, 1975)

Species diversity is low in the taiga—there are literally thousands and thousands of square miles covered by just a few different tree species. The taiga is the world's largest forest region and its northern boundary line (the boundary line between the D and E climates) is the ***latitudinal treeline***, or the northern limit of woody plants in North America, Europe, and Asia.

Module 18 Objectives

You should now be able to:

- Use temperature data to differentiate D climates from the A, C, and E climates

- Compare and contrast the two main types of *continental climates*

- Discuss the geographic distribution of the continental climates and explain why they are located where they are

- Discuss the precipitation and temperature patterns of the continental climates and relate the patterns to the types of natural vegetation found in the continental climates

- List four characteristics of the *taiga*

- Draw the locations of the continental climates on a world map

Practice Exercise: What is the distinguishing difference between these two D climates?

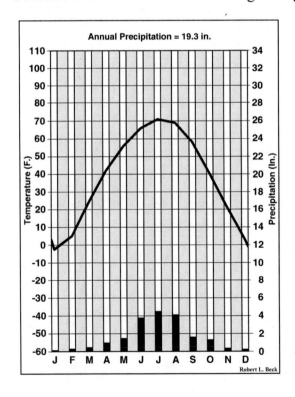

X

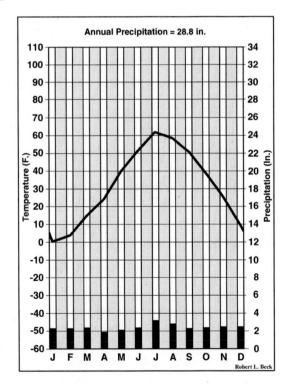

Y

231

CLIMOGRAPHS OF Df CLIMATES

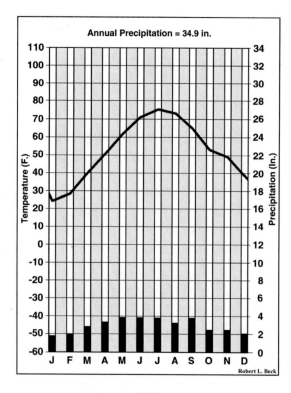

Dfa

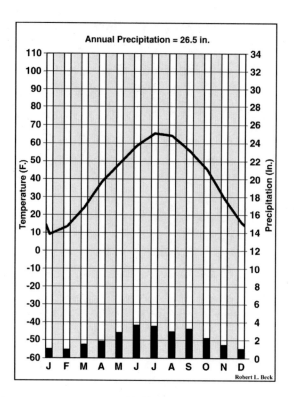

Dfb

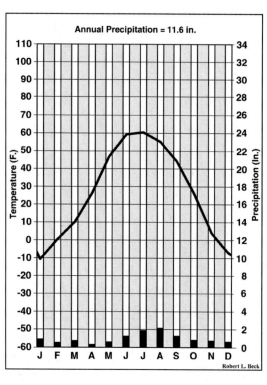

Dfc

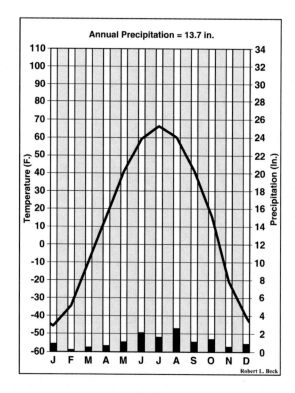

Dfd

MODULE 19: POLAR AND HIGHLAND CLIMATES

The polar climates are high latitude climates designated with a capital *E*. The average temperature of the coldest month of the E climates is less than 32°F, but the D climates use that same criterion. One has to use the average temperature of the warmest month to separate the D climates from the E climates. The D climates, being continental, have warm summers with the average temperature of the warmest month greater than 50°F. The E climates, being polar, do not have such warm summers. The average temperature of the warmest month in the E climates is less than 50°F.

Ice Cap Climate

In the high latitude areas of Earth one finds permanent glaciers; Antarctica and Greenland are mostly covered with a sheet of ice. In these areas the average temperatures of both the coldest month and the warmest month are below 32°F. The ice cap climates are designated *EF*, and they are colored light purple on my World Climate Regions map (http://www.iu.edu/~g107/mod16/World Climate Regions.jpg). To be classified as an E climate the average temperature of the warmest month has to be below 50°F, but when it is also below 32°F then the designation *F* is used to represent "perpetual frost."

The world's coldest average temperatures are found in the ice cap climate over Antarctica. One would expect the South Pole to be colder than the North Pole because it is near the center of a continent, whereas the North Pole is in the Arctic Ocean. Land climates are colder than water climates.

The EF climates might seem to receive a lot of moisture, but actually very little precipitation falls. What does fall remains there in the form of ice—little evaporation takes place when temperatures are consistently below freezing. In the Köppen system, however, these climates are not considered to be B climates because of the low evaporation rate. Precipitation, what little there is, exceeds evaporation in the E climates.

Tundra Climate

The *ET* climate is the tundra climate, so the *T* refers to *tundra*. Observe on the *World Climate Regions* map (p. 211) that the **tundra** climate is situated between the subarctic climate of northern Canada (Dfc) and the ice cap climate (EF) of the center of Greenland. Also observe the strip of tundra along the north shores of both Europe and Asia. The Antarctic Peninsula also has an ET climate. The areas on Earth with an ET climate are colored dark purple on my *World Climate Regions* map shown online.

There is a brief growing season in the ET climates, for the average temperature of the warmest month is greater than 32°F but less than 50°F. This period of warmth allows the top few inches of permanently frozen ground *(permafrost)* to thaw. Water will then collect on the earth's surface and, when coupled with the long daylight hours of summer, allow plants to grow a little. Tundra is a type of vegetation that consists of grasses, mosses, and lichens; this allows large herbivores such as caribou and reindeer to live in this environment (Fig. 19-1). Many geographers consider tundra to be polar grassland (Fig. 19-2).

Figure 19-1. Tundra, Northern Alaska
(Tim Brothers photo)

Figure 19-2. Tundra, Polar Grassland
(Tim Brothers photo)

The tundra is perhaps the world's most sensitive ecosystem. It takes dozens or hundreds of years for human disturbances in this environment to be erased by nature. I once saw a photograph of the track of a bulldozer that had been driven through the tundra of northern Alaska or Canada. The photograph, I believe, was taken in the 1980s, but the bulldozer had been driven through the tundra in the 1940s.

Practice Exercise: The climographs of four E climates are shown below. Which one represents a different type of climate than the others? Why?

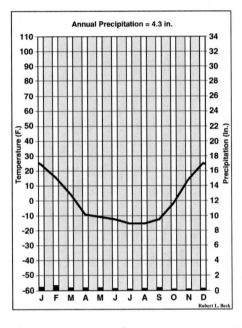

1

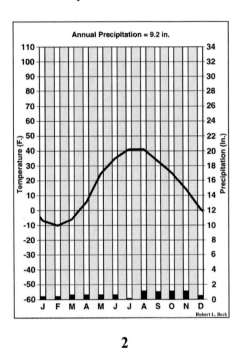

2

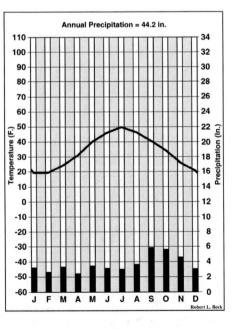

3

4

235

Summary of the Trewartha-modified Köppen System

The Trewartha-modified Köppen system is summarized in Fig. 19-3. This chart should help you to quickly differentiate between the major Köppen climate groups. Keep in mind that the B climates are not shown on the chart because they are defined using precipitation totals and not average temperatures of the coldest and warmest months.

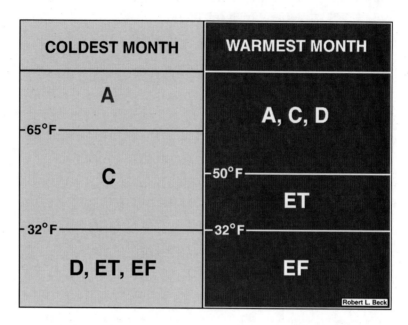

Figure 19-3. Climate Groups Classified by Temperature of the Coldest and Warmest Months

If you try to memorize the Köppen system too quickly, without spending the time to understand it, I am sure your brain will be cluttered with seemingly meaningless letters and numbers. Many geographers who do not like the Köppen system preach against it by saying, "it is not used anymore" or "students find it confusing, so I do not cover it in the courses I teach" or "it is a waste of time, why bother learning about all of this confusing terminology." I have the belief, however, that studying the Köppen system really helps one to grasp the world patterns of climate and vegetation. The system has many faults, but I believe the benefits of the system outweigh the frustrations some students feel as they study it. I enjoyed learning about climates this way, but I know many people do not.

To classify climates using the Köppen system, it is best to begin with an analysis of a certain set of temperature data starting with the coldest month. Whenever I am confronted with such data the first step I follow, assuming it is not a B climate, is to separate the A, C, and D/E climates from each other using the coldest month as the determining factor.

I then examine the warmest month to (1) separate the D climates from the E climates, and (2) separate the ET climates from the EF climates. Flow charts have been constructed by some geographers to show this graphically, but I think those charts make complex something that is not too difficult to understand. After all, there are only three key numbers (65, 50, and 32) in Trewartha's modifications of Köppen's basic groups. **Practice Exercise**: What climate types are these? What types of vegetation would you expect to find in them?

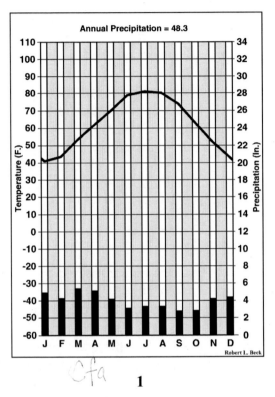

Cfa

1

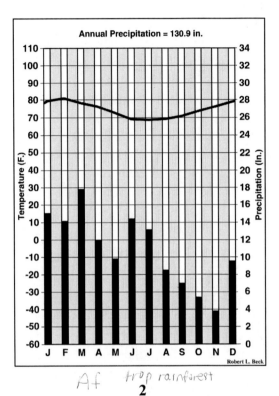

Af   trop rainforest

2

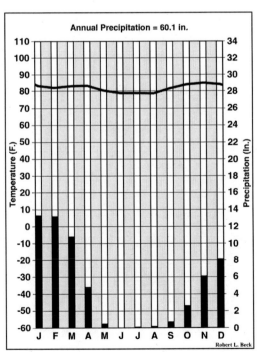

As / Am

3

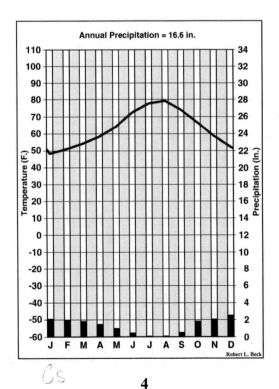

Cs

4

237

Highland Climates

The Köppen–Geiger system uses just five letters—A, B, C, D, E— to classify the world's climates into major groups. The high mountain areas such as the Himalayas and the Andes are considered to be E climates largely because they have permanent ice fields near their summits. Trewartha added a sixth letter, a capital *H*, to represent *highland* climates in which one encounters climatic changes that occur vertically while ascending a mountain. Many individual mountains in the Andes have permanent ice fields near their summits, but others have rainforests at their bases, near sea level. One can logically argue, therefore, when using the Köppen–Geiger system, that a mountain might be classified as being either an A, C, D, or E depending on the elevation above sea level where the classification takes place. Trewartha's system eliminates this problem, for the areas of Earth where climates vary vertically are designated as highland climates. These H climate regions are shown on my *World Climate Regions* map (p. 211). H climates are most prominent in the low and middle latitudes. In the high latitudes the entire mountain from base to summit will be cold and will therefore be properly classified as a D or E climate.

High mountains in the low and middle latitudes are ringed with vegetation zones. If one starts at the base of a mountain and climbs to the peak, he or she might walk through four or five major vegetation zones on the upward ascent (Fig. 19-4). If the mountain is on the Equator, one might begin the climb through a zone of tropical rainforest (A climate), thence through a zone of deciduous forest (C climate), thence through a zone of needleleaf forest (D climate), thence through a zone of alpine tundra (ET climate), finally reaching an ice field at the peak (EF climate). In essence, you have traveled from the Equator to a pole by going up the mountain. This vertical

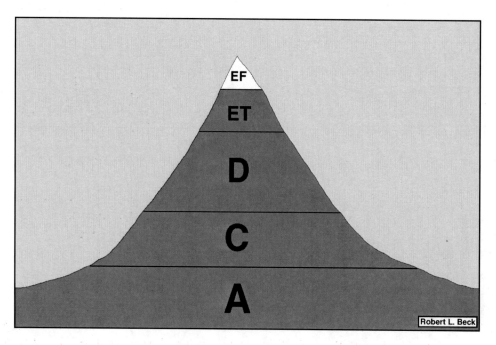

Figure 19-4. Altitudinal Zonation of Climates on Mountains in Low Latitudes

separation of vegetation is, of course, related to the temperature and moisture changes that occur with elevation on the mountain. While traveling from the Equator to a pole, one encounters a **latitudinal** zonation of vegetation, but while traveling up a high mountain one encounters an **altitudinal** zonation of vegetation.

Latin Americans have names for these various climate zones related to elevation. The *tierra caliente* is the "hot land" at the base of the mountain that extends upward to an elevation of about 2,000 feet above sea level (Fig. 19-5). In this zone one finds not only tropical rainforest vegetation, but also crops that like hot, humid weather, such as bananas and sugarcane. From about 2,000 feet to 6,000 feet is the *tierra templada*, the "temperate land." Deciduous forest is found at this elevation, but so also are the crops of coffee and corn (Fig. 19-7). From 6,000 feet to 11,000 feet is the *tierra fria*, the "cold land." Needleleaf forest is found here, but also the crops of potatoes, barley, and wheat. Finally, above 11,000 feet is the *tierra helada*, the "ice land." Alpine tundra and permanent glaciers are located here. The tundra might be used as pasturage for livestock.

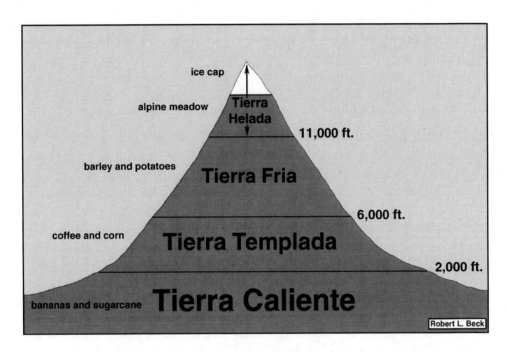

Figure 19-5. Vertical Climate Zones in Latin America

Quito, Ecuador, is one of the world's classic highland cities. Its elevation of 9,200 feet above sea level puts it in the tierra fria, and its location on the Equator (0° 12' S. Lat.) gives it a sun angle of at least 66½ degrees every day. The temperature curve of Quito is almost flat—every month of the year averages about 58°F (Fig. 19-6).

Quito is classified as a Cfb climate in the Köppen–Geiger system, and it is shown as such in the 22nd edition of *Goode's World Atlas* (p. 30). In Trewartha's system, and also in this textbook, Quito is classified as an H climate, for its climate has a lot more to do with its altitude than its latitude. Quito is shown as an H climate on my *World Climate*

239

Regions map (p. 211); it was also shown as an H climate in the 21st edition of **Goode's World Atlas** (p. 14).

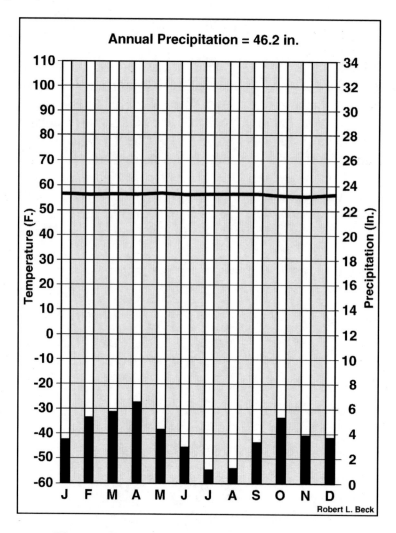

Figure 19-6. Climograph of Quito, Ecuador

The switch in editions of **Goode's World Atlas** caused a switch in the climatic classification of Quito, which is a good example of why many people despise classification systems in general. Classification systems are often based on opinions, so what one person views as a good system another person might view as bad. Many geographers believe it is more important to understand how the seven climate controls interact to produce a climate rather than quibbling about the details and merits of any particular classification system. Those geographers often argue for the elimination of climatic classification systems to eliminate the controversy concerning them. I believe the intent of Köppen and Trewartha, however, was to produce a general model explaining the world distribution of climate so that people might begin to understand geographic patterns without being concerned about minor exceptions to the general model. If a student understands a general model of any concept, then he or she should be able to analytically identify specific exceptions; however, if a student is taught only specific instances of some earth feature (without being exposed to the general model) then he or she is rarely able to synthetically produce a general model by integrating specific examples.

I teach the Trewartha-modified Köppen system as a general model without worrying about its specific flaws. Other geographers worry about the specific flaws, so they do not teach the Köppen system because of them; their students are set adrift to flop about with no guiding model to assist them in figuring out the world distribution of climates. Remember, however, climate is abstract; only weather is real, so do we really need to study climate? And especially climate regions, which are often based on opinions, likes, and dislikes? Many geographers view climatology as a science, which requires quantification, precision, predictability, and minimal interjection of opinion. I understand that viewpoint, but I also see climatology as an art, for it can be a subjective way to begin to understand Earth's complicated patterns of long-term weather and how those influence the world distribution of natural vegetation. Furthermore, I find fascinating the concept of region-building with the intent to depict regional boundaries on maps artistically, but based on quantitative data.

Figure 19-7. Tierra Templada, Dominican Republic
(Tim Brothers photo)

Module 19 Objectives

You should now be able to:

- Use temperature data to differentiate E climates from the A, C, and D climates

- Compare and contrast the two main types of *polar climates*

- Discuss the geographic distribution of the polar climates and explain why they are located where they are

- Discuss the precipitation and temperature patterns of the polar climates and relate the patterns to the types of natural vegetation found in the polar climates

- Draw the locations of the polar and *highland climates* on a world map

- Discuss why Trewartha added the H climates to Köppen's climate groups

- List the four main types of H climates found in Latin America and briefly discuss the differences between them

- Discuss why the latitudinal variations of vegetation are similar to the altitudinal variations of vegetation found in the H climates

- Describe the general changes one encounters in the natural environment in an ascent from the base to the summit on a Latin American mountain situated near the Equator

- Briefly explain why some geographers do not like classification systems in general

Figure 19-8. Ketchikan, Alaska, is one of the rainiest places in North America. Its annual precipitation exceeds 137 inches. Its wettest month, October, receives over 20 inches; its driest month, July, receives over 6 inches. It is at sea level and its coldest month is January with an average temperature of about 33°F. Ketchikan has four months of the year with an average temperature above 50°F, but its warmest month, August, averages only about 59 degrees. You should now be able to tell me what type of climate is found in Ketchikan. You should also be able to tell me if it is near the center of one of Trewartha's climate regions or near the margins.
(Robert L. Beck photo, 1975)

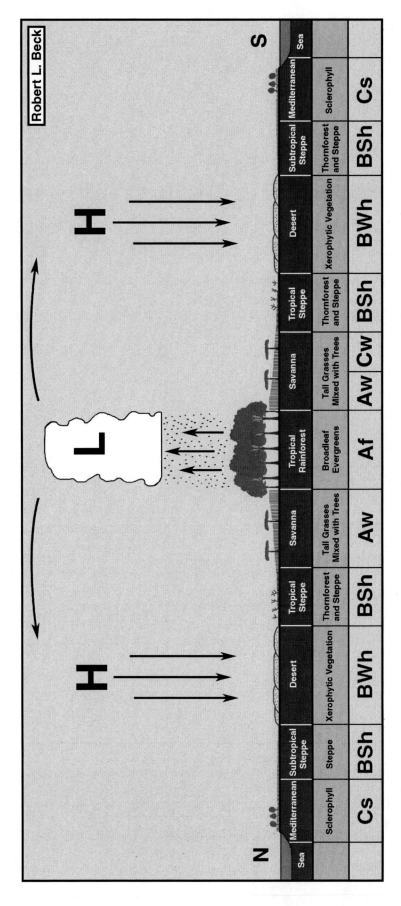

Figure 19-9. A generalized model of the climate and vegetation regions across Africa from north (left) to south (right) is shown in this drawing. The Equatorial Low is positioned over the Af climate region, which indicates the SSP is located near the Equator. The subtropical high pressure cells are situated over the Sahara Desert and the Kalahari Desert. What season, or calendar months of the year, might this drawing represent for the lands bordering the Mediterranean Sea?

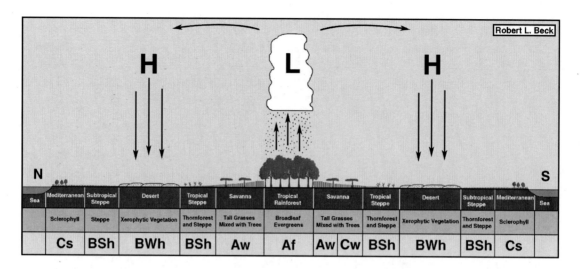

Figure 19-10. This drawing is a repeat of Figure 19-9.

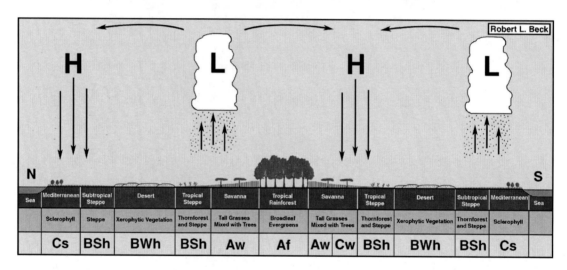

Figure 19-11. What season, or calendar month of the year, does this drawing represent?

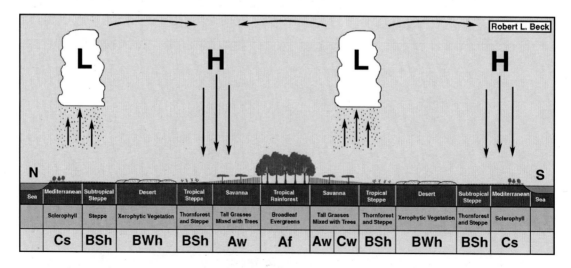

Figure 19-12. What season, or calendar month of the year, does this drawing represent?

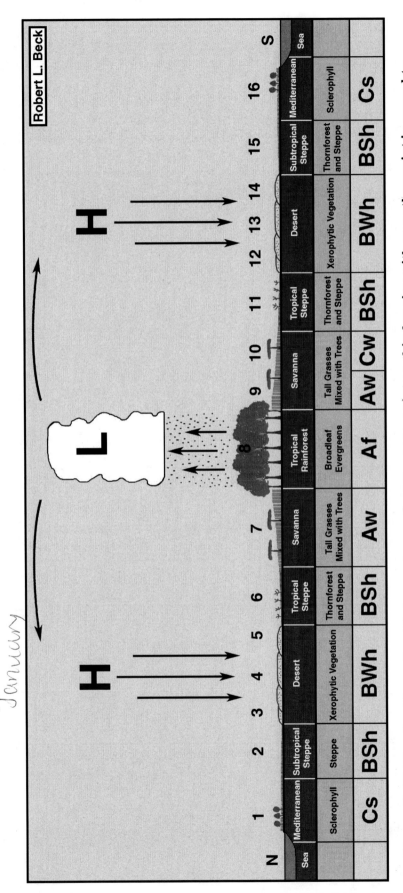

Figure 19-13. You should now be able to compare and contrast any point on this drawing with any other point in regard to season of precipitation, calendar month of precipitation, wind patterns, drought, season of drought, calendar month of drought, and position of the SSP. For example, when does one expect precipitation to occur at Point #2, and what precipitation producing condition will bring it? Another question, what wind belt is affecting Point #11 in this drawing? You should use this drawing (and also Figure 19-10, Figure 19-11, and Figure 19-12) to assist your understanding of the interrelationships between climate and vegetation. Comprehending the climate patterns in Africa goes a long way in helping one to understand the world patterns of climate, especially in the A, B, and C climate groups. This drawing is also useful in demonstrating your ability to apply what you have learned from your reading and studying of Modules 15, 16, and 17.

Practice Exercise: Assume the numbers in the drawing below represent temperatures in degrees F for some area on Earth. Also, all lines (A–E) are the same length. Answer the following questions using the information in the drawing.

What is the temperature at Point V, W, X, Y, and Z? Which line has the steepest temperature gradient? Which line has the weakest temperature gradient? What is the general shape of the 55° isotherm? What is the general shape of the 60° isotherm?

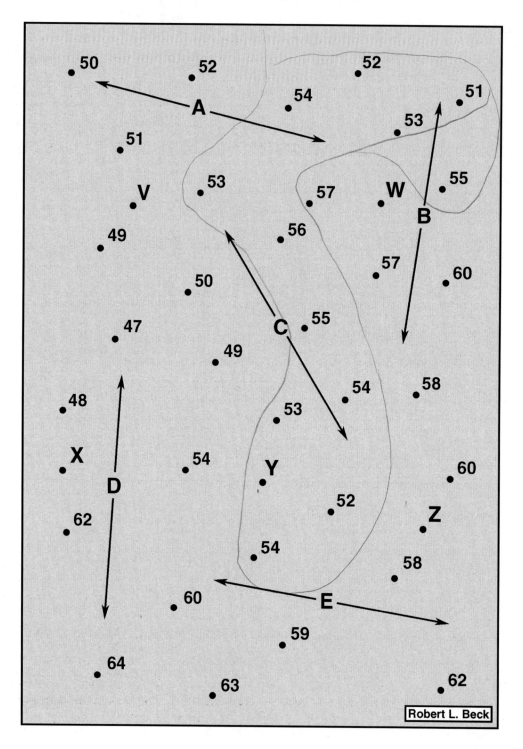

MODULE 20: VEGETATION

This module is meant to enhance the coverage of vegetation introduced in the climate modules. I like to link vegetation with climate, but there are other aspects of vegetation that students should be exposed to in an introductory physical geography course. This module is my attempt to provide such exposure.

Biomes

The vegetation patterns discussed in the climate modules represent the dominant vegetation of large areas of Earth. The vegetation zones identified in my previous modules are known more precisely as *biomes*, which specifically refer to the assemblages of plants and animals that interact with their environments in large areas of Earth. The savanna is a biome, so is the taiga, the tropical rainforest, the steppe, and all the others. The biomes can be grouped into three major categories: the forest biomes, the grassland biomes, and the scrubland biomes (Fig. 20-1).

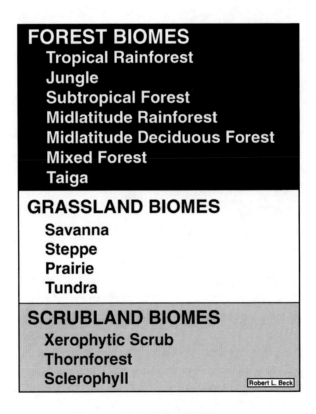

FOREST BIOMES
Tropical Rainforest
Jungle
Subtropical Forest
Midlatitude Rainforest
Midlatitude Deciduous Forest
Mixed Forest
Taiga

GRASSLAND BIOMES
Savanna
Steppe
Prairie
Tundra

SCRUBLAND BIOMES
Xerophytic Scrub
Thornforest
Sclerophyll

Robert L. Beck

Figure 20-1. World Biomes

Vegetation Controls

In Modules 15 to 19, I tried to make the point that there is a strong connection between climate and vegetation. The Köppen system is based on the idea one can see climate in vegetation. Climate is such a strong control in the distribution of vegetation that some climates are even known by their vegetation names, for example, the tropical rainforest climate, the steppe climate, and the tundra climate.

The distribution of plants in the middle of the United States is certainly influenced by climate, especially by amount of precipitation. The tall grasses (bluestems) of the *prairie* lands of Indiana, Illinois, Iowa, and eastern Nebraska (Dfa climate) give way to medium-height steppe grasses (needle grass and wheat grass) in central Nebraska (BSk climate), which give way to short grasses (grama grass and buffalo grass) in eastern Wyoming (also BSk climate), which give way to sagebrush in Wyoming's Red Desert (BWk climate). A climographic transect from Kentland, Indiana, to Rock Springs, Wyoming, depicts the decrease in precipitation as one moves from east to west on the transect (map, p. 249). Seven cities are shown on the map, and they are all about 200 miles apart and situated near the 41° N. Latitude line. Kentland receives an annual precipitation of 37.0 inches, but Rock Springs gets only 8.7 inches. The temperature curves of the cities do not vary greatly; precipitation is thus a bigger factor than temperature in influencing the distribution of plants in this area of the country. Bluestem is the dominant grass from Kentland to York; needle grass and wheat grass are the dominant grasses around North Platte; grama grass and buffalo grass are the dominant grasses around Cheyenne; and sagebrush dominates around Rock Springs. To verify this please see the "Natural Vegetation" map in *Goode's World Atlas*, pp. 92–93.

Climate, however, is only one vegetation control. Other factors also help shape the world pattern of vegetation. This is especially the case when examining local or regional patterns. The distribution of precipitation influences the vegetation pattern in the central United States, but other factors such as soil quality certainly play a role. I cannot explain the pattern of vegetation around my rural property in Putnam County by only considering that northern Indiana has a humid continental climate. Other factors are also operating that influence the types and spatial arrangements of both the natural and introduced vegetation surrounding my lawn and gardens. Geographers, and biogeographers in particular, take great delight seeing these patterns when they venture into the field.

Topography is a vegetation control. The shape and arrangement of landforms, especially hills and depressions, influences the distributions of plants and animals. In humid areas, depressions are places where water might frequently pool, producing wetland spots on the landscape. Only water-loving, or water-tolerating, plants live in such an area. In this instance topography might be a stronger control than climate.

I mentioned in Module 19 that vegetation zones ring mountains so that in high mountains one might encounter several bands of vegetation in an ascent from base to summit (Fig. 20-2). Mountains and hills can also deprive certain areas of sunlight by keeping those areas in shade virtually the entire year. North-facing slopes tend to be much cooler and wetter than south-facing slopes, so *aspect*, or exposure to the sun, might be the dominant vegetation control where slopes occur. We have a classic example of such a situation in Indiana. Sugar Creek, in Parke County, is perhaps Indiana's most scenic stream because it has deeply downcut into Indiana's sedimentary rock layers on its approach to the Wabash River. Sugar Creek flows from east to west (more specifically

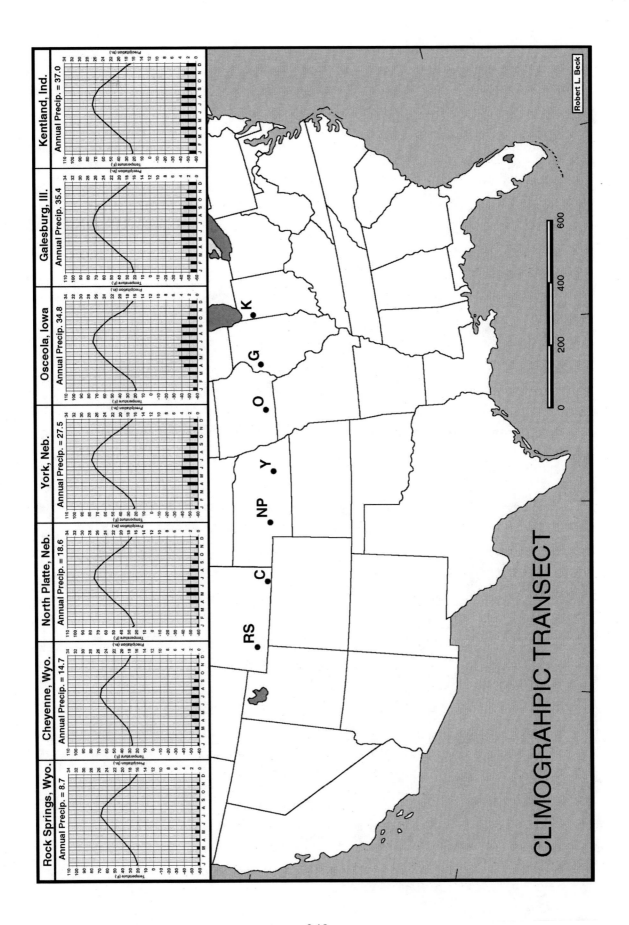

CLIMOGRAHPIC TRANSECT

Robert L. Beck

249

east-northeast to west-southwest), and therefore the north-facing slope of the valley through which it flows is in shade for a large part of the year. This slope is considerably cooler and damper than the south-facing slope facing it across Sugar Creek. This north-facing slope is one of the few areas in Indiana where native pine and hemlock trees grow. The ancestors of the pines and hemlocks became established in central Indiana during the Pleistocene Ice Age, so the modern pines and hemlocks are a living legacy of the Ice Age (Fig 20-3). They have been able to remain living on this site because it is still relatively

Figure 20-2. Altitudinal Zonation of Vegetation, Colorado
(Robert L. Beck photo, 1987)

Figure 20-3. Hemlocks, Pine Hills Nature Preserve, Central Indiana
(Robert L. Beck photo, 2009)

250

cool and wet, even though the last Ice Age glacier left Indiana about 10,000 to 14,000 years ago. Aspect, produced by topography, appears to be the dominant control here because these trees should be found in the taiga far to Indiana's north. Another factor operating here, however, is that pines and hemlocks grow well in the acidic sandstone outcrops found in the nature preserve.

Disturbance is also a vegetation control. This includes any event that quickly disturbs the environment by altering Earth's surface in a short period of time (usually in a few hours). Disturbances include events such as fire, flood, landslide, tidal wave, volcanic eruption, or high winds. Disturbances do **not** include events that put stress on plants over a long period of time, such as drought. Of course, disturbance can be produced by human actions as well as natural events, but we are concerned with natural disturbances in this course.

Fire is one of the major disturbance controls. In general, fire benefits herbaceous vegetation such as grass and forbs (non-grass flowering plants) while harming woody vegetation such as trees and shrubs. Grasses benefit from fire because they grow differently than woody plants. Grasses grow from the base upward instead of from the tips outward, as trees do (Fig. 20-4). When a fire burns a grassland area, the grass plants

Fig. 20-4. Growth Tip on a Blue Spruce
(Robert L. Beck photo, 1985)

Figure 20-5. Jack Pine Cone
(Robert L. Beck photo)

just start growing again from their bases, but when a fire burns a wooded area most of the trees die. As humans spread over Earth, carrying fires with them, grasses have spread, too. Some trees have developed strategies to survive, or benefit from, recurring fires. The jack pine cone remains tightly closed until it is immersed in a fire, which causes the cone to open allowing its seed to spread (Fig 20-5). I have been carrying a jack pine cone in my briefcase for nearly 35 years . . . it is still tightly closed waiting for a chance to open.

Another tree, the southern longleaf pine, waits for a fire by enveloping itself in fire-resistant needles (known as the grass stage) when it is a young seedling about 6 inches high (Fig. 20-6). After a fire goes through the area in which it is living, it will begin to grow upward rapidly, for the fire helped remove nearby competing plants (Fig. 20-7).

Fig. 20-6. Young Southern Longleaf Pine
(Robert L. Beck photo, 2000)

Fig. 20-7. Southern Longleaf Pine Woodland, S. Miss.
(Tim Brothers photo, 2000)

Forest fires are one of the worst natural hazards of the Canadian Shield, a huge, horseshoe-shaped area of crystalline rocks mostly surrounding Hudson Bay (the area of the Canadian Shield is shown on p. 24 in *Goode's World Atlas*, and it is colored orange for those of you who are interested). When a forest fire burns a swath through the taiga that consisted of needleleaf trees, the first trees to reoccupy the burn site are usually aspens, small broadleaf, deciduous trees (Fig. 20-8). One could argue, with some conviction, that fire was a stronger control than climate in helping to establish the aspen community.

Figure 20-8. Aspens Occupying the Burn Site of a 1947 Forest Fire, Acadia National Park, Maine *(Robert L. Beck photo, 1988)*

Surface material is another vegetation control. This refers to the substance at the earth's surface in which plants have an opportunity to grow, such as decomposing rock and soil in which plants take root. Surface material includes unconsolidated substances such as sand, volcanic ash, glacial deposits, loess, or silt deposited by flooding streams. Surface material also includes consolidated substances such as sedimentary rocks,

252

solidified lava, or crystalline rocks. Surface materials vary chemically, and this too can greatly influence the pattern of vegetation. Some surface materials are highly acidic, others have a high degree of toxicity to plants, and still others are highly alkaline. Some plants have the ability to live in alkaline materials, such as sagebrush (Fig. 20-9).

Figure 20-9. Sagebrush, Red Desert, Southern Wyoming *(RLB photo, 1975)*

Other plants, like azaleas, thrive in acidic materials; so do blueberries, cranberries, and rhododendrons. Potatoes like a loose soil that has a low amount of calcium in it. Peas like a soil with relatively large amounts of calcium. Eastern red cedars thrive in thin soils over a solid limestone base (Fig. 20-10), whereas pin oaks are often found in areas underlain with claypans. Buttonbushes live in waterlogged materials where daffodils rot. Many oaks and hickories like dry, sandy materials . . . beeches and sugar maples like cool, wet materials; red maples like dry slopes; sycamores grow near streams (Fig. 20-11). There are just hundreds and hundreds of examples of plants with quite specific requirements about the surface materials in which they desire to live.

Figure 20-10. Eastern Red Cedars in an Abandoned Limestone Quarry, Indiana
(Robert L. Beck photo, c. 2006)

253

I have been an active gardener for most of my adult life. It seems that every day I learn something new about a plant, usually a flower, which I did not know the day before. If you want to have beautiful flowers, then you have to pay attention to their wants and needs. This usually means you have to plant them in a spot in which they want to grow. I am careful to select my flowers for their ability to grow in the places around my yard that suit their requirements.

Figure 20-11. Sycamores Growing near Big Walnut Creek, Indiana. Their white bark makes them easy to identify from a considerable distance away. Imagine how difficult it would be to explain the distribution of all plants in this one small area of Earth. It is much easier to focus on the distribution of one species.
(Robert L. Beck photo, 2009)

Explaining the pattern of vegetation in the natural areas surrounding my property is not an easy activity, for it requires a lot of thought and knowledge to understand why certain plants choose to grow where they do. One cannot explain the distribution of plants growing in every site in Indiana simply by stating that the state has a humid continental or humid subtropical climate. All vegetation controls need to be considered when examining the mosaic of plants that cover the landscape. As I walk through the wooded areas near my house, I look for vegetation patterns and try to explain those patterns with my relatively limited knowledge of vegetation controls. The place in the forest where a certain community of plants is living might be explained by a disturbance event that occurred many years ago, or perhaps there is something in the soil that aids that plant community, but maybe the plants' presence is due to topographic conditions. All the vegetation controls operate together to produce a complicated arrangement of plants, even in the small wooded area near my rural home.

Succession

Plant communities do not remain unchanged indefinitely—rather they are partly or completely destroyed by disturbances. After a disturbance, the previous community does not usually replace itself directly, because the postdisturbance environment is so different (more light, greater fluctuations of temperature and humidity, perhaps removal of the soil and its nutrient pool, or maybe simply lack of seeds). What happens is a sequence of plant community changes called *succession*, in which the environment is occupied, and modified, by groups of plants that move into the disturbed site.

Plants have a tendency to change the site in which they are growing, giving invading plants an opportunity to displace the plants currently growing in that site. For example, some trees prosper in warm, dry habitats. If those trees grow to maturity, their foliage will shade the ground, making it cooler; this results in less evaporation beneath the tree making the soil a little wetter; in the autumn, when the trees shed their leaves, they collect at the base of the trees helping to keep water in the soil. These trees, in effect, have changed a warm, dry habitat into a cooler and wetter one. This assists trees that prosper in cooler, wetter habitats to invade and thus displace the first set of trees. The first set of trees changed the environment allowing the invasion of the second set of trees to succeed.

Succession is the process by which a community of plants and animals is replaced by a different community. In some instances, succession occurs on recently deposited surface material in which no soil is present. For example, lava and ash fields laid down by a recent volcanic eruption are eventually occupied by plants even though there is no soil present in the environment. This type of succession is known as *primary succession*, and it occurs when plants and animals occupy and replace one another on recently formed sites in which no soil is present (Fig. 20-12).

**Figure 20-12. Primary Succession in a Lava and Volcanic Ash Field,
Craters of the Moon National Monument, Idaho**
(Robert L. Beck photo, 1975)

Most succession on Earth is *secondary succession*, the replacement process that occurs when a soil is present. Secondary succession often involves some sort of disturbance in which the existing vegetation of an area is removed, or radically altered, by a short-term event such as by fire or storm. Secondary succession also occurs, however, when plants are slowly replaced by other plants over a long-term time span. In this case the first set of plants lives their natural life, dies, and is replaced by young plants of the second set that were growing around and among the first set when they were still alive.

In the traditional description of succession, the first plants to occupy a site are known as *pioneers*, and they are usually weeds, which includes annual grasses (Fig. 20-13). Pioneers are opportunists. If they find an open spot mostly free of competing plants, they grow there. Most weeds are opportunists that have a short, fast life cycle. Weeds live quickly and thus so spread their seed. Weeds can hold onto a site through reseeding, but when weeds are growing they help protect the site from erosion, and their leaves provide a limited shade. Seeds from perennial grasses are slow to

Figure 20-13. Weeds in a Disturbed Site (l) and Pioneer Grasses Growing in Sand (r)
(Robert L. Beck photos)

germinate compared to annual seeds from weeds. While the weeds were growing, reseeding, and dying, a few perennial grass plants took root in the site. At first, the grasses do not appear to be much of a threat to the weeds. The perennial grasses are soft, tender, and seem to be weak. Many grasses, however, send out subsurface runners to colonize new areas. When the perennial grasses become established they are tough to dislodge and eventually, with no disturbance, push out the weeds. Perennial grasses replace weeds and thus these grasses succeed weeds. Then why do people find weeds in their lawns? Do not grasses push out weeds? Well, every time someone mows the lawn he or she creates a disturbance that gives weeds an opportunity to grow, so they do. When we mow the lawn, sunlight might now be able to hit a bare spot between individual grass plants giving a weed seed an opportunity to germinate and establish itself in your lawn. If you do not want weeds in your lawn, you should not mow your lawn, but then you give your neighbors an opportunity to complain, which they probably will do. It is just less hassle to mow the lawn and view it as an opportunity to watch the plant competition occurring in your piece of turf. I do, however, set aside small patches in my backyard with the intent to let nature work the succession process. I do not mow these areas, and if asked about them, I just mention I am trying to grow wildflowers there.[3] People seem to accept that notion, for at least I am mowing most of my lawn. Please be reminded again that some grasses are weeds; one of the most common is annual bluegrass; it will come up in any disturbed patch in your lawn, but can be crowded out by its perennial relative, Kentucky bluegrass (which is from Europe, just as is annual bluegrass).

Moles are nasty little critters. They create disturbed sites in my lawn! The mounds they produce are outstanding sites for weed seeds to germinate, and they do. One day you gaze at your lawn thinking that it looks good, but the next day you notice disturbed sites just waiting for weeds to appear. Highly frustrating. Tim Brothers, another geography instructor at IUPUI, told me that in his yard squirrels bury walnuts in his mole mounds. The soil is easily workable, so the squirrels are naturally attracted to it. Mole and squirrel activity certainly adds diversity to the plants found in Hoosier lawns.

Perennial grasses might occupy a site for a long time, but eventually woody species grow above the grasses and drive them out. Woody tissue can support a greater weight than herbaceous tissue, so woody plants can grow higher than the grasses, spread out a leaf canopy above the grasses to capture sunlight, and in doing so deprive the grasses of what they need to survive—light. Grasses grow almost everywhere on Earth. One can find grasses growing in the hot tropics, at the edges of deserts, in wetland areas, in the middle latitudes, and in tundra environments adjacent to the ice caps. Grasses are tough. They survive fires, floods, human disturbances, and chemical alterations of the soil. They survive extreme cold, heat, wetness, and dryness. But most grasses do not survive without light. This is their weakness, for few grasses live in deep shade; bamboos are the prominent exceptions.

The first woody plants to grow above the grasses are often small woody plants that grow relatively quickly, shrubs. They might take a few years to grow above the grasses, but eventually they do so and thus deprive the grasses of light. Shrubs replace grasses in the succession process (Fig. 20-14). Shrubs, with their leaf canopy, shade the surface causing it to become much cooler than what was the case when only the grasses were present. The site will not evaporate as much water, so it is likely to become a little wetter. The leaf litter lying on top of the soil also helps hold water in the soil. These actions change the site and help the next set of plants to become established.

Trees push out shrubs in the forested areas of the Midwest. With their leaf canopy high above the shrub level, they deprive the shrubs of light. Some shrubs have evolved into living beneath a tree canopy, but many shrubs need light to prosper. It takes a long time for the tree to grow to maturity, so when a tree seed germinates, it might have done so when weeds occupied the site many years ago. The tree grew slowly through the grass phase and through the shrub phase until it was ready to assume full occupancy of the site.

---

[3]Many small birds are attracted to my wild areas. Some birds are especially fond of grass and weed seeds.

The first set of trees, at least in Indiana, to occupy successional sites are often trees that live in warm, dry habitats. They change the site to allow other sets of trees to occupy the area, which are typically trees that favor cool, wet sites. The last group of plants to occupy an area, and can theoretically hold it indefinitely without being replaced by succession processes, is known as the *climax vegetation*. Beech-maple forest is the climax vegetation of most of central Indiana (Fig. 20-15).

Figure 20-14. Shrubs Replacing Grasses in Little Bluestem Prairie Nature Preserve, Vigo County, Indiana *(Robert L. Beck photo, 1993)*

Figure 20-15. Beech-Maple Forest, Putnam County, Indiana
(Robert L. Beck photo, 2006)

Disturbances can interrupt the succession processes I have outlined. If a fire goes through a forest and kills the trees and shrubs, then the succession process might start all over again, with the burn site first being occupied by weeds. Humans affect plant succession by causing disturbances such as keeping cattle on an area too long so that it is overgrazed. Long-term climate changes can also affect succession.

When the environment is changing so that succession appears to be working in reverse order, the process is then known as *retrogression*. For example, overgrazing a grassland area, such as a pasture, might result in the killing of the grass plants, which allows weeds to reoccupy the site.

In summary, what I have presented here is the traditional view of plant succession in a forested environment such as central Indiana. Weeds first occupy an open site; they are replaced by grasses, which are replaced by shrubs, which are replaced by trees. It is important to realize that succession in the natural world is a more complicated process than what I have outlined here. Successional sequences differ depending on the environmental characteristics of the place. The successional processes operating in the desert are different than those operating in chaparral, tundra, or prairie. Further, the full sequence of succession may not have time to play itself out in frequently disturbed sites, such as beaches, river banks, and avalanche tracks; here the vegetation remains in a state of persistent disequilibrium, often constantly dominated by pioneers.

Fig. 20-16. Deciduous Trees, Fern Cliff, Putnam County, Indiana
(Robert L. Beck photo, 2007)

It also needs to be mentioned that animal communities are associated with plant communities, so when plant replacement occurs, so does animal replacement. Squirrels live mostly in climax forests, but deer live in the grass-shrub stage in the intermediate stages of succession. Deer benefit from forest fires because those fires burn holes in the forest cover, which allows shrubs to populate the area producing berries deer can eat. Squirrels are hurt by forest fires because those fires kill the trees supplying the squirrels with food, such as oak trees, which produce acorns. Bird populations are the same way. Some birds live mostly on weed seeds and are found in open environments, but others, like warblers, live in climax forests. Human alteration of vegetation will benefit some animals and birds, but it will harm others.

Please do not assume from the previous discussion that succession occurs only on land environments. Water bodies, too, are subject to plant invasion and replacement as vegetation infills the body—generally from the shore to the middle (Fig. 20-17). Circular patterns ringing small ponds typically represent different groups of plants collectively taking over the pond, and, given enough time, will eventually drive the water from it turning it into a marsh and maybe later a forest. This process is aided by the deposition of sediment, such as soil, into the pond. Dead and decaying organic matter (such as leaves, branches, stems, and animal bodies) also help infill the pond not only directly by adding biomass, but also by decomposing thus adding nutrients to the pond that can be taken up by living plants and animals.

Figure 20-17. Water Plants and Water-tolerant Plants in the Process of Infilling a Small Pond in Wisconsin. As the floating plants expand toward the center they will be replaced by herbaceous plants rooted near the shoreline; they, in turn, will be replaced by trees if no disturbance occurs to interfere with the succession process. All small water bodies have a limited lifespan not only because of deposition of sediment into them, but also because plants move into them from nearby areas.
(Robert L. Beck photo, 1980)

260

Fire Suppression

For hundreds, or thousands, of years before Europeans arrived in North America the American Indians had been setting fires to clear tracts of land. Their reasons for doing this are many, but one of the principal reasons was to improve pasturage for wild game. Certain animals favored by American Indians as hunting targets (bison, for example) do not prosper in heavily forested environments, so to help increase the range and abundance of such animals the American Indians deliberately set fires to burn-off woody plants. The fires set by these people enabled grasses to spread widely over the continent. Repeated burnings helped maintain the grasslands once they were established. To survive, trees living in the grasslands had to be fire-resistant, which the burr oak is.

It is now widely believed the American Indians were mostly responsible for the establishment of a wedge of grasslands that extended east from the central Great Plains of Nebraska to the northwestern corner of Indiana. This area has a humid continental climate (Dfa), so it should be covered with deciduous forest. At the time of European exploration and settlement, however, it was mostly populated with grasses, but trees were found along streams, near natural springs, and in some poorly drained wetland areas. Today this area is known as the *Prairie Wedge* or the *Prairie Peninsula*, and it lies in the heart of the American Corn Belt (Fig. 20-18). Bluestem grasses came to dominate this prairie land, and fires helped maintain bluestem prominence. American Indians referred to the prairie as *maskotia*, which means "place of fire." The season of fire began in August or September when the bluestem grasses dried up and turned brown.

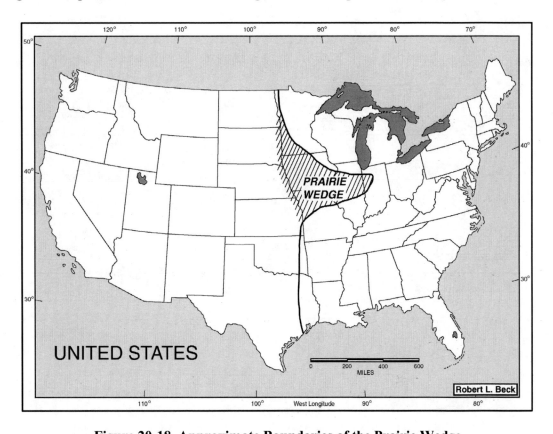

Figure 20-18. Approximate Boundaries of the Prairie Wedge

In New Mexico, Texas, and other parts of the Southwest grasses also covered large areas of the continent at the time of European settlement. Europeans introduced cattle and sheep (domesticated animals from the Old World continents) to graze these grasslands. The establishment of permanent settlements such as farms and towns changed the perception of fire, for now it was viewed as a property threat. Fire suppression became the order of the day with the more intensive economic development of the land by Europeans. The American Indians living in the Great Plains were mainly hunters, not farmers, so fire assisted their efforts in using the land. European settlers who arrived in the 1800s were mainly farmers or ranchers, not hunters, so fire ultimately came to been seen as a threat, but initially even the Europeans used fire to help clear land.

The concept of suppressing fires, instead of starting them, changed the vegetation composition of the areas once subjected to repeated burnings. Shrubs, especially, have benefitted greatly through the virtual elimination of fire in grassland environments. In the southwestern United States, and Texas in particular, shrubs have taken over lands formerly covered with grasses. One such shrub, *mesquite*, is an invader of the first order (Fig. 20-19). It is difficult to remove in the absence of fire, so it just keeps expanding its range. Cattle that eat mesquite further contribute to its expansion through the spreading of mesquite seeds in their droppings.

Figure 20-19. Mesquite in Texas
(Robert L. Beck photo, 1987)

The elimination of prairie fire is the main reason mesquite is now viewed as a plant pest. Many conservationists advocate the return of fire to control plant invaders. ***Prescribed burning*** is the term used today when fires are deliberatively set by conservation workers to help remove woody vegetation and thereby assisting grasses or other herbaceous plants. Some Indiana nature preserves are grasslands, but to maintain the grassland requires the application of fire every so often. Permanently suppressing the fire in these grassland preserves would enable shrubs and trees to push out the grasses resulting in the destruction of the preserve. It is therefore ironic that the only way such nature preserves can be maintained is through human intervention. Left to its own, nature would take over the preserve by sending in various woody species. Nature requires human activity to maintain nature in these instances.

Fire suppression was, for a long time, advocated by Smokey the Bear of the U.S. Forest Service. Conservationists today are not as anti-fire as they were in the 1940s and 1950s. Fires remove dead materials from the forest floor, which reduces the likelihood of more severe fires later on. Fires also help recycle nutrients quickly and they have been used to kill insect pests that attack trees. Insects kill more trees every year in the United States than do fires.

Module 20 Objectives

You should now be able to:

- Define a *biome*

- Classify the world's vegetation regions into one of three general biome categories

- List the four vegetation controls

- Describe how the vegetation controls produce distinctive patterns in the distribution of vegetation in local areas

- Define, or identify, the following words or phrases: *aspect, disturbance, succession, pioneers, climax vegetation, retrogression, prairie*

- Describe, using examples, why fire is beneficial to certain plants and animals and harmful to other plants and animals

- Compare and contrast *primary succession* with *secondary succession*

- List the four stages in the traditional succession model

- Describe how short-term events affect the succession process

- Discuss why mesquite is a problem in the southwestern United States

- Describe how mole activity contributes to the development of weedy lawns

- Explain why jack pine cones remained closed for long periods of time

263

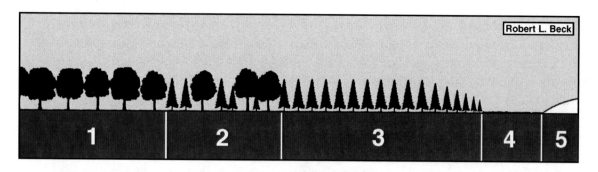

Figure 20-20. What climate and vegetation zones do these numbers represent?

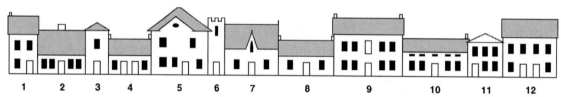

Figure 20-21. These are just a few of the house types studied in my
***North American House Types* class taught at IUPUI.**
(Robert L. Beck drawing, 2010)

Figure 20-22. Sycamore Trees,
Putnam County, Indiana
(Robert L. Beck photo, 2007)

Figure 20-23. Installing Geothermal
Tubes in My Front Yard
(Robert L. Beck photo, 2008)

MODULE 21: INTERIOR STRUCTURE OF THE EARTH

In this module we begin the study of the geosphere. It is important to know something about the interior structure of Earth, including rocks, before one studies the landforms observable on Earth's surface.

Classes of Rocks

There are three classes of rocks on Earth—igneous rocks, sedimentary rocks, and metamorphic rocks. *Igneous rocks* are formed from molten, rock-forming material known as *magma*. These rocks are sometimes said to be the "fire rocks." *Ignis* is the Latin word for "fire." Igneous rocks were Earth's first rocks, for the solidification of the hot material from which Earth formed produced igneous rocks.

Igneous rocks are composed of *minerals*, which are naturally occurring inorganic substances with a certain chemical composition and fairly recognizable physical characteristics (Fig. 21-1). For example, the igneous rock *granite* is mostly composed of varying amounts of the following minerals: quartz, orthoclase feldspar, hornblende, and biotite mica (Fig. 21-2). Different igneous rocks have different combinations of rock-forming minerals.

Figure 21-1. Quartz is not a rock, it is a mineral found in many rocks.

GRANITE

Hornblende

Orthoclase
Feldspar

Biotite
Mica

Quartz

Granite is composed of these common igneous minerals.

Figure 21-2. Granite is an igneous rock composed of many minerals, including an abundance of quartz and orthoclase feldspar; lesser minerals found in granite include hornblende and biotite mica. *(Robert L. Beck photo and drawing)*

Some igneous rocks form when magma, from the mantle, rises in a crack in the earth's crust and solidifies beneath the earth's surface; such rocks are known as ***intrusive igneous rocks*** (Fig. 21-3). These rocks are also known as ***plutonic*** rocks. Other igneous rocks are formed when magma is extruded onto the earth's surface; such rocks are known as ***extrusive igneous rocks*** (Fig. 21-4). Igneous rocks, therefore, are classified on the basis of where they form—above ground or below ground.

Being formed underground, intrusive igneous rocks take a long time to cool, and as a result the ***mineral crystals*** composing the rock grow to be quite large and can be seen directly with the human eye. Extrusive igneous rocks, being formed on the earth's surface, cool quickly, for wind and water carry away much of the heat in the magma. The mineral crystals in these rocks are small, for they do not have the time necessary to grow large because they are cooled so quickly. The mineral crystals in extrusive igneous rocks are typically too small to be seen using the human eye without the benefit of a magnifying instrument.

Intrusive igneous rocks and extrusive igneous rocks have different names, even if they have the same mineral constituency. ***Granite*** is a common intrusive igneous rock, so it has large mineral crystals; ***rhyolite*** is an extrusive igneous rock composed of the same minerals as in granite, but it has small mineral crystals because it cooled rapidly.

One of the most common uses of granite today is in the manufacturing of tombstones. The famous *Rock of Ages* quarry at Barre, Vermont, has traditionally been a major supplier. Granite is popular as a tombstone because it is colorful and because it is highly resistant to weathering and erosion. Names and dates carved in granite will last a very long time compared to the names and dates carved in marble or limestone. Granite is also fashionable as a kitchen countertop, but its cost is prohibitive for most people.

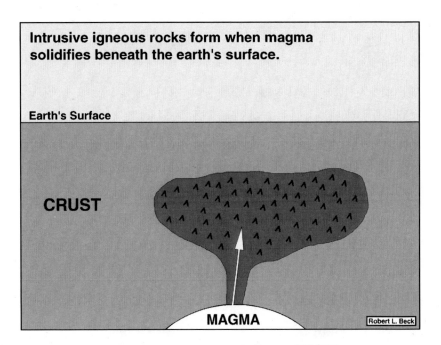

Figure 21-3. Intrusive Igneous Rocks

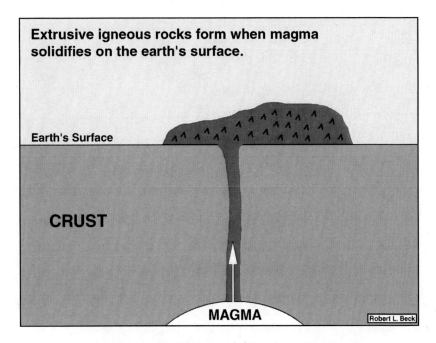

Figure 21-4. Extrusive Igneous Rocks

When igneous rocks form, the mineral crystals in them solidify in seemingly random patterns; and because they form from magma, they do not have fossils in them. Common igneous rocks include *granite*, *basalt*, *diorite*, and *gabbro* (Fig. 21-5).

Figure 21-5. Common Igneous Rocks

Figure 21-6. The Presidential Heads at Mount Rushmore are Carved in Igneous Rock
(Robert L. Beck photo, 1993)

Sedimentary rocks, as the name indicates, form when sediments become cemented together under pressure. A source of sediment must be present for these rocks to originate, and it is usually a nearby landform of some sort being eroded away. The first sedimentary rocks to form were probably composed of particles eroded from igneous rocks that originated with the formation of Earth.

Four factors are necessary to produce sedimentary rocks: (1) a **sediment** must be present—sand, silt, clay, weathered minerals from preexisting rocks, and the organic remains of plants and animals are some examples of sediments; (2) a **cement** is necessary to bind the particles of sediment together; (3) the cementing process must occur under **pressure**, or under the weight of millions of tons of loose materials; and (4) **time** is necessary to allow the loose particles to be transformed into solid rock. Sediment compressed under a lot of weight over a long time will not turn into solid rock unless a cementing agent is present. Concrete is an example of a sedimentary rock made by humans. To make concrete one typically mixes sand and small pebbles with a cement mix, pours in a small amount of water to dampen the mix, spreads out the wet concrete in a mold or form, and then waits a few days for it to solidify. Concrete is often misnamed "cement," but cement is only one part of concrete—sand and pebble sediments are also present.

Sedimentary rocks **always form in layers** (Fig. 21-7), and they often have fossils in them. They are sometimes said to be "soft rocks," for they are relatively easy to erode, especially when compared to igneous rocks. Sedimentary rocks are often positioned on top of igneous rocks (Fig. 21-8).

Figure 21-7. Sedimentary Rock Layers in Putnam County, Indiana
(Robert L. Beck photo)

Figure 21-8. Sedimentary Rocks Covering Igneous Rocks in Southeastern Missouri. As you see in this photograph the sedimentary rocks are layered, but the igneous rocks are not.
(Robert L. Beck photo, 1982)

Indiana's bedrock surface is composed of sedimentary rocks. No matter where you go in the state, if you drill down into the earth the first native rock your drill hits is a sedimentary rock (Fig. 21-14, p. 275). Common sedimentary rocks include *shale*, *limestone*, *siltstone*, *sandstone*, *dolomite*, and *coal* (Fig. 21-9).

Figure 21-9. Common Sedimentary Rocks

Heat and pressure turn preexisting rocks into ***metamorphic rocks***, which are rocks that have undergone a mineral change as a result of that heat and pressure. Igneous rocks when subjected to heat and pressure turn into metamorphic rocks; for example, the igneous rock ***granite*** turns into the metamorphic rock ***gneiss***. Sedimentary rocks when subjected to heat and pressure turn into metamorphic rocks; for example, the sedimentary rock ***limestone*** turns into the metamorphic rock ***marble***. And even metamorphic rocks when subjected to heat and pressure turn into different types of metamorphic rocks; for example, the metamorphic rock ***slate*** turns into a different type of metamorphic rock known as ***schist*** (Fig. 21-10). Igneous and metamorphic rocks, collectively known as ***crystalline rocks***, are sometimes said to be "hard rocks," for most do not weather and erode easily.

Figure 21-10. Common Metamorphic Rocks

Compositional Structure of the Earth's Interior

There are two ways to view the structure of Earth's interior. One way is to examine the composition of materials that lie below the earth's surface, and the second way is to examine the physical state of those materials. Imagine you take a glass jar and fill it with a mixture of oil and water. You then shake it to make sure the two substances are thoroughly mixed. Finally, you let it sit for a few hours on a flat, immovable surface. You later come back to examine the mixture; what will you see? You will see that the oil and water have separated, for oil is not as dense as water. The oil molecules rise to the top and float on the water molecules. Oil spills in water bodies are cleaned up in part by skimming the water surface to remove floating oil.

271

A broadly similar process was in place when Earth formed billions of years ago, but instead of having a mix of oil and water the different substances at that time were lightweight minerals, heavyweight minerals, and extremely heavyweight minerals. As Earth cooled, the minerals apparently separated by density and rocks eventually formed from them. Igneous rocks formed from lightweight minerals are known as *felsic rocks*, for they have a lot of silicon in them; igneous rocks formed from heavyweight minerals are known as *mafic rocks*; and igneous rocks formed from extremely heavyweight minerals are known as *ultramafic rocks* (Fig. 21-11).

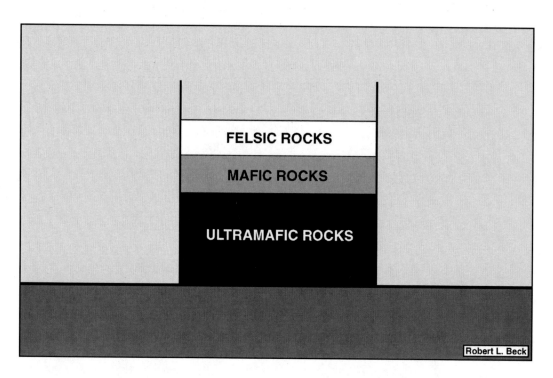

FELSIC ROCKS

MAFIC ROCKS

ULTRAMAFIC ROCKS

Robert L. Beck

Figure 21-11. Felsic, Mafic, and Ultramafic Rocks Sorted by Density

The outer layer of Earth is known as the *crust* (Fig. 21-12). As you might suspect, the crust is mostly composed of lightweight minerals, and it is thickest over the continents, which I like to think of as being big globules of felsic materials floating on mafic (or ultramafic) magma. Over the ocean the crust is only about 5 miles thick, but over the continents it is dozens of miles thick.

The *Moho* is the boundary line that separates the crust from the *mantle*, which lies beneath the crust. Mafic and ultramafic materials compose the mantle, which extends 1,800 miles downward into the earth from the bottom of the crust. The mantle is the largest part of Earth's interior (Fig. 21-12).

The *outer core* is positioned below the mantle (Fig. 21-12). It is composed of heavy minerals thought to be in a molten, or liquid, state. It extends an additional 1,300 miles downward into the earth to a depth of about 3,100 miles below the surface. The *inner core* is positioned below the outer core (Fig. 21-12). It occupies the center of Earth and is thought to be composed of extremely dense and heavy materials in a solid state.

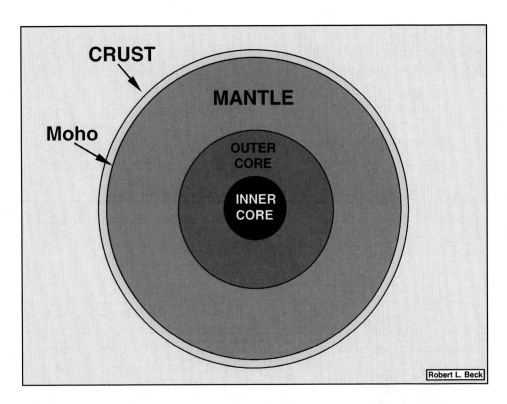

Figure 21-12. Compositional Structure of Earth's Interior

Numerous people have commented that the compositional structure of Earth's interior is similar to an egg. The shell of the egg is thin, rigid, and can easily be broken, just like the earth's crust; the white of the egg is the largest portion of the egg and is rather viscous, just like the mantle; and the yolk of the egg is at its center, just like the core. Of course, there is no solid interior in an egg.

Physical State Structure of the Earth's Interior

Instead of viewing Earth's interior as consisting of layers based on the heaviness of earth materials, one might analyze the interior to examine the physical state characteristics of those materials. All the crust and the upper part of the mantle are known as the *lithosphere* (Fig. 21-13). This outer layer of Earth is composed of rigid and brittle rock that can break. In fact, the lithosphere is composed of a large number of sections that are separated from each other by fault lines or cracks (Fig. 21-13). Each one of these distinctive sections of the lithosphere is known as a *lithospheric plate*, or more simply as a *plate* (*Goode's World Atlas*, pp. 22–23). The boundaries between these lithospheric sections are known as *plate boundaries*.

Below the lithosphere is a zone of weak, soft, and semiplastic rock known as the *asthenosphere* (Fig. 21-13). The earth materials here are denser than the lithospheric materials, but they are semiliquid and not rigid like the lithosphere. As a consequence, the lithospheric materials are slipping and sliding on the asthenosphere. In other words,

273

the lithospheric plates are moving around on top of the asthenosphere, which in a sense is providing the lubrication for this movement to occur. As the lithospheric plates move around, they bump into each other producing earthquakes, volcanoes, and mountains.

The asthenosphere is underlain by the ***mesosphere***, which is the bottom part of the mantle (Fig. 21-13). Here the earth materials are again thought to be rigid. In effect, the fluid asthenosphere is positioned between two rigid sections of Earth's interior—the lithosphere and the mesosphere. Earth's core is positioned below the mesosphere.

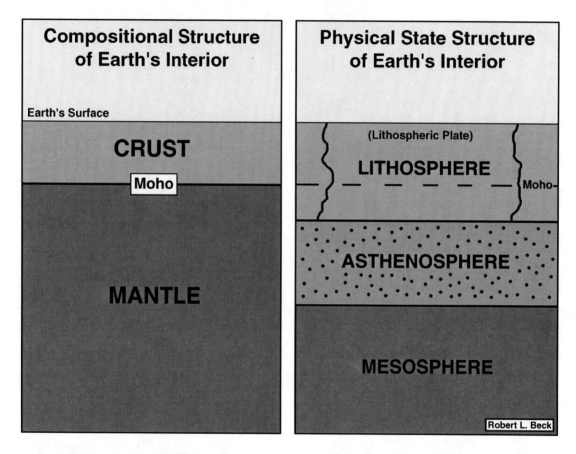

Figure 21-13. A Cross-section Comparison of (1) the Compositional Structure of Earth's Interior (left) with (2) the Physical State Structure of Earth's Interior (right)

Module 21 Objectives

You should now be able to:

- List the three classes of rocks and describe the differences between them

- Describe the difference between a *mineral* and a *rock*

- Compare and contrast *intrusive igneous rocks* with *extrusive igneous rocks*

- Identify the names of 14 common rocks and classify them into one of the three rock classes

- List the four factors necessary to form a *sedimentary rock*

- Describe how *metamorphic rocks* originate

- Discuss the difference between *felsic*, *mafic*, and *ultramafic* rocks

- Draw the compositional layers of the earth and briefly discuss their differences

- Compare and contrast the *lithosphere*, *asthenosphere*, and the *mesosphere*

- Define a *lithospheric plate*

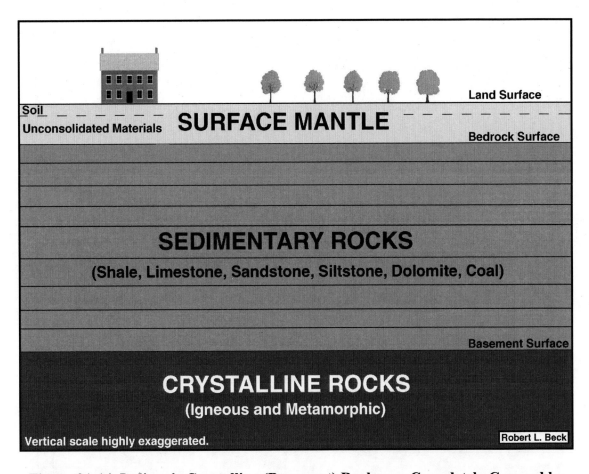

Figure 21-14. Indiana's Crystalline (Basement) Rocks are Completely Covered by Sedimentary Rocks. The basement surface lies thousands of feet below sea level in Indiana. This drawing has been included for illustrative purposes only—it greatly diminishes the thickness of the state's sedimentary rock layers.

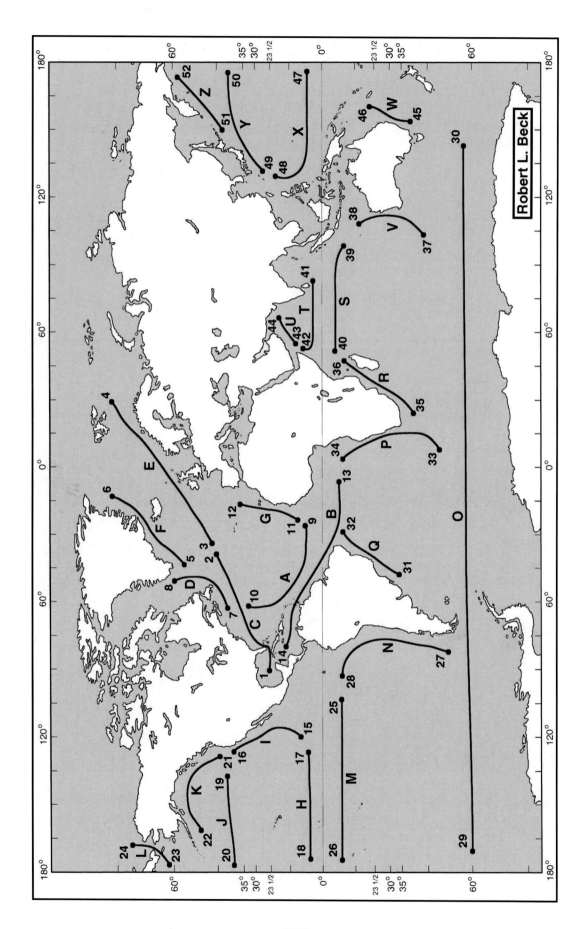

Robert L. Beck

276

MODULE 22: TECTONIC PROCESSES

The discipline of geography overlaps a little bit with the discipline of geology (Fig. 22-1). This overlap concerns the study of landforms—earth features of interest to both geologists and geographers. The study of landforms is known as *geomorphology*, which as an academic course offered at a university might be taught in either a geography department or in a geology department. At IUPUI, geomorphology is taught in the earth sciences (geology) department.

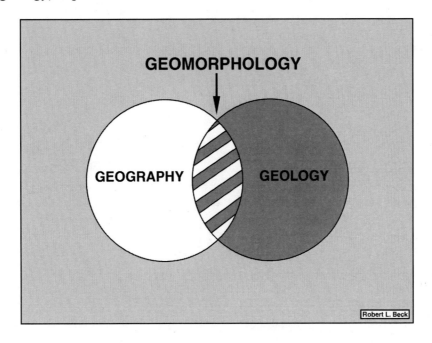

Figure 22-1. Overlap of Geography and Geology

Geomorphology textbooks are often broken down into two main parts. The first part concerns the processes that build up landforms. These processes are known as the *tectonic processes*—*tecton* is a Greek word for "builder." The second part of the textbook concerns the processes that tear down landforms—the *landmass degradation processes*. In this module I focus on the building processes; the following module examines the landmass degradation processes.

Plate Tectonics

In the early part of the 20th century (1910s and 1920s) a German meteorologist, Alfred Wegener, promoted the idea that at one time Earth's continents were all connected into one supercontinent, which he named *Pangaea*. He further argued that the present arrangement of the continents occurred as the gigantic continent broke into smaller continents that drifted apart and away from the center of Pangaea. His ideas, although not totally original to him, became known as the *continental drift theory*. A few years ago an IUPUI reference librarian, Jim Baldwin, told me that Wegener was Köppen's son-in-law.

Geologists at the time scoffed at Wegener, for he was not a geologist (so obviously he was not enlightened and could therefore know nothing about Earth), and he did not provide an explanation for why the continents drifted apart. The continental drift theory was largely discounted as child's play, even though the coastlines of the continents seemed to match up—the western coast of Africa, for example, is nearly a perfect match with the eastern coast of South America (Fig. 22-2).

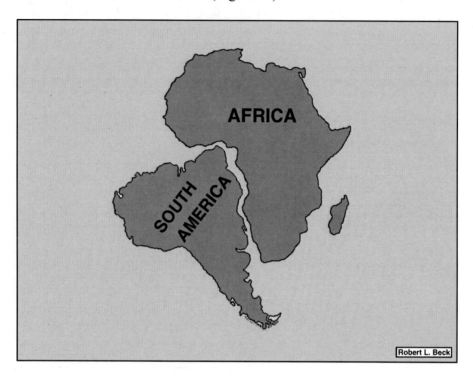

Figure 22-2. Coastline Matching of South America and Africa

The continental drift theory proposed that Pangaea broke into two continents—a northern one named ***Laurasia*** and a southern one named ***Gondwanaland***. Laurasia broke apart to form the modern continents of North America, Europe, and most of Asia. Gondwanaland broke apart to form the modern continents of South America, Africa, Australia, and Antarctica; India and the Arabian Peninsula were also attached to Gondwanaland (examine the sequence of maps shown in ***Goode's World Atlas***, p. 22). The University of California maintains an online animation of continental drift on one of their websites (http://www.ucmp.berkeley.edu/geology/anim1.html).

It was not until the mid-1960s that most geologists started to accept the idea that perhaps Wegener was right. The fossil remains of extinct animals in South America matched the fossil remains of extinct animals in Africa, so it appeared the continents had indeed been connected. Further, the rock types in Africa matched the rock types in South America, and seafloor research showed the ocean floors are of a very young age when compared to the age of the continents, which indicates the ocean floors are constantly moving and are continually recycled. Today the continental drift theory is known as ***plate tectonics theory***, which, as we will see, provides an explanation for why the continents have drifted apart.

The major lithospheric plates of Earth are depicted on the "Plate Tectonics" map shown in *Goode's World Atlas*, pp. 22–23. Observe many of the plates have a continent or a major landmass as a passenger, so they are known as *continental plates*, but even on the continental plates there are substantial areas of ocean. For example, the South American plate is a continental plate, but a large area of the South Atlantic Ocean is considered to be a part of it. Other plates are found almost exclusively in the ocean. The Nazca Plate, the Scotia Plate, the Philippine Plate, the Cocos Plate, and the Juan de Fuca Plate are all *oceanic plates*, for they are not carrying a major landmass on them as they slide about on the asthenosphere.

PLATE MOVEMENT AND PLATE COLLISION

The blue arrows on the map show the direction the plates are moving. The length of the arrows is proportional to the speed of plate movement. The northern part of the Pacific Plate, for example, is moving about 10.3 centimeters (4 inches) per year. The blue lines with blue triangles show **convergent plate boundaries**, or the places on Earth where *plate collision* is occurring. The South American Plate is moving to the west, but it is colliding with the Nazca Plate, which is moving to the east. In this case an oceanic plate is colliding with a continental plate, and whenever that occurs, the edge of the oceanic plate is forced beneath the edge of the continental plate. Recall that continents are composed mostly of felsic rocks, where the crust is thick. The ocean plates have a thin crust and lesser amounts of felsic material on them, so when a plate mostly composed of mafic materials (such as an oceanic plate) collides with a plate mostly composed of felsic materials (such as a continental plate), the heavier plate descends beneath the lighter plate in a process known as *subduction*. The place where this happens is known as a *subduction zone*, and an *ocean trench* is produced when subduction occurs (Fig. 22-3).

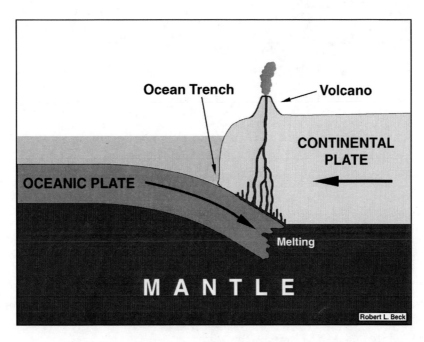

Figure 22-3. Subduction: Oceanic Plate Colliding with a Continental Plate

Some other examples of where continental plates are colliding with oceanic plates include the Cocos Plate collision with the Caribbean Plate and the Philippine Plate collision with the Eurasian Plate. You should now be able to answer the following question. Is the Philippine Plate descending (subducting) beneath the Eurasian Plate or is it the other way around? Yes, the Philippine Plate is subducting beneath the Eurasian Plate because it is an oceanic plate, whereas the Eurasian Plate is a continental plate mostly composed of lightweight felsic materials.

Oceanic plates can also collide with other oceanic plates. The Pacific Plate, an oceanic plate, is colliding with the Philippine Plate, also an oceanic plate. In this case the triangles of the blue line indicate that the Pacific Plate is subducting beneath the Philippine Plate. When two oceanic plates collide the denser one will subduct beneath the lighter one (Fig. 22-4).

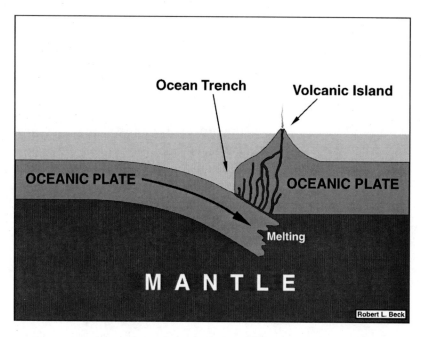

Figure 22-4. Subduction: Oceanic Plate Colliding with an Oceanic Plate

Continental plates collide with continental plates. Both India and the Arabian Peninsula were originally part of Gondwanaland and, in effect, broke off Africa. India is part of the Indo-Australian Plate, and when it collided with the Eurasian Plate about 35 million years ago, the Himalayan Mountains began to form. Mountains are the result of continental plate collisions (Fig. 22-5). The collision of the Arabian Plate with the Eurasian Plate produced the Zagros Mountains in Iran (***Goode's World Atlas***, p. 232). When continental collision occurs, one plate is forced beneath the other plate, but the bottom plate is too buoyant to subduct into the mantle. Plateaus are often produced behind mountain chains where continental collision has occurred. The Plateau of Tibet is behind the Himalayan Mountains (***Goode's World Atlas***, p. 221), and the Plateau of Iran (which is labeled in the 21st edition of ***Goode's World Atlas***, p. 196, but not in the 22nd edition) is behind the Zagros Mountains.

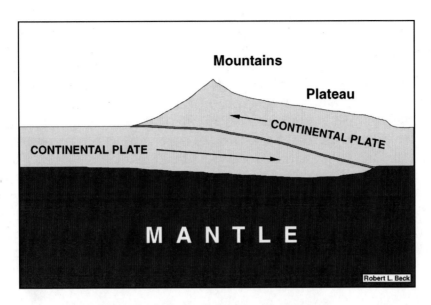

Figure 22-5. Continental Collision

Many plates on Earth are moving away from each other instead of moving toward each other. When this happens, a **divergent plate boundary** is produced, and the process that produces such a boundary is known as *rifting* (Fig. 22-6). Running down the middle of the Atlantic Ocean is a divergent plate boundary, for both the African and Eurasian plates are moving toward the east, whereas the North American and South American plates are moving toward the west (***Goode's World Atlas***, p. 23). Earth's crust is essentially being torn apart along this line, but as the plates spread apart, magma rises from the mantle to solidify and form new ocean floor. The rising magma is extruded onto the earth's surface, so the resulting igneous rocks cool quickly and thus form small crystals. Rifting mostly occurs in the middle of the ocean, where felsic material is thin or nonexistent (***Goode's World Atlas***, pp. 22–23). The extrusive igneous rock produced as a

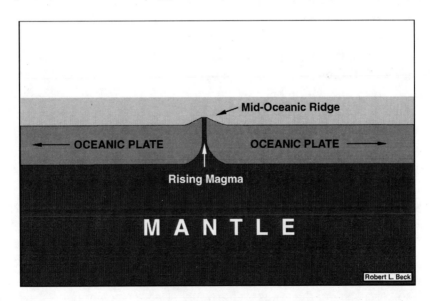

Figure 22-6. Rifting

result of the rifting is composed of mafic minerals, and it is one of the world's most common rocks, **basalt**.

The plate tectonics map in **Goode's World Atlas** does not show it, but a section of eastern Africa is being torn off the main mass of Africa. The place where this is happening is known as the East African Rift Valley. The long, linear lakes of East Africa are in this valley. Lake Nyasa, Lake Tanganyika, Lake Edward, and Lake Albert are four of the largest. The Rift Valley cuts diagonally across Ethiopia from Lake Rudolph to the small country of Djibouti on the Red Sea (**Goode's World Atlas**, p. 263).

Iceland is another land area being rifted. The midoceanic rift in the Atlantic Ocean goes right through Iceland. The eastern half of the country is being carried to the east by the Eurasian Plate while the western half of the country is being carried to the west by the North American Plate. Iceland is getting bigger as a result.

Many lithospheric plates are moving adjacent to each other without colliding or rifting; when this occurs it is known as a **transform movement**. Mexico's Baja Peninsula and a piece of southwestern California are located on the Pacific Plate, which, as you see on the map, is moving to the northwest. The remainder of California and Mexico is located on the North American Plate, which, in this area of the continent, is moving to the southeast. Transform boundaries are shown on the map as orange or light brown lines (**Goode's World Atlas**, pp. 22–23). The famous San Andreas Fault of California is a transform fault produced by a transform movement.

Earthquakes are produced by plate movements, especially transform movements or plate collision. Observe on the map the close correlation between the type of plate boundary and the occurrence of earthquakes (**Goode's World Atlas**, pp. 22–23). The earthquakes throughout the Eurasian Plate are mostly produced by continental collisions; for India, the Arabian Plate, and the African Plate are crashing into the Eurasian Plate, subducting beneath it, and generating earthquakes as a result.

No one really knows the cause of lithospheric plate movement. It is thought there are hot areas in Earth's core that produce convection cells in the mantle much like hot earth surfaces produce convection cells in the atmosphere (Fig. 22-7). Hot molten rock in the mantle rises above the hot areas in the core. The molten material cools as it rises, and near Earth's surface it starts to flow laterally thus causing plate collision, rifting, or transform movements. The magma cools even more with lateral movement, and eventually it sinks in the direction of the core to start the process all over again (Fig. 22-7).

The discipline of geology has been profoundly altered in the past 60 years as plate tectonics theory has become widely accepted by professional geologists as the means to explain why earthquakes occur and to explain the distribution of most of the world's volcanoes. One must understand plate tectonics theory and the different composition of igneous rocks to comprehend the types and arrangements of volcanoes. Plate tectonic theory, then, is an important prerequisite to the study of volcanism.

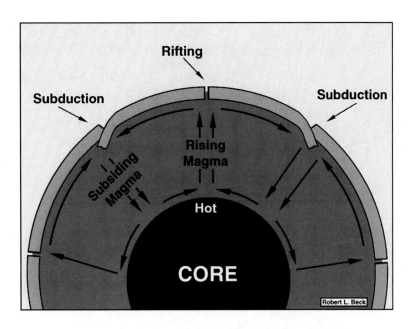

Figure 22-7. Convection Cells in the Mantle

Volcanism

A high percentage of the world's volcanoes are found along subduction zones and especially along the zones where oceanic plates are colliding with continental plates (*Goode's World Atlas*, pp. 22–23). Felsic materials are eroded off the continents and deposited into the ocean environments around them. When these felsic materials are carried by the oceanic plates, via subduction, into the mantle, they melt and being lightweight they rise and become volcanoes when they are extruded onto the earth's surface. These types of volcanoes are known as *stratovolcanoes* (Fig. 22-8.). They have steep sides produced from lightweight *felsic magmas*, which are notoriously explosive. Occasionally such magmas are filled with gases that sometimes blow the whole top of a volcano away.

Volcanoes also form where *hot spots* are found. The Hawaiian volcanoes, for example, are not found along a subduction zone—they are in the middle of the Pacific Plate near a hot spot (*Goode's World Atlas*, pp. 22–23). The Hawaiian Islands were formed as a result of the Pacific Plate carrying them over the hot spot. The islands are lined up (Hawaii maps, p. 127) as if they have been formed along a subduction zone, but close inspection of the island chain shows that the larger islands, including the big island of *Hawaii*, are located in the southeastern section of the chain. The island chain extends from the southeast to the northwest because the Pacific Plate is moving them to the northwest. As the Pacific Plate carries an island off the hot spot, a new island starts to form to the southeast of the preceding one. Weathering, erosion, and mass wasting wears away the islands once they are carried off the hot spot, so the northwestern islands are much smaller than the southeastern ones.

Please examine the locations of Earth's major hot spots on the "Plate Tectonics" map in *Goode's World Atlas*, pp. 22–23. As you see on the map, almost all are in the oceans. The major exception is the hot spot beneath Yellowstone National Park near the center of the North American landmass, which has a lot of felsic material around it.

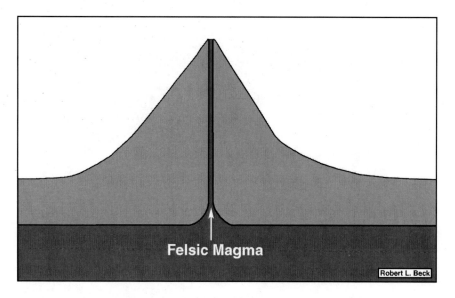

Figure 22-8. Profile of a Stratovolcano

Volcanoes located in the middle of oceanic plates or on divergent plate boundaries where rifting occurs are composed of *mafic magmas*, which are dense, heavy, and have a lack of gases in them. Such volcanoes are not explosive, and when magma is extruded as lava from them it flows downslope as a thick liquid. These volcanoes are known as *shield volcanoes*. They have gently sloping sides produced from heavyweight mafic magmas (Fig. 22-9). The Hawaiian volcanoes are the world's classic examples of shield volcanoes.

The Pacific Ocean is mostly circled with subduction zones that have volcanoes located nearby. This circle of volcanoes around the Pacific, as you might already know, is the "Ring of Fire."

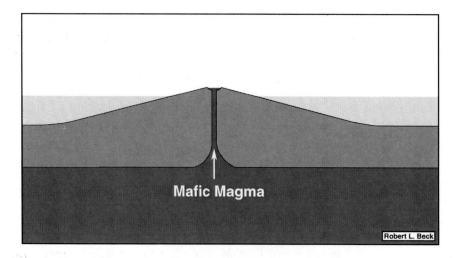

Figure 22-9. Profile of a Shield Volcano

VOLCANIC LANDFORMS

Several distinctive landforms are produced by volcanic activity (Fig. 22-11). As magma rises in the earth's crust, it might solidify underground to form a large igneous intrusion known as a **batholith**, which can cover thousands of square miles. For instance, the Idaho Batholith covers an area of 16,000 square miles forming the rugged, mountainous core of the state. Batholiths cool slowly underground, but they are exposed when the rock layers above them are removed by weathering and erosion. Although the Idaho Batholith is now solid, it is still warm as indicated by the numerous hot springs in the central part of the state. The rocks originally covering the Idaho Batholith have been removed by weathering and erosion, so today when a person visits that area he or she can walk on top of it even though it solidified underground with the cooling of intruded magma (Fig. 22-10).

Figure 22-10. Idaho Batholith
(Marty Nelson photo, 1985)

Rising magma might find a seam between sedimentary rocks layers where it can spread out horizontally underground and cool to form a **sill**, or if it cools in a vertical position it produces a **dike**. If magma domes upward after having spread out laterally, a **laccolith** is formed, which has a mushroom shape with a rounded top and a flat bottom. Hydrothermal solutions (hot water) rising off magma carry soluble minerals (such as gold) into small cracks, and when the minerals solidify they form **veins**. Igneous intrusions such as these are common volcanic landforms that can be uncovered when weathering and erosion removes the earth materials above them (Fig. 22-12 and Fig. 22-13).

Magma can be carried to the earth's surface in a **pipe**, and when it is extruded it then becomes known as **lava** (Fig. 22-14). The hole through which lava pours out of a volcano is known as a **crater**. Sometimes magma solidifies in the pipe preventing rising gas from venting itself to the atmosphere. When this happens, the gas pressure inside the

285

volcano can become so great it might explode and blow the top of the volcano away, producing a *caldera*, or a large hole where the volcano once stood. Crater Lake, Oregon, is actually a caldera now filled with water. If lava solidifies in a vertical position in a pipe, and the volcano becomes extinct, weathering and erosion eventually expose the pipe and start to decompose it, producing a *volcanic neck* (Fig. 22-15).

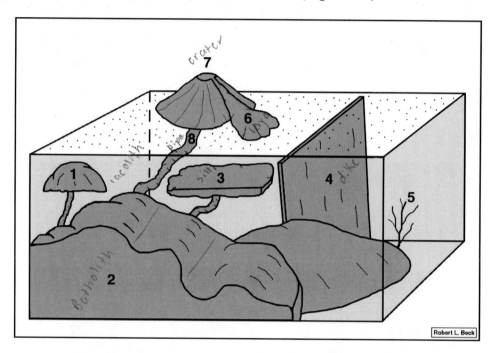

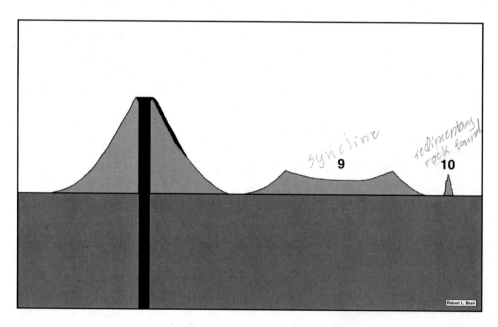

Figure 22-11. Based on the readings in the textbook, you should be able to identify these ten volcanic landforms. The top drawing is a block diagram of a volcanic area; the bottom drawing is a cross-section of a volcanic area.

Figure 22-12. This *dike*, in New Mexico, stands about 15-20 feet above the surrounding flatlands. The dike was formed underground, but weathering and erosion has uncovered it.
(Robert L. Beck photo, 1987)

Figure 22-13. Weathering and erosion has exposed this *laccolith*, located in Colorado, by removing the earth materials above it, which were there when it formed.
(Robert L. Beck photo, 1987)

Figure 22-14. Steel fenceposts mark the location of a wire fence that has been constructed across this solidified *lava bed* in New Mexico. This lava bed is in a lowland, which indicates the lava is of recent age. A lava bed on top of a sedimentary landform usually indicates the lava is of old age, for the lava is probably acting as a caprock to protect the softer rocks beneath it from weathering and erosion. *(Robert L. Beck photo, 1987)*

Figure 22-15. Sedimentary rock formations surround these *volcanic necks* in Arizona.
(Robert L. Beck photo, 1987)

Folding

Lithospheric movements exert considerable pressure on rock layers. Folding occurs when rock layers are slowly compressed, or pushed together (Fig. 22-16). Slow *compression*, the cause of folding, causes rock layers to bend or warp (Fig. 22-17). There are many types of folded landforms, but the two basic ones are *anticlines*, where rock layers have been folded upward to form a hill or ridge, and *synclines*, where rock layers have been downfolded to form a valley or trough (Fig. 22-17).

Figure 22-16. Folded Rock Formations, Arizona
(Robert L. Beck photo, 1987)

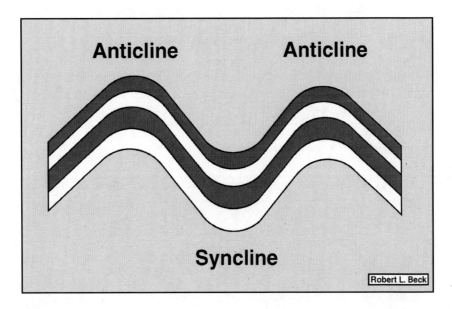

Figure 22-17. The two most basic folded landforms—anticline and syncline.

Faulting

Faulting occurs when crustal movements cause rock formations to break or fracture along a line, which produces an earthquake. Faulting can occur due to *compression* (when rock formations are pushed together) or *tension* (when rock formations are pulled apart). In this sense, then, faulting is more complicated than folding, which is only caused by compression.

It is necessary to understand a few fault terms before one can properly analyze and correctly classify faults. *Tension faults* and *compression faults* both occur on a well-defined line, the *fault line* (Fig. 22-18). When a fault occurs, it is analyzed using a *marker formation*, or a distinctive layer of rock that allows one to assess the vertical displacement of rocks produced by the fault (Fig. 22-18). Faults involve moving two blocks of the earth's crust. One block is known as the *headwall*, and the other block is known as the *footwall* (Fig. 22-18).

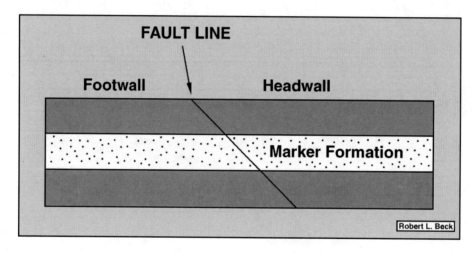

Figure 22-18. Fault Terms

To differentiate between a headwall and a footwall, imagine the fault line is a mine shaft instead of a line-of-contact between two blocks of earth. If a person walks down the shaft, that person's feet would touch the footwall, and his or her head would touch the headwall (Fig. 22-19). Headwalls are also known as *hanging walls* because miners would drive bolts or hooks into the headwall to hang lanterns on.

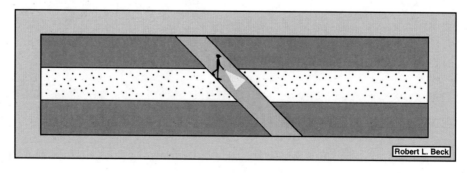

Figure 22-19. Headwall and Footwall

We are now ready to classify faults using these terms. By examining Figure 22-20 one should be able to see that the headwall has been **lowered** with respect to the footwall. Such a fault is known as a *normal fault*. What produces normal faults, tension or compression? Normal faults occur when the earth is being pulled apart, so tension produces them. Tension causes the headwall to slip along the fault line.

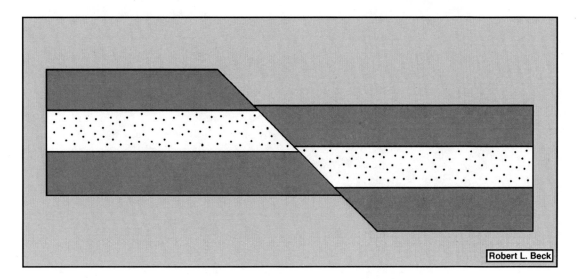

Figure 22-20. Normal Fault

A *reverse fault* occurs when the headwall is **raised** with respect to the footwall (Fig. 22-21). Compression is the cause of reverse faulting. Imagine you are holding two blocks of wood (with your hands) separated from each other by a 45°-angle cut. Pushing them together would force the headwall to rise relative to the footwall.

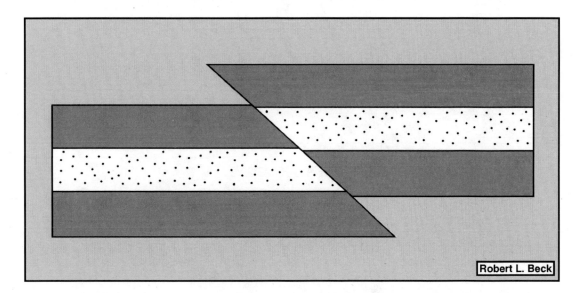

Figure 22-21. Reverse Fault

Is the fault shown in Figure 22-22 a normal fault or is it a reverse fault? Which side is the headwall? Which side is the footwall?

reverse

Figure 22-22. Fault, British Columbia
(Robert L. Beck photo, 1975)

How about the fault shown in Figure 22-23? Note also the folded rock formations in Figure 22-23.

normal

Figure 22-23. Fault, British Columbia
(Robert L. Beck photo, 1975)

292

When a headwall is forced on top of a footwall, a ***thrust fault*** has occurred (Fig. 22-24). These faults are also produced by compression, so I like to think of them as being, in effect, a super reverse fault. Thrust faults are also known as ***overthrust faults***, and they usually are found on low-angle fault lines.

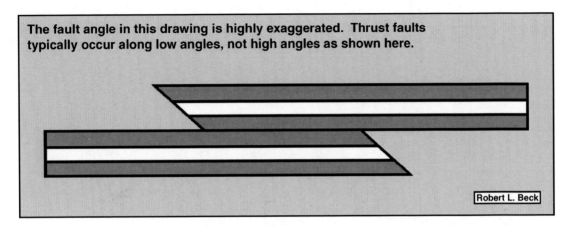

Figure 22-24. Thrust Fault

A ***transform fault*** occurs when blocks of the earth slide along each other and are displaced horizontally with little or no vertical displacement (Fig. 22-25). This type of fault occurs along the transform boundaries between the lithospheric plates. Transform

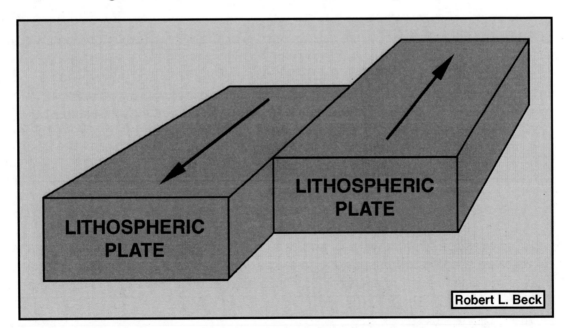

Figure 22-25. Transform Fault

faults are also known as ***strike-slip faults*** or as ***transcurrent faults***. Streams often show a noticeable change in angle as they flow across transform fault lines. Roads, railroads, fences, and sidewalks are torn apart and displaced horizontally when strike-slip faults occur (Fig. 22-26).

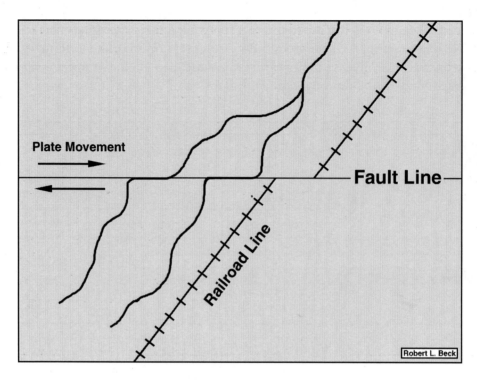

**Figure 22-26. Overhead View of the Displacement of
Linear Features by Transform Faulting**

In a few places around the world individual blocks of the earth have been either raised or lowered with respect to the land on both sides of them. A block raised relative to the land on both sides is known as a *horst* (Fig. 22-27), which is the German word for **aerie** (a place where eagles live). A block lowered relative to the land on both sides is known as a *graben* (Fig. 22-28), the German word for **grave**. Horsts and grabens are produced by *block faulting*. An examination of the headwall and footwall relationships in

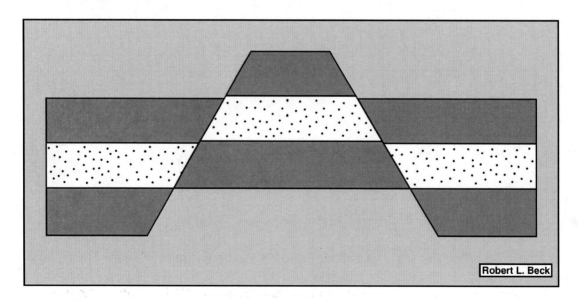

Figure 22-27. Horst

both the horst and graben (Fig. 22-27 and Fig. 22-28) reveals that block faulting is produced by tension, for the headwall has been lowered with respect to the footwall in both the horst and graben.

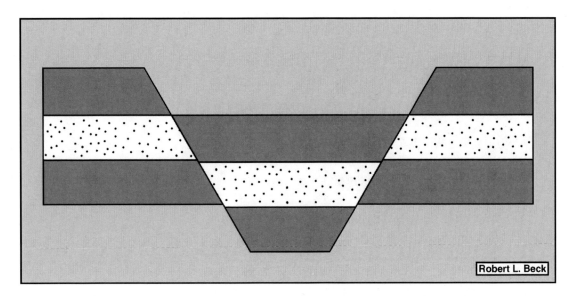

Figure 22-28. Graben

Module 22 Objectives

You should now be able to:

- Discuss how the discipline of geography overlaps with the discipline of geology

- Explain how the *continental drift theory* is related to *plate tectonics theory*

- Discuss the plate tectonics theory

- Compare and contrast *plate collision, rifting*, and *transform movements*

- Discuss what happens when a continental plate collides with an oceanic plate

- List the evidence that supports the idea that lithospheric plates do move

- Compare and contrast *subduction zones* with *rifting zones*

- Describe how the Himalayan Mountains were created

- Identify the major plates on Earth and their directions of movement

- Discuss how the world distribution of volcanoes is related to plate tectonics

- List the two main types of volcanoes and discuss their major characteristics

- Identify at least ten volcanic landforms

- Link volcano types with magma types

- Compare and contrast *folding* and *faulting*

- Describe the difference between tension and compression as it relates to faults

- Identify the two main folded landforms

- Classify faults using the *headwall–footwall concept*

- Compare and contrast the principal types of faults

- Define or identify: *marker formation, horst, graben, hot spot, Pangaea, Gondwanaland, Laurasia*

- Examine a photograph or drawing of a fault and classify it by type

Practice Exercise: Using a blue colored pencil, draw Earth's major convergent plate boundaries on this map.

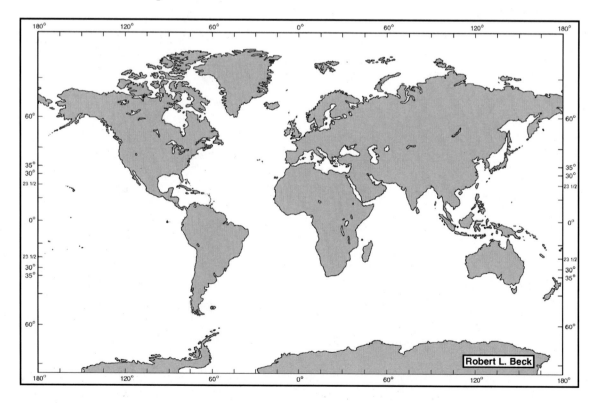

Practice Exercise: Using a red colored pencil, draw Earth's major divergent plate boundaries on this map.

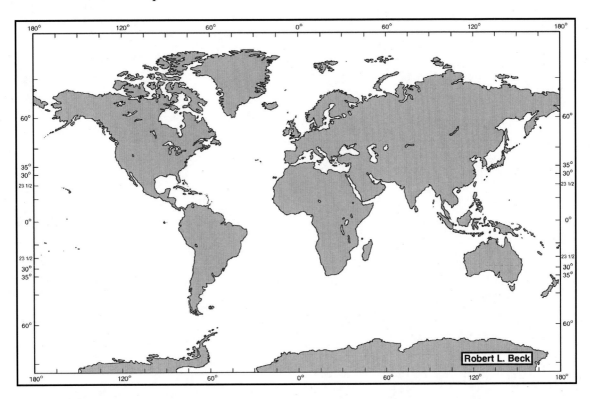

Practice Exercise: Using a green colored pencil, draw Earth's major transform plate boundaries on this map.

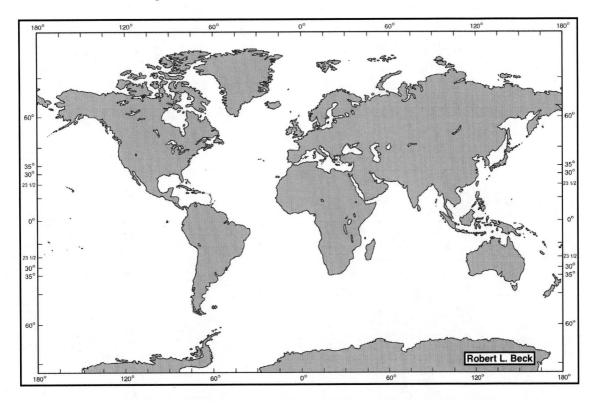

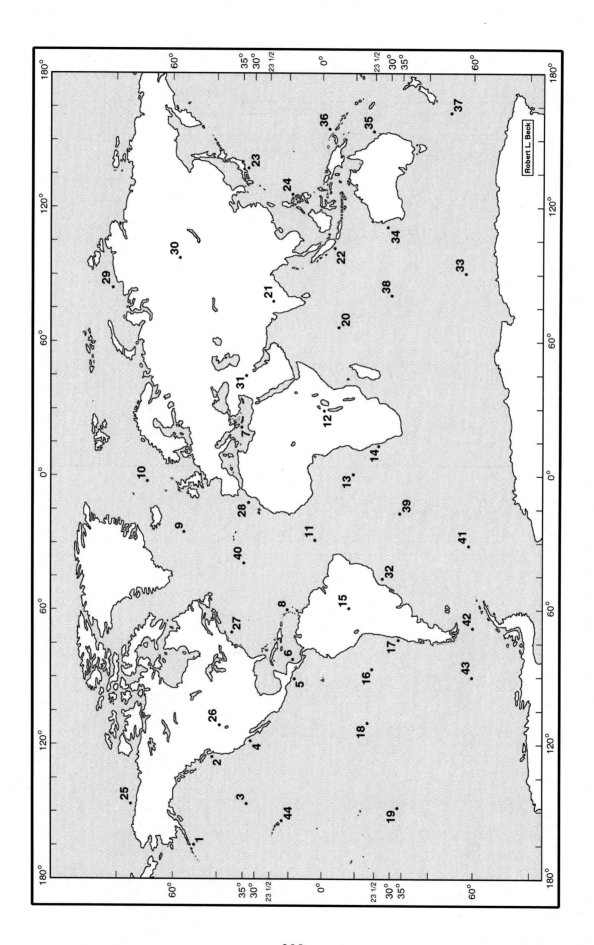

Robert L. Beck

MODULE 23: LANDMASS DEGRADATION PROCESSES

The focus of this module is to identify and discuss some of the major natural processes that tear down landforms. I separate the processes for purposes of organization and discussion, but they really are interrelated.

Weathering

The process by which rock (and other substances) is disintegrated and decomposed during exposure to atmospheric influences is known as *weathering*. Weathering does not mean the same thing as *erosion*, for weathering does not involve the transportation of loose materials. In effect, weathering softens a rock and erosion carries away the softened or loosened material.

PHYSICAL WEATHERING

Also known as mechanical weathering, *physical weathering* occurs when rocks are disintegrated and decomposed without any change in their chemical composition. *Frost action* is a good example of a physical weathering process. Water is a substance that expands when it freezes (most other substances on Earth contract when they freeze), so if some of it freezes in the crack of a rock it will exert pressure on that rock. Repeated freezing and thawing of the water in the crack will eventually cause a piece of the rock to loosen or fall off (Fig. 23-1).

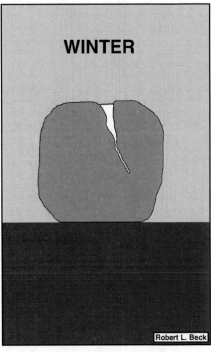

Figure 23-1. Frost Action

Thermal expansion helps to decompose rock. I mentioned earlier that granite is an intrusive igneous rock, so it has large crystals. Granite is one of the hardest rocks abundant on Earth; it is quite resistant to weathering and erosion. But even granite, just sitting out in the sun day after day, will be decomposed by physical weathering processes. As the sun shines on a piece of granite, its black minerals (mostly hornblende) will absorb more radiation than its white or light-colored minerals (quartz and orthoclase feldspar). Small hot spots are produced in the granite due to this differential heating of minerals. When the minerals get hot, they try to expand, which puts stress on the rock. One day a sand grain happens to fall off the granite because of the thermal expansion that repeats itself every day. Given enough time, and without any other disturbances, a piece of granite will be reduced to a pile of sand by simply sitting in the sun. When small pieces of a rock fall off it, over a long period of time, the process is known as ***granular disintegration*** (Fig. 23-2).

Figure 23-2. This group of rocks, sitting in the sun in Arizona, is being reduced to a pile of sand by the weathering process known as *granular disintegration.*
(Robert L. Beck photo, 1987)

In high mountain areas a physical weathering process known as ***shattering*** disintegrates rock. Mountain environments tend to have temperature extremes because of the thin atmosphere. Depending on their exposure, some rocks get very hot during the day and very cold at night. The repetition of alternative periods of hot and cold sometimes causes the rocks to explode with a loud bang. When a rock shatters, it tends to produce a sharp edge. ***Felsenmeer*** (rock sea) is a term used to describe fields of shattered rocks at high elevation (Fig. 23-3). One can simulate the shattering process by throwing a water-soaked sedimentary rock into a hot fire, but stand back, for in a few minutes the rock will explode, and when it does sharp pieces of it will fly outward from the fire in all directions. I tried this in my backyard; when the rock exploded a piece was thrown on top of my roof.

In the natural world plants will grow wherever they have an opportunity to do so, even in places that might not be ideally suited for them. Some plants grow in the spaces between rocks or even in the crack of a rock, for that is where the seed from which they germinated happened to land. As a plant grows, its roots exert pressure on the rock as they try to wedge their way into any available space. This action loosens the rock and helps to decompose it. ***Plant root growth*** is another physical weathering process, but some people consider it to be, more specifically, a biological weathering process (Fig. 23-4).

Figure 23-3. Felsenmeer
(Tim Brothers photo, c. 1969)

Figure 23-4. Plant Root Growth
(Robert L. Beck photo, 1984)

Rainwater falling in desert areas carries salts and other minerals into the ground. As the water is percolating down into the ground through pore spaces and openings in the rock, it might hit an impermeable rock layer forcing it to flow laterally. If the water then seeps out the side of a cliff, it will evaporate leaving the salts behind on the side of the cliff. The salts crystallize, and with their growth pressure is exerted on the surrounding rock, which helps to disintegrate it. Desert areas often have ***niches*** in rock faces produced by ***salt crystallization***, another physical weathering process (Fig. 23-5 and Fig. 23-6).

Magma that solidifies beneath the earth's surface into an intrusive igneous rock does so with many millions of tons of rock, soil, and unconsolidated deposits pressing on it from above. If this weight is removed through weathering and erosion processes the rocks often crack in response to the weight removal. A physical weathering process known as ***unloading*** is at work when rocks crack and otherwise decompose through the removal of overlying materials. Sheets of rock, both thin and thick, break off the original rock and fall nearby in a process known as *exfoliation* or *spalling*. Exfoliation domes such as Stone Mountain (in Georgia) or Enchanted Rock (in Texas) are two examples where large sheets of rock have spalled off the dome and have been carried to the base of it by gravity (Fig. 23-7).

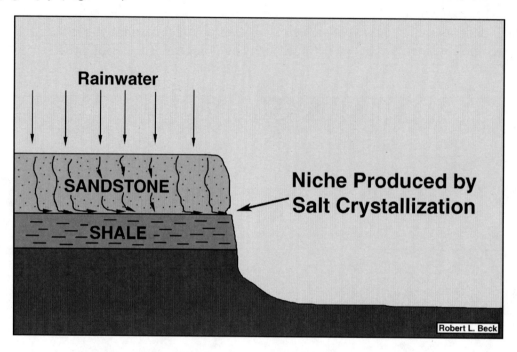

Figure 23-5. Rainwater and Salt Crystallization

Figure 23-6. Niches
(Robert L. Beck photo, 1987)

Figure 23-7. Enchanted Rock Exfoliation Dome, Central Texas
(Robert L. Beck photo, 1982)

CHEMICAL WEATHERING

Chemical weathering is a second type of weathering process that occurs when a rock is decomposed through the chemical alteration of its minerals. Chemical weathering and physical weathering usually work jointly to disintegrate a rock, but they are studied separately for ease in understanding the differences between the two.

Rainwater is naturally acidic, for it reacts with carbon dioxide in the atmosphere to produce a weak acid, carbonic acid. Limestone and other sedimentary rocks are slowly dissolved by carbonic acid in a process known as *carbonation*, a chemical weathering process. Southern Indiana is famous for its *karst* features—sinkholes, swallow holes, caves, and underground rivers—that have been produced by a combination of chemical weathering and erosion of limestone rock formations (Fig. 23-8, Fig. 23-9, and Fig. 23-10).

Hydrolysis is a chemical decomposition process in which water joins with another substance to produce a new compound that is almost always weaker and softer than the original. Erosion processes have a much easier time removing the weaker and softer compound than the original hard substance. Igneous rock is particularly susceptible to this chemical weathering process.

Oxidation is a third chemical weathering process in which dissolved oxygen in water combines with metallic elements in rock to produce new substances that are soft and easily erodible. The reaction of oxygen with iron-bearing minerals produces iron oxide, more commonly known as *rust*.

303

Figure 23-8. Sinkhole, Southern Indiana
(Robert L. Beck photo, c. 1976)

Figure 23-9. As is the case with many sinkholes in Indiana, this sinkhole, in Putnam County, has trees growing in it because it is in the middle of a field cropped for corn and soybeans. Farm machinery cannot drive over the sinkhole, so trees have established themselves in it as a result. Limestone underlies this area of the county.
(Robert L. Beck photo, 2007)

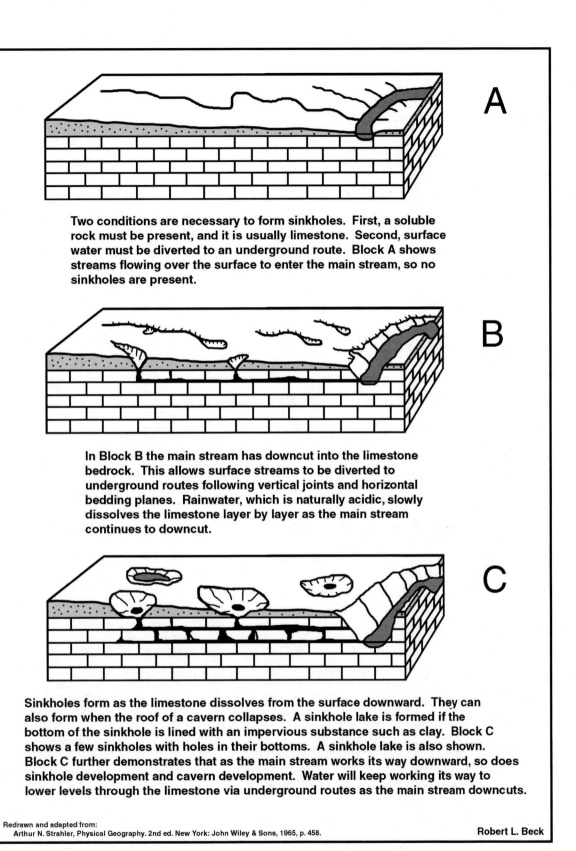

A

Two conditions are necessary to form sinkholes. First, a soluble rock must be present, and it is usually limestone. Second, surface water must be diverted to an underground route. Block A shows streams flowing over the surface to enter the main stream, so no sinkholes are present.

B

In Block B the main stream has downcut into the limestone bedrock. This allows surface streams to be diverted to underground routes following vertical joints and horizontal bedding planes. Rainwater, which is naturally acidic, slowly dissolves the limestone layer by layer as the main stream continues to downcut.

C

Sinkholes form as the limestone dissolves from the surface downward. They can also form when the roof of a cavern collapses. A sinkhole lake is formed if the bottom of the sinkhole is lined with an impervious substance such as clay. Block C shows a few sinkholes with holes in their bottoms. A sinkhole lake is also shown. Block C further demonstrates that as the main stream works its way downward, so does sinkhole development and cavern development. Water will keep working its way to lower levels through the limestone via underground routes as the main stream downcuts.

Redrawn and adapted from:
Arthur N. Strahler, Physical Geography. 2nd ed. New York: John Wiley & Sons, 1965, p. 458.

Robert L. Beck

Figure 23-10. Sinkhole Formation

Erosion

Erosion involves the **transportation** of loose materials from one area of Earth to another. There are five major erosion agents—streams, lakes, oceans, ice, and wind. It is important to keep in mind that when a loose particle is picked up by one of these agents that it will be deposited (dropped) somewhere else. Loose particles dropped by streams are known as *alluvial* deposits; those dropped by lakes are known as *lacustrine* deposits; those dropped by oceans are known as *marine* deposits; those dropped by ice are known as *glacial* deposits; and those dropped by wind are known as *eolian* deposits. Erosion is therefore linked with deposition—what is carried will be dropped.

The three smallest soil particles sizes are sand, silt, and clay. Sand is the largest of the three, followed by silt, and then by clay. When wind erodes the soil it has the ability to transport particles of these three sizes. Sand, being the largest and heaviest, will fall first; silt and clay will be carried greater distances because they are lighter, but eventually they too will fall (Fig. 23-11). The wind, then, is a good *particle size separator*. Over

Figure 23-11. Particle Size Separation

long periods of time the sand-sized particles collect to form a *sand dune*, a type of eolian deposit. Silt- and clay-sized particles collect to form a deposit known as *loess*, a second type of eolian deposit (Fig. 23-11 and Fig. 23-12). Before the invention of threshing machines, people separated grain from chaff by throwing the mix of it into the air on a windy day. The grain, being heavy, fell near their feet, but the chaff was blown away.

306

Figure 23-12. People have carved their names in this loess deposit in western Missouri. The deposit is about 25 feet thick. *(Robert L. Beck photo, 1987)*

Unlike wind, which can erode both uphill and downhill, water erodes downhill only, so I like to begin the study of the ***water erosion sequence*** by starting at the top of the hill, with raindrops falling from the atmosphere (Fig. 23-13). When a raindrop strikes the earth's surface the impact might cause some loose particles to be transported downhill

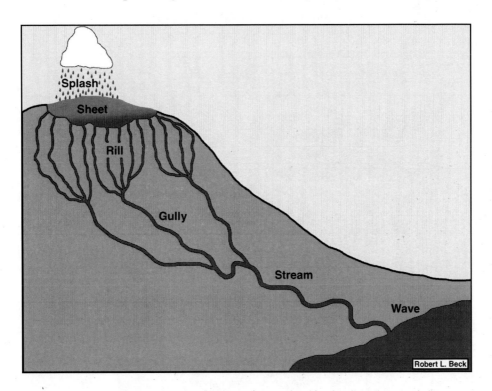

Figure 23-13. Water Erosion Sequence

307

in a process known as ***splash erosion*** (Fig. 23-14). As the water from the raindrops collects on the surface, it starts to flow downhill carrying particles in a film of moving water in an erosion process known as ***sheet erosion***. Water moving downhill as a sheet of water quickly starts to collect in small channels known as ***rills***; particles are carried downhill in these small channels by moving water and is known as ***rill erosion*** (Fig. 23-15). Rills begin to merge into larger channels and the result is known as ***gully erosion*** (Fig. 23-16).

Figure 23-14. Splash Erosion
(Natural Resources Conservation Service photo)

Figure 23-15. Rill Erosion, Vigo County, Indiana
(Robert L. Beck photo)

Gullies join together to form streams, which continue to flow downhill causing *stream erosion* (Fig. 23-17). Streams ultimately enter the ocean (or a lake) and the moving water in it produces *wave erosion* (Fig. 23-18).

Figure 23-16. Severe Gully Erosion, South Dakota
(Robert L. Beck photo)

Figure 23-17. Stream Erosion, Wabash River, Southwestern Indiana
(Robert L. Beck photo, 1987)

To minimize the adverse effects of water erosion, it is important to protect the earth's surface during the entire water erosion sequence, from hilltop to ocean. Sheet and rill erosion account for more than 50% of the tonnage of sediment moved every year in Indiana by water erosion processes.

Figure 23-18. Wave Erosion along the Coast of Maine
(Robert L. Beck photo, 1988)

Figure 23-19. A *spit* is a landform produced by the action of waves. Spits are attached to the seashore, but they can extend seaward many miles. Homer Spit, in Alaska, was about five miles long when this photograph was taken.
(Robert L. Beck photo, 1975)

Some rocks are resistant to erosion and some are not. In general, crystalline rocks resist weathering and erosion to a greater degree than do sedimentary rocks, but even they have varying degrees of resistance. Sandstone, a sedimentary rock, resists weathering and erosion in the humid climates of the eastern United States; it is much more erodible in the dry climates of the western United States. Limestone is just the opposite; it weathers quickly in humid climates and it resists erosion in dry climates. The phrase ***differential weathering and erosion*** refers to a situation in which rocks weather and erode at different rates depending on their mineral constituency.

EROSIONAL LANDFORMS

Distinctive landforms are produced by differential weathering and erosion as they tear down the earth's surface. A **plateau** is a large, flat, upland surface, but differential weathering and erosion will eat away at the plateau until its surface is highly dissected (cut up) by small streams. When that happens it is known as a **dissected plateau** (Fig. 23-20). The Appalachian Plateau in the eastern United States is a good example of a dissected plateau. If you travel to eastern Kentucky and West Virginia looking for a large, flat, upland surface known as the *Appalachian Plateau*, you will not find it, for it has been dissected by weathering and erosion into mountainous topography.

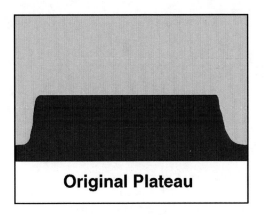
Original Plateau

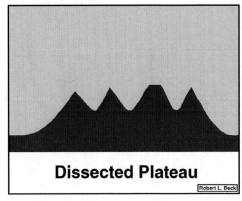
Dissected Plateau

Figure 23-20. Plateau Dissection

The Colorado Plateau in the southwestern United States is a different story. That plateau has extensive, flat, upland tracts only slightly dissected by streams. Major streams have deeply cut into it, but the upland tracts of low relief are easily seen both in the air and on the ground (Fig. 23-21 and Fig. 23-22).

Fig. 23-21. The flat, upland tracts of the Colorado Plateau are marked by the light colored rocks. The dark strip is a major stream cutting down into the plateau.
(Tim Brothers photo, 1990)

311

Figure 23-22. The Gunnison River in western Colorado has made a deep incision into the Colorado Plateau, but the upland tracts away from the canyon have only been slightly cut up by weathering and erosion. *(Robert L. Beck photo, 1987)*

A number of distinctive erosional landforms found in the western United States have been produced by differential weathering and erosion. Mesas, buttes, and pillars are eroded remnants of a plateau surface. A *mesa* is a large remnant of a plateau, whereas a *butte* is a small remnant, and a *pillar* is a standing column of rock (Fig. 23-23 and Fig. 23-24). The flat tops of pillars, buttes, and mesas are typically at the same elevation as the flat top of the plateau from which they have been cleaved (Fig. 23-23). When the

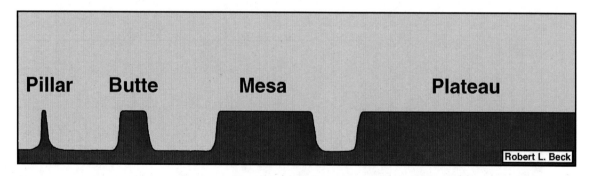

Figure 23-23. Erosional Landforms

tops of adjacent landforms are all at the same elevation above sea level this concept is known as *accordant elevations*. Unless he or she is standing on the edge, the horizon will appear to be flat to a person standing on top of a plateau because he or she will not see the eroded sections between the plateau and the smaller landforms around it.

Figure 23-24. Buttes and Pillars, Monument Valley, Arizona
(Christy Herris photo)

Weathering and erosion produce recognizable landforms adjacent to mountains. *Pediments* are gently sloping flat surfaces composed of the same rocks as the mountain from which they have been formed (Fig. 23-25 and Fig. 23-26). Weathering and erosion tear down the mountain—producing pediments in the process. Small hill-like features in pediments composed of resistant bedrock are known as *inselbergs* (Fig. 23-25 and Fig. 23-27).

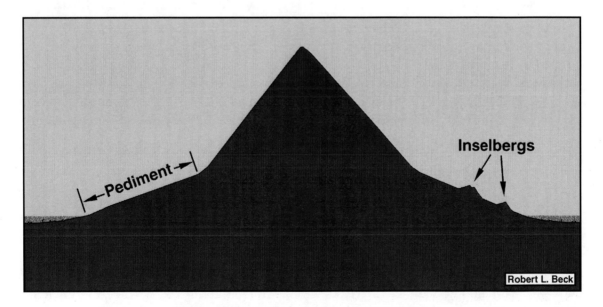

Figure 23-25. Pediments and Inselbergs

313

Figure 23-26. In this photograph, a *pediment* is seen as the light colored strip of land positioned between the mountains and the vegetation occupying the land near the stream in the middle ground. The photo was taken on the western side of the Tobacco Root Mountains in Montana. *(Tim Brothers photo, 1989)*

Figure 23-27. *Inselbergs* Situated in a *Pediment* in Southern Arizona
(Robert L. Beck photo, 1987)

Hill lands formed through weathering and erosion of exposed edges of gently dipping sedimentary rock formations are known as **cuestas**. They typically occur in areas where sedimentary rock layers alternate between erosion-resistant formations and easily erodible formations (Fig. 23-28). Some of southern Indiana's hill lands are cuestas (Fig. 23-29). The top drawing in Figure 23-28 shows an original flat surface on Earth underlain with dipping sedimentary rocks varying in their ability to resist weathering and erosion—the harder rocks are shaded a dark color. Over time, weathering and erosion easily remove the softer rocks (light color) leaving behind a hill land (cuesta) capped with erosion-resistant rocks (bottom drawing, Fig. 23-28).

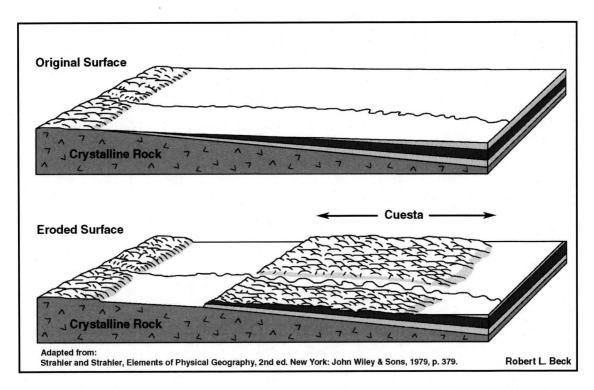

Adapted from:
Strahler and Strahler, Elements of Physical Geography, 2nd ed. New York: John Wiley & Sons, 1979, p. 379.

Robert L. Beck

Figure 23-28. Erosion produces a hill land known as a *cuesta* in gently dipping sedimentary rock formations even though the original surface was almost flat.

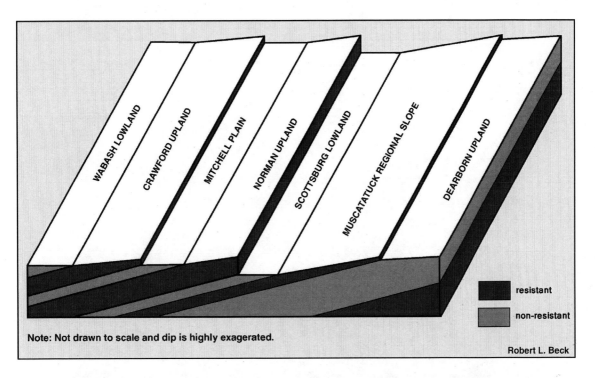

Note: Not drawn to scale and dip is highly exaggerated.

Robert L. Beck

Figure 23-29. Generalized Block Diagram of Southern Indiana's Physiographic Regions. Which regions in southern Indiana are cuestas?

Elongated ridges of eroded rock formations known as *hogbacks* are the result of differential weathering and erosion of alternating layers of steeply inclined hard and soft rocks (Fig. 23-30). Igneous intrusions are often partially responsible for the formation of hogbacks, for when an intrusion occurs any sedimentary rocks positioned above it might be tilted upward into a nearly vertical arrangement (Fig. 23-31). A hogback emerges when the softer sedimentary rocks on both sides of it are removed by weathering and erosion. Hogbacks and cuestas differ, however, for a cuesta has a gentle slope on one side and a steep slope on the other. Hogbacks have steep slopes on both sides because they form from steeply inclined rocks. Cuestas form when rock formations are gently sloping, not steeply sloping.

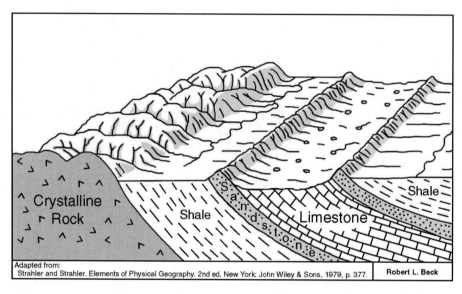

Adapted from:
Strahler and Strahler. Elements of Physical Geography. 2nd ed. New York: John Wiley & Sons, 1979, p. 377.   Robert L. Beck

Figure 23-30. Sandstone Hogbacks

Fig. 23-31. The uplift that produced the Rocky Mountains turned the Dakota Sandstone on edge, which today is standing as a *hogback* in the Garden of the Gods in Colorado. *(Robert L. Beck photo, 1987)*

Mass Wasting Processes

The pull of gravity on earth materials is known as **mass wasting**, and it can occur with or without water. Weathering and erosion are aided by gravity, but mass wasting specifically refers to situations where gravity pulls earth materials downhill. Earth materials laid down by gravity are known as **colluvial deposits**.

In humid areas the absorption of water by the soil makes it especially heavy, so gravity slowly pulls it downhill in a process known as **soil creep**. Not only does the soil slowly move downhill, but substances in the soil or on top of the soil are also pulled downhill. Turned or tilted telephone poles, leaning fence posts, displaced tombstones, and broken retainer walls are all visible evidence of soil creep (Fig. 23-32).

Figure 23-32. Soil Creep Pushed Over this Retaining Wall in Southern Indiana
(Robert L. Beck photo, 1986)

An **earthflow** occurs when the top layer of a water-saturated hillside slides downhill in a few hours, so it is a faster process than soil creep. A noticeable scar is left in the hillside after the earthflow has ended (Fig. 23-33). A type of earthflow in which a hillside sags with the bottom of it being pushed out by the weight of the mass above it is known as **slump** (Fig. 23-34). Earthflows can bury trees, houses, and roadways. They are even known to have dammed streams resulting in the formation of natural lakes. Like soil creep, earthflows are mostly found in humid areas.

A **mudflow** is not the same thing as an earthflow, for mudflows occur in arid areas, and they move much faster, sometimes so fast that even a person driving a car might not be able to outrun them (Fig. 23-35). Mudflows occur after a period of heavy rain, such as after a cloudburst. When the precipitation hits the ground, the lack of

317

vegetation causes the water to quickly start flowing over the earth's surface, where it is rapidly channeled into stream valleys. It rushes downhill as a mass of mud-filled water. Its energy allows it to pick up virtually anything in its path and carry it downslope.

Figure 23-33. An Earthflow Threatening to Move onto Interstate 70 in Indiana
(Robert L. Beck photo, 1986)

Figure 23-34. Slump has Affected this Hillside in Southern Indiana
(Robert L. Beck photo, 1985)

Mudflows move faster than earthflows because they have much higher water content. When mudflows disgorge from narrow valleys the energy in them is dissipated, and the sediments and other materials in them are deposited helping to form *alluvial fans* (Fig. 23-36 and Fig. 28-8).

Figure 23-35. This Mudflow, in California, Destroyed Many Houses
(Kim Greeman photo)

Figure 23-36. Alluvial Fan *(Kara Holmes drawing)*

The mass wasting process of **rock fall** occurs when individual rocks fall off the side of a hill and collect at the bottom, usually in a small mound known as a **talus cone**, also known as **scree** (Fig. 23-37). Rock fall does not require water. Weathering simply loosens a piece of rock and gravity carries it downhill. The rapid sliding of large masses of rock is known as a **landslide**. It is another mass wasting process that does not require water.

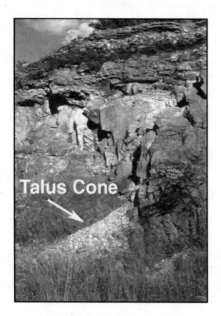

Figure 23-37. Talus Cone
(Robert L. Beck photo)

Figure 23-38. Granite Quarry
(Robert L. Beck photo, 1988)

Module 23 Objectives

You should now be able to:

- Discuss the differences among *weathering*, *erosion*, and *mass wasting*

- List the two main weathering processes and give several examples of each

- Identify the names of five erosional deposits

- List, and briefly discuss, the six steps of the water erosion sequence

- Identify the three smallest *soil particle sizes*

- Discuss how the wind acts as a *particle size separator* and relate that to the nature of *eolian deposits*

- List, and briefly discuss, at least seven erosional landforms

- Discuss the principal mass wasting processes

- Explain the difference between a *hogback* and a *cuesta*

MODULE 24: STREAMS

A *stream* is a long, narrow body of water, occupying a channel, moving to a lower level under the influence of gravity. South America's Amazon River is a *stream*, but so is Pogues Run in Indianapolis. Some people have the mistaken impression that a river is not a stream, for does not everyone know a river is large and a stream is small? Rivers, runs, creeks, branches, forks, and brooks are all streams.

In the field it is difficult to pinpoint the exact location where a stream begins. Technically, streams begin where gullies end, but the point at which a gully turns into a stream is often a matter of opinion.

Features of Streams

The place where a stream begins is known as its *head*, and the place where a stream ends is known as its *mouth*, which might be located at an ocean, at a lake, or at another stream. Streams that flow into a larger stream are known as *tributaries*, and streams that flow out of a larger stream are known as *distributaries*. The Wabash River is a tributary of the Ohio River, and it is a tributary of the Mississippi River, which breaks up into distributaries before reaching the Gulf of Mexico. The place where a tributary joins a larger stream is known as the *confluence* (Fig. 24-1).

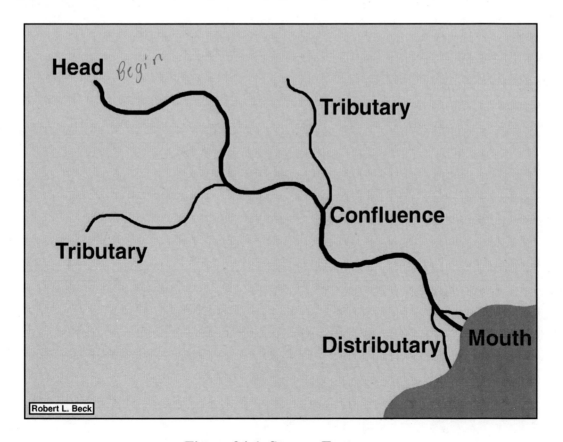

Figure 24-1. Stream Features

321

The ***channel*** is a trenchlike depression in which the stream flows. The bottom of the channel is known as the ***streambed***, and the two sides of the channel are known as the ***stream banks*** (Fig. 24-2). Stream channels swing back and forth across the land, and these looping features of the channel are known as ***meanders***. The strip of land between the outside points of the meanders on both sides of the stream is known as the ***meander belt***, and the piece of land between two meanders is a ***meander neck*** (Fig. 24-3). The

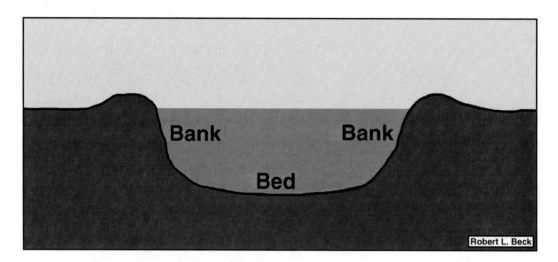

Figure 24-2. Channel Features

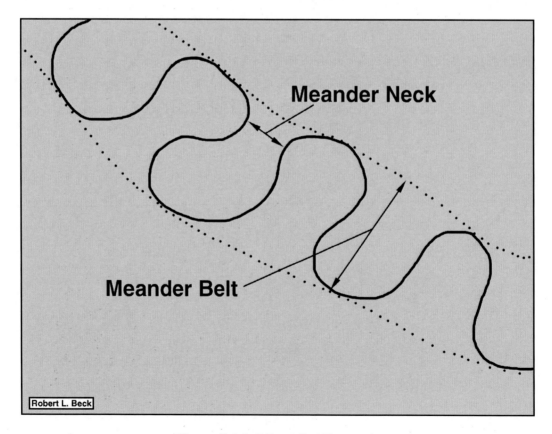

Figure 24-3. Meander Features

lower Wabash River has numerous meanders and meander necks south of Terre Haute (Fig. 24-4 and Fig. 24-5).

Figure 24-4. Meander and Meander Neck, Wabash River
(Robert L. Beck photo, 1987)

Figure 24-5. Meander Neck, Wabash River
(Robert L. Beck photo, 1987)

Load

Streams have the ability to carry solid matter. Anyone who has observed the streams of Indiana and the midwestern United States knows they almost always look muddy, for they are carrying soil particles and other solid materials that have been washed into them from various sources. *Load* is the solid matter carried by the stream.

Some of the solids carried by the stream are too lightweight to settle to the bottom, so they remain floating in the stream. These floating solids are known as *suspended load* (Fig. 24-6). If you dip a cup in the White River in Indianapolis and observe the water in it, you will notice solid particles are floating in it.

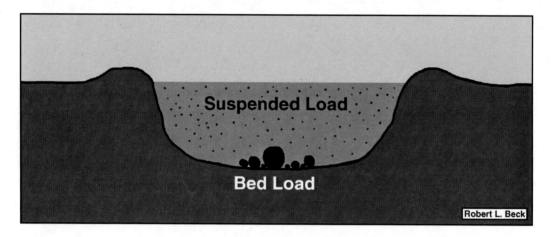

Figure 24-6. Stream Load

Heavy solids settle to the bottom of the stream, but they will not just sit there indefinitely unless they are extremely heavy. The stream water pushes the heavy solids along on the streambed. Cobblestones, boulders, and other large rocks slide, roll, or jump along the streambed. The heavy solids moving along the bed of the stream are known as the *bed load* (Fig. 24-6).

Every morning at breakfast I like to drink a cup of tea, but I want it to be sweetened, so I stir two teaspoons of sugar in with my spoon. After I have stirred it, I can taste the sugar in the tea but I cannot see it with my eyes. Stream water is similar to this because it has dissolved solids in it, which include salts of various sorts. The dissolved solids carried by streams are load in *solution*.

The maximum load a stream can carry is its *capacity*, for obviously a stream cannot carry an unlimited amount of solid materials. The capacity of a stream is influenced by the amount of water it is discharging and by the speed the water is moving. If the amount of water in the stream is increased, such as due to flooding or a heavy rainfall event, the capacity of that stream will be increased, which will allow the stream to add more load through increased erosion. If the discharge falls, then some of the load will be dropped as an alluvial deposit. The amount of load dropped is equal to the amount necessary to bring the stream into equilibrium with its capacity.

Organization of Streams

A *drainage basin* is the area drained by a stream and its tributaries. It is also known as a *watershed*. For example, the Wabash River has its head at Grand Lake, Ohio, and its mouth at the Ohio River. Nearly 85% of the area drained by the Wabash River and its tributaries lies in the state of Indiana, but some of the area drained by it is in Illinois and some of it is in Ohio (Fig. 24-7). The divide between streams that drain into the Atlantic Ocean and those that drain into the Pacific Ocean is known as the *continental divide* (Fig. 24-8).

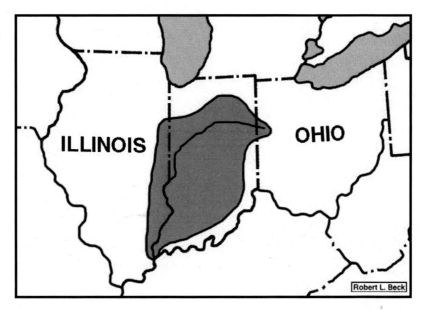

Figure 24-7. Wabash River Drainage Basin

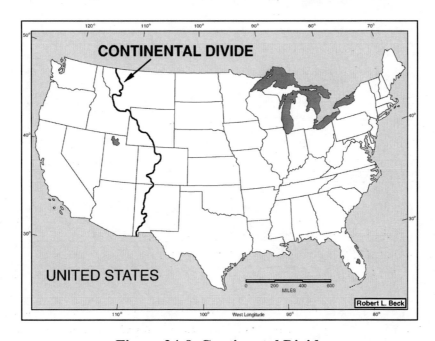

Figure 24-8. Continental Divide

325

Stream order is a concept used to describe stream arrangement within a watershed. The smallest streams are first-order streams, and they are tributaries to second-order streams, which are tributaries to third-order streams, which are tributaries to fourth-order streams, and so on (Fig. 24-9). The Amazon River is an 11th-order stream, the world's highest stream order.

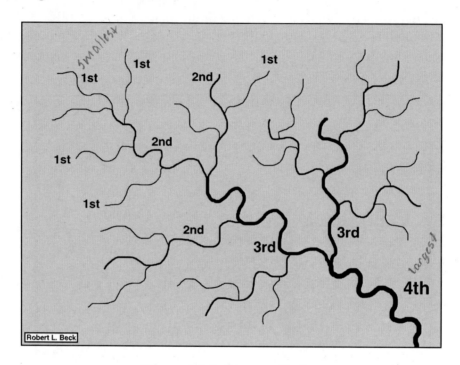

Figure 24-9. Stream Order

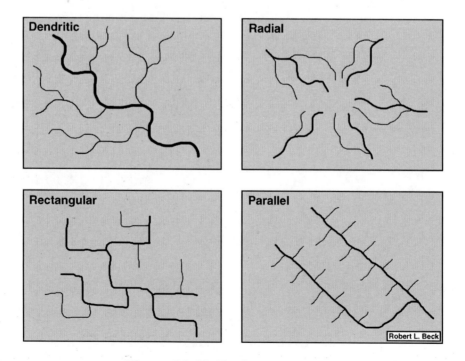

Figure 24-10. Drainage Patterns

As streams flow over the earth's surface, they produce recognizable ***drainage patterns*** that can be seen on maps or from an airplane (Fig. 24-10). These drainage patterns reflect the structure of the underlying deposits—rocks or unconsolidated materials. Streams that have a ***dendritic*** (treelike) drainage pattern are most likely flowing over flat-lying sedimentary rocks; streams that have a ***radial*** drainage pattern are flowing outward in all directions from a central high point, usually a mountain or hill; streams that have a ***rectangular*** drainage pattern with numerous 90° turns are typically flowing over jointed bedrock; streams that have a ***parallel*** drainage pattern are flowing between long narrow ridges that might be moraines deposited by a glacier; and streams that have a ***deranged*** drainage pattern are usually flowing over a flat, poorly drained area that lacks stream development. I have mentioned here just a few of the many stream drainage patterns recognized by geomorphologists.

Types of Streams

There are several different types of streams. The larger streams in Indiana are ***perennial streams*** (Fig. 24-11), or streams that flow year-round, such as the White River in Indianapolis. Perennial streams originate in areas of the world where precipitation exceeds evaporation. Indianapolis receives about 38–40 inches of precipitation every year, but only about 26 inches of it evaporates, so the remainder either infiltrates into the soil or runs off into the White River or one of its tributaries.

Figure 24-11. Big Walnut Creek Flows All Year, So it is a Perennial Stream
(Robert L. Beck photo, 2011)

Perennial streams cannot originate in B climate regions; for in those environments potential evaporation is greater than precipitation, so any water that does fall from the atmosphere will soon evaporate. But perennial streams do flow through deserts and steppes. The Nile River flows through the Sahara Desert in Africa, but the Nile originates in the tropical rainforest climate near the Equator. Streams that flow through dry climate regions are known as *exotic streams*—a stream not native to the area through which it flows.

Many small streams in Indiana flow only during the late winter, spring, and early summer— when rainfall is plentiful. During the late summer and fall they dry up. Such streams are known as *intermittent streams*—streams that flow seasonally. Small streams that flow only after a rain are known as *ephemeral streams*; one flows through a ravine in my backyard.

Braided streams lack a well-defined channel (Fig. 24-12). They flow through a maze of twisting and turning minichannels that might join together briefly and then break up again. These streams often flow on nearly flat surfaces filled with sand and gravel deposits. The Platte River, in Nebraska, is one such stream. It is extremely wide relative to its depth, for it is commonly described as "a mile wide and an inch deep." Thick deposits of sand and gravel, washed out of the Rocky Mountains by flood and snowmelt, fill the Platte River Valley. Alaska's Tanana River is another example of a braided stream, but in this case the deposits were expelled from glaciers residing high in the mountains near the head of the stream.

Figure 24-12. Braided Stream, Tanana River, Alaska
(Robert L. Beck photo, 1975)

Stream Erosion

Base level is the term used to describe the lowest level to which a stream can erode its channel. The *ultimate base level* for all streams on Earth is the ocean, but the *local base level* of a stream can be either above or below sea level. If a dam is constructed on a stream, the portion of the stream above the dam can erode down only to the water level of the dam's reservoir. Such a stream would have the water level of the reservoir as its local base level, and it might be situated many hundreds of feet above sea level. Some areas of Earth are below sea level because they are situated in a down-dropped block of Earth's crust (such as the Dead Sea). Streams flowing into these areas will erode down to the level of the block, even if it is below sea level. ***Downcutting*** is the term used to describe the action of the stream in eroding downward toward its base level. As streams downcut into a block of earth, they often cut a ***V-shaped valley*** (Fig. 24-13) early in the stream erosion process.

Downcutting

Figure 24-13. V-shaped Valley, Yellowstone National Park
(Robert L. Beck photo, 1975)

As streams erode downward, they also erode back and forth in their channels. This side-to-side erosion by streams is known as ***lateral cutting***, and it occurs as a stream erodes into one of its banks. A drawing of a meandering stream is shown in Figure 24-14. Line A–B crosses one of its meanders, and an enlarged cross-section of that line is shown below the stream. Observation of the drawing reveals that streams have two distinctly different sides at the meander. One side is known as the ***slip-off slope***, and it is found on the inside bend of the meander. The other side is found on the outside bend of a meander, and it is known as an ***undercut bank*** (Fig. 24-14). The photograph in Figure 24-15 shows both the slip-off slope and the undercut bank of a small stream in Putnam County, Indiana. Sand often collects at the slip-off slope forming a *point bar*.

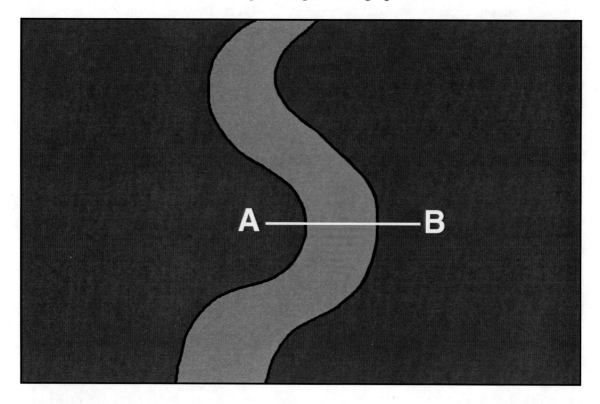

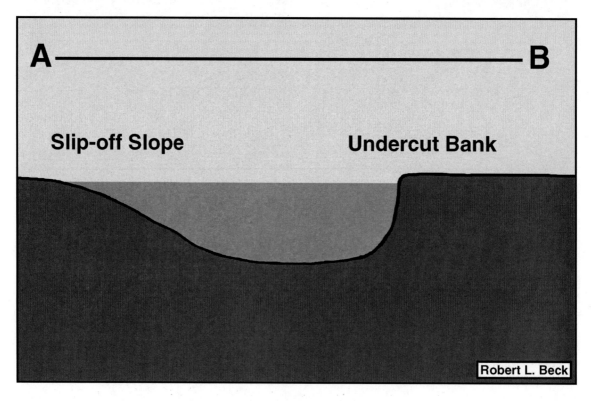

Robert L. Beck

Figure 24-14. Meandering Stream

Figure 24-15. Undercut Bank (left) and Slip-off Slope (right)
(Robert L. Beck photo, 1987)

Water moving in a stream flows faster on the outside bend of a meander than on the inside bend, so the stream erodes its undercut bank while depositing some of its sediment on the slip-off slope. A ***meander cut-off*** occurs when a stream erodes though a meander neck (Fig. 24-16). The old river channel eventually becomes an ***oxbow lake*** (Fig. 24-17). Over time oxbow lakes fill with sediment and organic debris to become ***meander scars*** (Fig. 24-18).

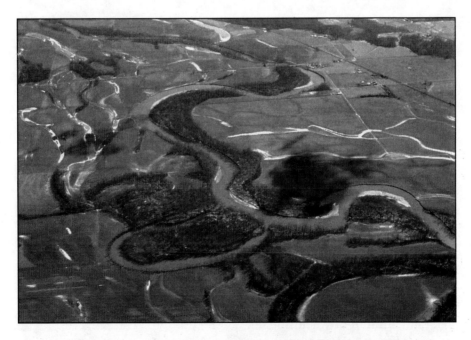

Figure 24-16. Meander Cut-off, East Fork White River, Indiana
(Robert L. Beck photo, 1999)

Figure 24-17. Oxbow Lake, Southwestern Indiana
(Robert L. Beck photo, 1987)

Figure 24-18. Meander Scar, Southwestern Indiana
(Robert L. Beck photo, 1987)

The combination of downcutting and lateral cutting by streams results in the formation of a belt of low, flat land on both sides of the stream known as a ***floodplain***. Both sides of a floodplain are marked by ***stream bluffs*** (Fig. 24-19).

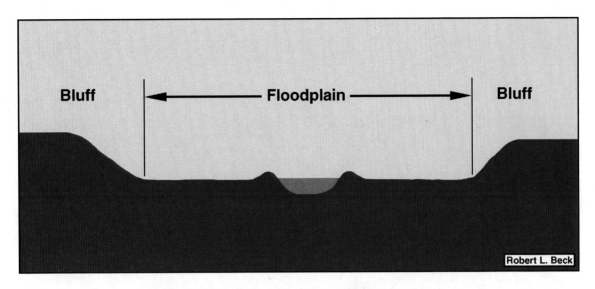

Figure 24-19. Floodplain and Stream Bluffs

Stream erosion and deposition produce a number of *fluvial landforms*. When a stream overflows its banks, its water spills out onto the floodplain and in doing so drops its load of sediment, resulting in an *alluvial deposit*, also known as *alluvium*. The stream drops its heavy load first, adjacent to the stream, and with repeated flooding this deposit begins to get higher and higher, ultimately forming a *natural levee*. Between the relatively high natural levee and the stream bluffs are the *backswamps*, or the areas where floodwaters sit after a flood event (Fig. 24-20).

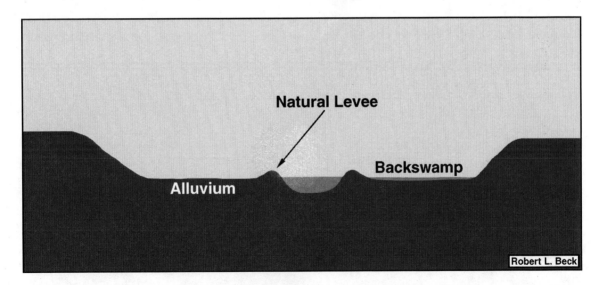

Figure 24-20. Fluvial Landforms

The best place to build a house on most floodplains is on top of the natural levee. Houses built on stilts can be found on the lower Wabash River, in Illinois, across the river from Merom, Indiana (Fig. 24-21). Natural levees sometimes prevent tributary streams, flowing through the backswamps, from entering the main stream. Such tributary streams are known as *yazoo rivers*.

333

Figure 24-21. Floodwaters are standing in the backswamps of the Wabash River in southern Illinois, but the land near the natural levee, upon which the houses are built, is relatively dry. Many houses in the lower Wabash River valley are built on stilts.
(Robert L. Beck photo, 1985)

When a stream enters a lake or ocean, its velocity drops, so it deposits some of its sediment load to form a ***delta*** (Fig. 24-22). If a stream leaves a mountainous environment

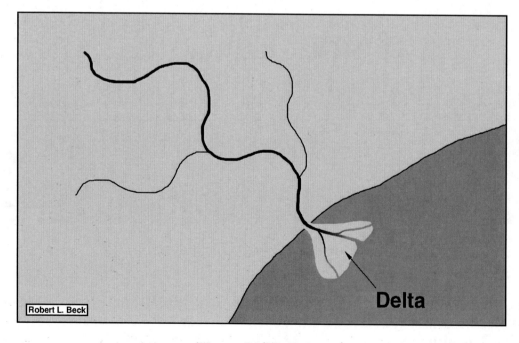

Figure 24-22. Delta

to enter a plain, it will also deposit its sediment load, but this deposit, as you know from Module 23, is an ***alluvial fan*** (Fig. 23-29, p. 316).

In central Indiana water from the melting glaciers of the Pleistocene Ice Age, which began about 1 to 2 million years ago, filled many of our stream valleys with sand and gravel washed out of the ice sheets. These sand and gravel deposits are known as ***valley train*** (Fig. 24-23 and Fig. 24-24). Post–Ice Age streams downcutting into these

Figure 24-23. Valley Train

Fig. 24-24. The sand and gravel deposits in Big Walnut Creek, in Putnam County, are known as *valley train*. Many streams in central Indiana are filled with valley train deposited by meltwater flowing out of the last Ice Age glacier as it began to recede beginning about 20,000 years ago. *(Robert L. Beck photo, 2007)*

valley train deposits have produced *alluvial terraces* as a result of the erosion process (Fig. 24-25). Alluvial terraces are found along many streams, large and small, in southwestern Indiana (Fig. 24-26 and Fig. 24-27). The city of Terre Haute (high land) is built on alluvial terraces above the Wabash River. Alluvial terraces are easy to spot in

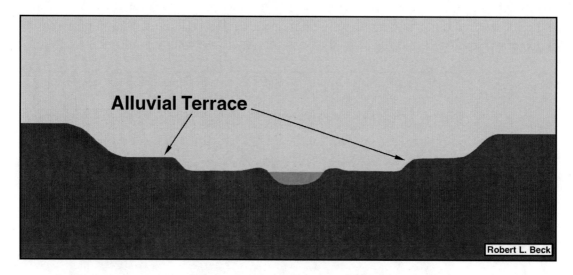

Figure 24-25. Alluvial Terrace

Figure 24-26. The change in angle of the fence and the road mark the edge of an alluvial terrace situated in the valley of Little Raccoon Creek, Parke County, Ind.
(Robert L. Beck photo, 1986)

terrain lacking dense vegetative cover such as in cropland areas, pastures, and western rangelands (Fig. 24-28 and Fig. 24-32).

Figure 24-27. This farmstead is built on an alluvial terrace of the Wabash River south of Terre Haute. The wheat stubble in the foreground is on the floodplain.
(Robert L. Beck photo, 1986)

Figure 24-28. Terraces of the Madison River near Ennis, Montana. One terrace is especially easy to see. It is positioned to the right of the stream between the floodplain of the stream and the forested slope of the distant bluff.
(Tim Brothers photo, 1989)

337

Channelization

Humans have historically used streams as transportation lines. Streams are naturally formed, and they penetrate far inland from the sea. The development of commerce and the desire to move goods faster from place to place led people to channelize streams to move freight more efficiently, but it also produced some negative environmental effects.

Channelization involves deepening and straightening the channel, so instead of a stream flowing along looping meanders, after channelization it can move along straight lines (Fig. 24-29). Suppose City A is situated on a meandering river at an elevation of 1,000 feet above sea level and that City B is situated on the same river at an elevation of 800 feet above sea level. Further suppose that the meandering river connecting the two cities has a length of 200 miles. In this example the *stream gradient*, or distance of fall between the two cities, would be 1 foot per mile (1,000' − 800' = 200' / 200 miles = 1).

A fluvial engineer shows up at City A one day and convinces the people living there that they need to channelize the river so it flows along a straight line to City B, which will result in their trade goods moving more efficiently. Now suppose the length of the channelized river is only 100 miles (instead of the 200 miles that was the length of the

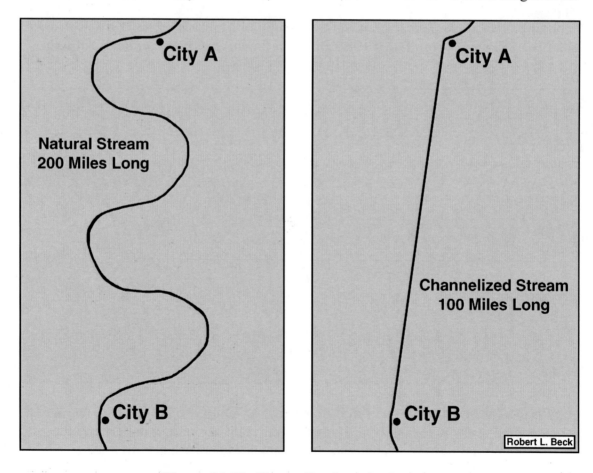

Figure 24-29. Channelization of a Stream

338

natural river), but the elevations of the two cities have not changed. Water flowing in the channelized river now drops 200 feet in 100 miles, so the stream gradient is 2 feet per mile (1,000′ − 800′ = 200′ / 100 miles = 2). This causes the stream velocity to increase, which helps boats move more quickly between the two cities. An increase in the stream's velocity, however, will cause its capacity to increase, which will allow the stream to increase its sediment load, which will bring increased soil erosion somewhere near the stream.

In this instance, the environmental costs of farmland loss, habitat change, and soil erosion wrought by channelization might be greater than the economic benefits gained by it. Of course, the people who designed the channelization project, the people who did the work to install it, and the boat owners and merchants who use the channelized river will not be paying the environmental costs. The people who will be paying the environmental costs are the landowners and land users of the watershed. When environmental costs such as these are not included in the construction cost and are further not included in operating costs, they become known as **external costs**, and they are more specifically known as **negative externalities** because they negatively affect the environment.

Many streams in Indiana have been channelized to assist in the drainage of wetlands—especially in northern and central Indiana (Fig. 24-30). Just as in navigation, a straightened channel will increase the velocity of a stream flowing through a wetland, which will help remove the standing water from that wetland area (Fig. 24-31). Indiana has a higher percentage of its total area artificially drained than any other state, with the possible exceptions of Delaware and Louisiana (Fig. 24-30).

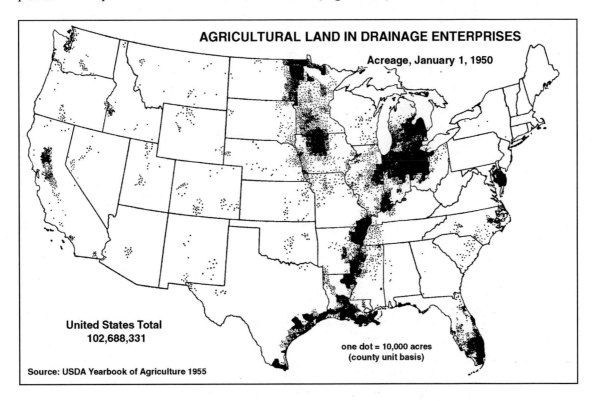

Fig. 24-30. Land Artificially Drained in the United States

WETLAND DRAINAGE
Benton County, Indiana

Sugar Creek Before Channelization

Sugar Creek After Channelization

Robert L. Beck

Figure 24-31. Sugar Creek, in northern Indiana, was channelized to help drain a large wetland known as the Kankakee Marshes.
(Elmore Barce photos)

Module 24 Objectives

You should now be able to:

- Define a *stream*

- Identify at least ten stream features

- Explain the difference between stream *load* and stream *capacity*

- Compare and contrast the three types of stream load

- Define a *drainage basin*

- Discuss *stream order*

- Identify five types of stream *drainage patterns* on a map

- Compare and contrast five types of streams

- Discuss stream erosion especially with regard to *lateral cutting* and *meander cutoff*

- Identify, and briefly discuss, at least ten types of landforms produced by stream erosion

- Define *channelization* and discuss the principal environmental impact of it

- Describe a situation involving a *negative externality*

- Use a drawing to identify various stream features

****

The master said to the student, *"Which is stronger, the mighty oak tree out in the courtyard or the little sapling down by the river?"* The student said to the master, *"The mighty oak tree is the stronger, only a fool would think otherwise."* The master said to the student, *"Which one will survive the next typhoon?"*

Figure 24-32. A prominent alluvial terrace is seen in this photograph. It is situated between the Grand Teton Mountains and the stream in the foreground.
(Tim Brothers photo, 1990)

BIRDS OBSERVED BY ROBERT L. BECK IN MADISON TOWNSHIP, 2001–2012

American Kestrel	Bald Eagle	Baltimore Oriole
Barn Swallow	Black Capped Chickadee	Broad-Winged Hawk
Blue Jay	Brown-Headed Cowbird	Brown Thrasher
Cardinal	Carolina Wren	Catbird
Cedar Waxwing	Chipping Sparrow	Common Bobwhite
Crow	Downey Woodpecker	Eastern Bluebird
Eastern Kingbird	Eastern Phoebe	Goldfinch
Grackle	Great Crested Flycatcher	Hairy Woodpecker
House Finch	House Sparrow	Indigo Bunting
Least Flycatcher	Mourning Dove	Northern Mockingbird
Pileated Woodpecker	Purple Finch	Red Bellied Woodpecker
Red Headed Woodpecker	Red-Shouldered Hawk	Red Tailed Hawk
Red Winged Blackbird	Robin	Rose-Breasted Grosbeak
Ruby-Crowned Kinglet	Ruby-Throated Hummingbird	Rufous-Sided Towhee
Scarlet Tanager	Slate-Colored Junco	Song Sparrow
Starling	Titmouse	Turkey Vulture
White-Breasted Nuthatch	White-Crowned Sparrow	White-Throated Sparrow
Wild Turkey	Yellow Bellied Sapsucker	Yellow Billed Cuckoo
Yellow Shafted Flicker		

****

MODULE 25: GLACIERS

Glaciers form in areas of Earth where more snow falls in the winter than melts away in the summer, so year after year new snow keeps piling on top of old snow, which turns the bottom layers of it into ice. The weight of continued accumulation eventually causes the ice to move outward from its area of accumulation producing a moving glacier.

Glaciers form in two areas: high latitudes and high altitudes. The two types of glaciers—***continental glaciers*** and ***mountain glaciers***—reflect the division between formation areas. Both types of glaciers produce distinctive landforms.

Glacial periods have occurred on Earth for hundreds of millions of years. The last period of glaciation, which began about 1 to 2 million years ago, is known as the Pleistocene Ice Age. There were four major glacial advances during the Pleistocene, and there might have been as many as 30 or 40 smaller advances. The four major ice advances (from oldest to youngest) were the Nebraskan Glacier, the Kansan Glacier, the Illinoian Glacier, and the Wisconsin Glacier, which left the state of Indiana only about 10,000 to 14,000 years ago. Periods of warmth known as ***interglacial stages*** occupied the time spaces between the major advances. Today, we might still be living in the Pleistocene Ice Age; perhaps the warm climate we are now experiencing is an interglacial stage between the last glacier, the Wisconsin, and the next glacier yet to arrive.

Continental Glaciers

Continental glaciers, as the name implies, cover large land areas. Both the modern Greenland and Antarctic ice sheets are continental glaciers. The continental glaciers today are found in the high latitudes, but about 20,000 years ago there was an ice sheet covering the northern half of Indiana, including the site Indianapolis now occupies.

The Wisconsin Glacier was the last Ice Age glacier to invade Indiana and the northern United States. It originated in the Hudson Bay area in Canada. A second ice sheet covered much of northern Europe at the same time; it was centered on the Gulf of Bothnia between the countries of Sweden and Finland. The area of the United States (excluding Alaska and Hawaii) that was glaciated by at least one of the four continental glaciers of the Pleistocene Ice Age is shown in Figure 25-1. This maximum line of advance is shown as a red line on the "Physiography" map in the 21st edition of ***Goode's World Atlas*** (pp. 70–71), but that map, which was an extremely useful map for teaching the *Geography of the United States*, was eliminated from the 22nd edition. The useful "Physiography" map in the 21st edition was replaced with the "Geology" map in the 22nd edition (pp. 96–97), and that map does not show the maximum line of Pleistocene glacial advance in the United States south of the Canadian border.

As continental glaciers advance outward from their area of origin, they scrape off the soil and loose material with which they come in contact. Some of these substances will become incorporated into the ice, but others, including large rocks, will be pushed by the ice in front of it much like a bulldozer moves objects of various sizes. If you ever have a chance to walk on a glacier, you will probably be able to see some of the loose debris carried by it (Fig. 25-2).

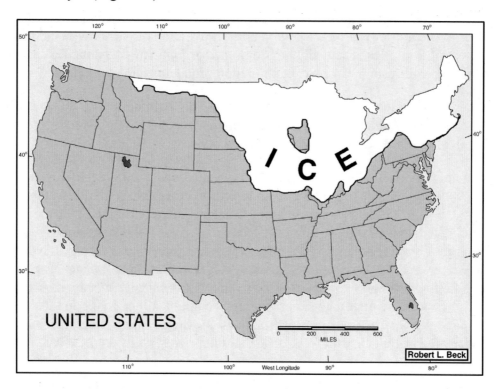

Figure 25-1. Area of the U.S. Covered by the Pleistocene Continental Glaciers

Figure 25-2. Debris Carried by a Mountain Glacier in Alaska
(Robert L. Beck photo, 1975)

It is necessary to distinguish between *glacial movement* and *glacial advance* to fully understand the process of glaciation. A glacier **moves** when the weight of accumulated ice at its center causes the basal ice underneath to expand outward, but if the glacier is melting at the same rate the ice is moving, then the glacier will not be advancing (pushing into new territory). If a glacier, however, is moving faster than it is melting, then it will be advancing into a previously unglaciated space. This leads to an important point concerning glaciers—they are either in equilibrium or disequilibrium with their climate.

A glacier in equilibrium with its climate will neither be advancing nor retreating, but it will still be moving! It will act like a big conveyor belt picking up rocks and loose material beneath the ice and transporting those substances to the edge of the glacier where they will be thrown out to produce a landform known as a *moraine*; which is a long, linear hill along the edge of the ice (Fig. 25-4 and Fig. 25-5). If the moraine is at the line of maximum glacial advance, it is then known as a *terminal moraine* (Fig. 25-4).

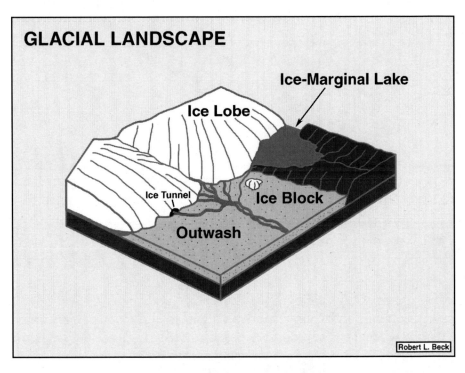

Figure 25-3. Glacial Landscape

If a glacier is in disequilibrium with its climate, it will either be advancing or retreating. If a glacier is advancing, its ice will be moving as the climate is getting colder, but if it is retreating, its ice might or might not be moving as the climate is getting warmer. For example, assume the ice of a glacier is moving but that the climate is getting warmer. The warming climate causes the glacier to be in disequilibrium with its climate, so it starts to retreat because its ice is melting faster than it is moving, but it is still moving! Glacially borne debris will be pushed out the front of the glacier by the moving ice.

345

A *recessional moraine* is produced by a retreating glacier (Fig. 25-4 and Fig. 25-5). As the climate warms, the glacier retreats back in the direction of its area of origin a few miles—to the point it is again in equilibrium with its climate, this allows a recessional moraine to form, because the ice is moving but the glacier itself is not advancing.

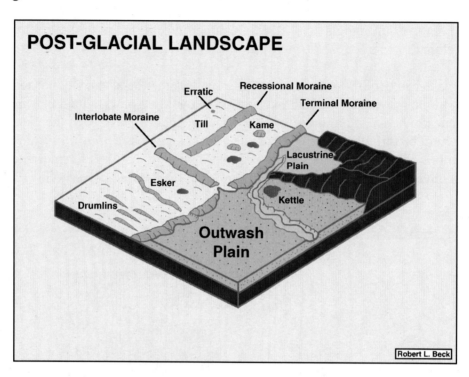

Figure 25-4. Postglacial Landscape

Figure 25-5. Recessional Moraine, Northern Indiana
(Robert L. Beck photo)

Continental glaciers usually do not advance as a single sheet of ice. Instead they advance as separate *lobes* of ice that eventually might collide with each other. Sand, gravel, boulders, and other debris collects in the depressional areas between lobes. When the glacier melts this debris emerges as an ***interlobate moraine***, which points in the direction of the ice movement (Fig. 25-4).

Streams flowing in, or on top of, the glacier also deposit earth materials that have been wrested from the ice by the action of liquid water. These streams often flow through tunnels in the ice, so the stream deposits are long and linear like the tunnels. When the ice melts, the stream-deposited material emerges as a long, sinuous hill known as an ***esker*** (Fig. 25-3, Fig. 25-4, and Fig. 25-6).

Figure 25-6. Esker, British Columbia
(Robert L. Beck photo, 1975)

When a glacier retreats rapidly or stagnates (stops moving), the material in the ice will be dropped to form ***ground moraine***, which is also known as glacial ***till*** (Fig. 25-4). Till deposits tend to flatten out the topography of the areas in which they occur, producing ***till plains***. The central one-third of Indiana, including Marion County, lies in a till plain. In Indiana this plain is known as the *Tipton Till Plain* (Fig. 25-7). It is named for Tipton County, the most featureless county in the state, which is situated near the center of the plain.

The till deposits of central Indiana have a lot of clay in them. During rainy periods the clay absorbs water and swells up, but during dry periods it loses most of its water and

347

shrinks. ***Swell and swale topography*** is the name given to the topography of clay-dominated till plains. These plains are not totally flat, for when the clay swells up it produces a slightly undulating surface (Fig. 25-8). The swales are the wide, shallow troughs between the swells.

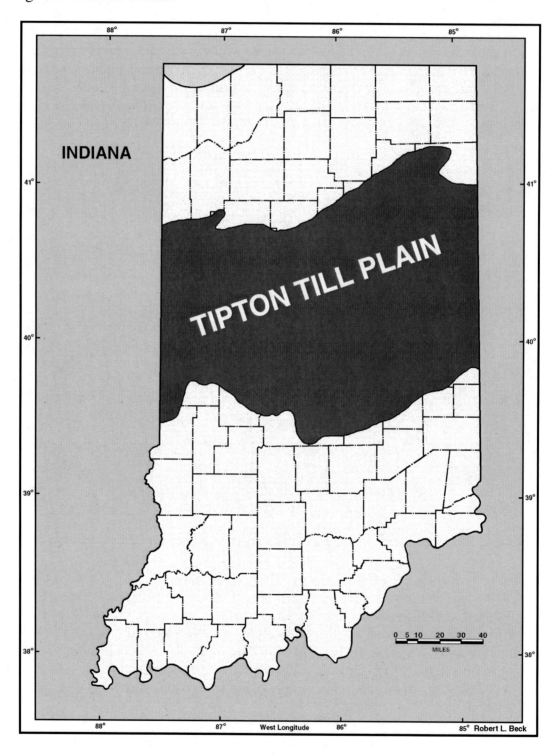

Figure 25-7. Tipton Till Plain

Figure 25-8. Swell and Swale Topography, Tipton Till Plain, Central Indiana
(Robert L. Beck photo, c. 1993)

Stagnating and retreating glaciers leave blocks of ice strewn about the landscape (Fig. 25-3) that often take a long time to melt, but when they do, the areas they occupied become depressions, which are surrounded by till and morainal deposits. Water often fills these depressions, known as **kettles**, to form small glacially formed lakes and ponds (Fig. 25-4 and Fig. 25-9).

Figure 25-9. Kettle, Northern Indiana
(Robert L. Beck photo, 1975)

349

Kettles are frequently found near **kames**, which are roundish hills produced by glacial meltwater deposition in close association with ice stagnation (Fig. 25-10). Kettles so often occur in conjunction with kames that the phrase, "kettle and kame topography" is commonly used to describe the physical landscape where they exist (Fig. 25-11).

Figure 25-10. The trees and the change in angle of the road mark the location of a *kame* in northern Indiana.
(Robert L. Beck photo, 1986)

Figure 25-11. Kettle and Kame Topography, British Columbia
(Robert L. Beck photo, 1975)

Water flowing off a glacier sometimes deposits huge amounts of sand and gravel in front of it to form an **outwash plain** (Fig. 25-3 and Fig. 25-4). Such a plain is found between Indianapolis and Chicago in the vicinity of Rensselaer, Indiana (**Goode's World Atlas**, p. 116). If the water is channeled into a stream valley, the sand and gravel that collects there is known as **valley train** (Fig. 24-24, p. 333).

Continental glaciers also produce **drumlins**, which are long, linear deposits that point in the direction the ice was moving (Fig. 25-4 and Fig. 25-12). The processes that produce drumlins are not known, but it is suspected they form when glacial ice reshapes deposits left by earlier glaciers.

Figure 25-12. This *drumlin*, in northern Michigan, is covered with coniferous trees.
(Robert L. Beck photo, 1992)

Large rocks and boulders dropped by a glacier are known as **erratics** (Fig. 25-13). Erratics might be found individually or in groups. In Indiana, they often mark the position of moraines. Farmers in the state pile them up in the corners of fields to keep them out of the way of farm machinery (Fig. 25-14). The fields behind our house in rural Putnam County were filled with crystalline erratics when we moved here in 2001. Indiana's bedrock consists of sedimentary rocks, so I knew these rocks had to have been carried in by a glacier and dropped when the ice melted. The abundance of them leads me to believe our house is situated on a moraine, probably the terminal moraine of the Wisconsin glacier. I asked the landowner if I could collect them to use around my flowerbeds. He readily agreed, for I was doing him a favor by supplying the labor to remove them from the fields. They are outstanding substitutes for plastic or wooden edging, for they do not rot, they are part of the natural landscape, and they are quite colorful and interesting.

Figure 25-13. Erratic, Central Indiana
(Robert L. Beck photo, c. 1983)

Figure 25-14. Pile of Erratics, Northern Indiana
(Robert L. Beck photo, 1975)

Mountain Glaciers

Glaciers that form in high altitudes are known as mountain glaciers, but some people prefer to call them *alpine glaciers* or *valley glaciers* (Fig. 25-15). These glaciers originate in *cirques*, which are bowl-shaped depressions high in the mountains (Fig. 25-16). The growth of the glacier eventually causes its ice to move out of the cirque and down into a valley, hence the name *valley glacier*.

Figure 25-15. Mountain Glacier, Alaska
(Robert L. Beck photo, 1975)

Figure 25-16. Cirques, Grand Tetons
(Robert L. Beck photo, 1975)

Like continental glaciers, mountain glaciers produce distinctive landforms. Erosional, toothlike ridges that separate valley glaciers are known as *arêtes* (Fig. 25-17). If several cirques erode into a mountain from many sides, the isolated mountain peak is then known as a *horn* (Fig. 25-18). If two cirques erode through the ridge separating them they create a mountain pass known as a *col* (Fig. 25-18).

Figure 25-17. Arêtes, Western Canada
(Deborah Melton photo, 2004)

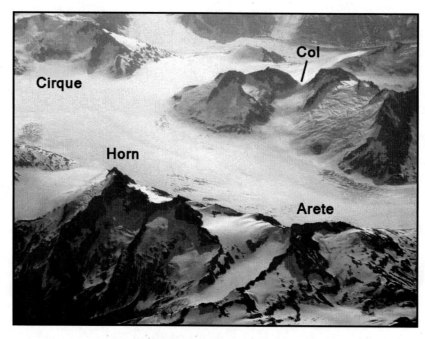

Figure 25-18. Mountain Glacial Landforms, Western Canada
(Deborah Melton photo, 2004)

Glaciers moving through mountain valleys erode into the sides of the valley causing them to become fairly wide. After the ice melts away it is easy to see where a mountain glacier has been, for the V-shaped valleys that were initially shaped by stream erosion will be replaced by **U-shaped valleys** shaped by glacial erosion (Fig. 25-19). Glacial erosion of mountain valleys also tends to straighten stream-eroded valleys.

Figure 25-19. U-shaped Valley, Western Canada
(Robert L. Beck photo, 1975)

If the glacier melts away completely, the cirque where the glacier originated is likely to have a depressional area near the center gouged out by the glacier. These depressional areas are usually filled with water to form high mountain lakes known as **tarns** (Fig. 25-20).

Figure 25-20. Tarn, Colorado
(Robert L. Beck photo, 1987)

As a glacier moves down a valley it might run into another glacier that originated in a different cirque. The glaciers then join to form a larger glacier known as a **piedmont glacier** (Fig. 25-21). Often small glaciers joining a larger one do so at a high elevation in the mountains. The melting of the ice might reveal that the small glaciers formed in high valleys vertically separated from the valley in which the larger glacier was situated. These high valleys are then known as *hanging valleys*.

Figure 25-21. Piedmont Glacier, Western Canada
(Deborah Melton photo, 2004)

Terminal moraines, recessional moraines, ground moraine, and outwash plains are produced by both continental glaciers and mountain glaciers. *Lateral moraines*, however, are only associated with mountain glaciers. These moraines form along the side of the glacier where debris lodges between the ice and the valley walls. A *medial moraine* is produced when two lateral moraines join through glacial coalescence, as during the formation of a piedmont glacier. From above, a medial moraine looks like a dark strip running down the valley embedded in the ice (Fig. 25-21). A medial moraine is the mountain glacier's equivalent of the continental glacier's interlobate moraine.

Indiana Glaciation

The Ice Age glaciers have greatly influenced the geography of Indiana. One cannot comprehend the landscape of the state without some knowledge of glacial processes and landforms. The state has been affected by at least three of the four major glacial advances. People who study glaciation have found Kansan, Illinoian, and Wisconsin glacial deposits in Indiana. The last glacier, the Wisconsin, is largely responsible for the landforms seen on the surface of the northern two-thirds of the state. Of course, Indiana's glaciers are of the continental variety; one must go to the mountains of the western United States and Canada to see abundant evidence of mountain glaciers. The five maps shown next specifically deal with glaciation as it applies to Indiana. The ancestors of the American Indians were probably here to see the last ice sheet.

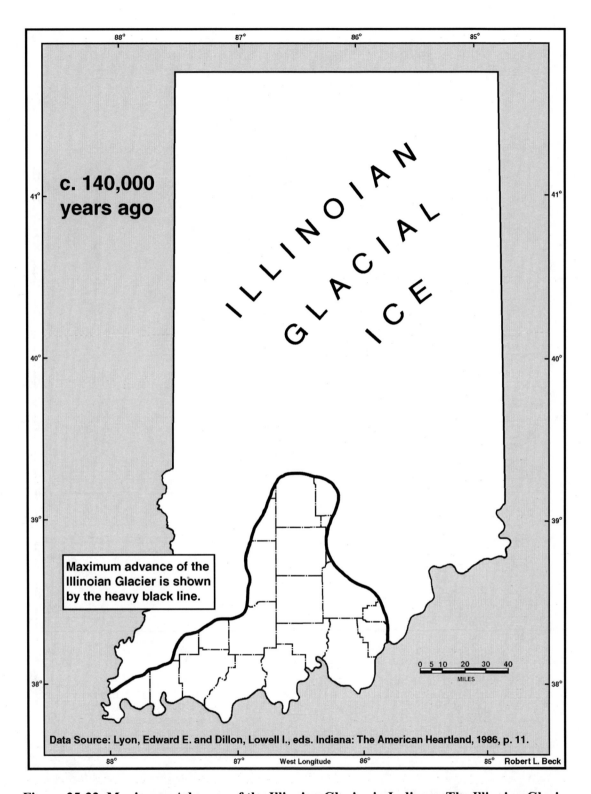

Figure 25-22. Maximum Advance of the Illinoian Glacier in Indiana. The Illinoian Glacier was the third of the four major Pleistocene Ice Age glaciers, and it advanced farther south than any other Ice Age glacier. The hills of southern Indiana kept it out of the south-central part of the state. The lack of hills in the lower Wabash River valley allowed it to advance as far south as the 38th parallel in Indiana and Illinois.

357

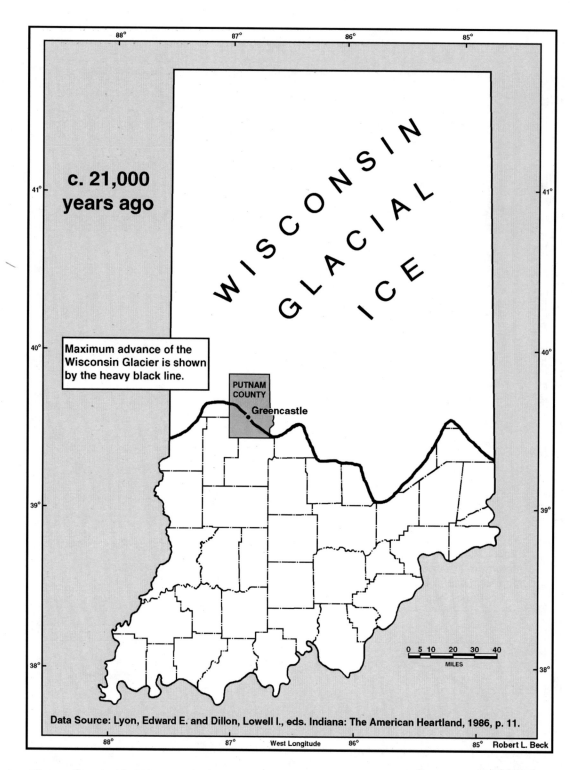

c. 21,000 years ago

WISCONSIN GLACIAL ICE

Maximum advance of the Wisconsin Glacier is shown by the heavy black line.

PUTNAM COUNTY

Greencastle

0 5 10 20 30 40
MILES

Data Source: Lyon, Edward E. and Dillon, Lowell I., eds. Indiana: The American Heartland, 1986, p. 11.

West Longitude

Robert L. Beck

Figure 25-23. Maximum Advance of the Wisconsin Glacier in Indiana. The Wisconsin Glacier was the fourth and last of the major Pleistocene Ice Age glaciers. Southwestern Putnam County was covered by Illinoian ice, but not Wisconsin ice. The Sangamon interglacial stage was situated between the Illinoian and Wisconsin Glaciers. The Wisconsin Glacier created the Tipton Till Plain (Fig. 25-7). Northern and eastern Putnam County has gently rolling swell and swale topography, but southwestern Putnam County is hilly. The city of Greencastle is situated on the terminal moraine of the Wisconsin Glacier.

358

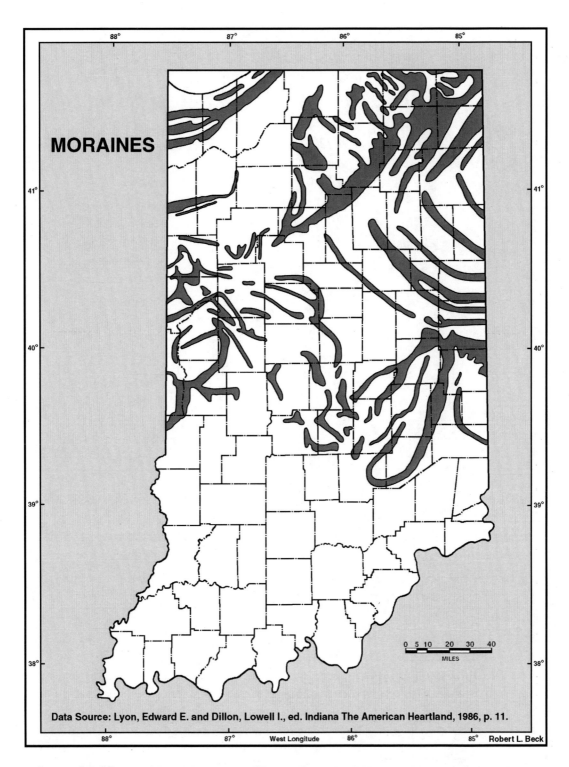

MORAINES

Data Source: Lyon, Edward E. and Dillon, Lowell I., ed. Indiana The American Heartland, 1986, p. 11.

Robert L. Beck

Figure 25-24. The recessional, interlobate, and terminal moraine deposits of Indiana are a legacy of the Wisconsin Glacier. Many of these deposits are hard to see in the field, for often only subtle differences separate a morainal deposit from the areas of the landscape around it. The Packerton Moraine, which extends southwesterly from Steuben County to Carroll County, is one of the largest interlobate moraines in the United States. It helped form the abundance of lakes in northeastern Indiana.

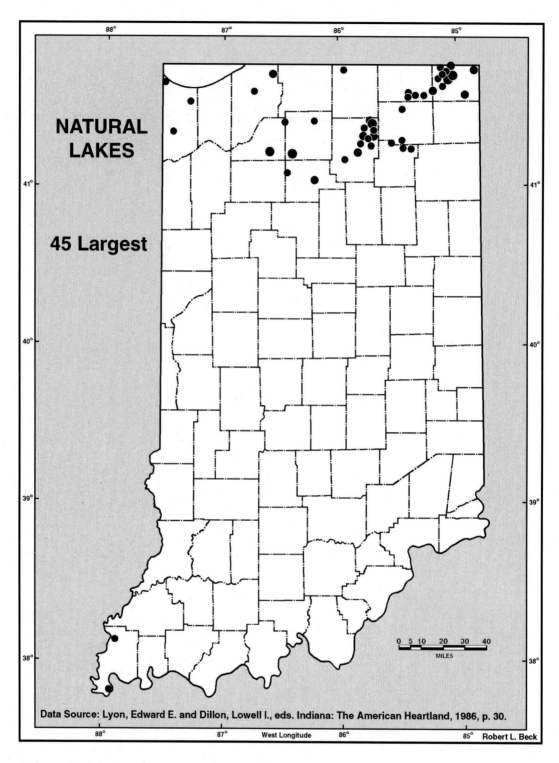

NATURAL LAKES

45 Largest

Data Source: Lyon, Edward E. and Dillon, Lowell I., eds. Indiana: The American Heartland, 1986, p. 30.

West Longitude

Robert L. Beck

Figure 25-25. Forty-three of the 45 largest natural lakes of Indiana are a legacy of the Wisconsin Glacier. The two lakes in Posey County, in the southwestern corner of the state, are oxbow lakes. Indiana has hundreds of lakes and ponds in the karst region near Orleans, but those water bodies, although natural, are too small to show up on this map.

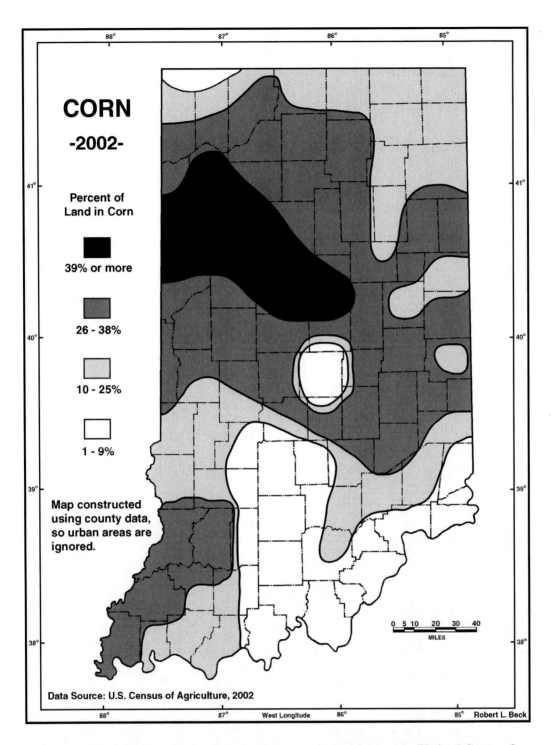

Figure 25-26. The *Corn Belt* stretches across the midwestern United States from Ohio to Nebraska. The southern margin of the Corn Belt in Indiana closely matches the southern margin of the Wisconsin Glacier (and also the Illinoian Glacier in the southwestern part of the state). Soils derived from glacial material in Indiana tend to be fertile, so the strong agricultural economy of the state is directly related to the physical geography of the state. One cannot fully understand the distribution of agricultural production on Earth, and Indiana in particular, while being blissfully ignorant of physical geography. Physical features influence cultural features.

361

Module 25 Objectives

You should now be able to:

- Explain why glaciers move

- List the two main types of glaciers and relate them to their areas of formation

- Discuss the *interglacial stage* concept

- Describe the difference between *glacial movement* and *glacial advance*

- Identify, and briefly discuss, ten types of landforms produced by *continental glaciers*

- Identify, and briefly discuss, nine types of landforms produced by *mountain glaciers*

- Identify the areas of Indiana where one might expect to find Wisconsin glacial landforms

- Explain why there are so many moraines and natural lakes in northern Indiana relative to southern Indiana

Figure 25-27. American Bison Grazing in Yellowstone National Park.
Can you identify the four spheres of the physical world in this photograph?
(Robert L. Beck photo, 1975)

MODULE 26: SOILS

It is fitting to have a module on soils positioned near the end of an introductory physical geography textbook, for to understand the distribution of soils requires knowledge of weather, climate, vegetation, rocks, and erosional processes. Soils, in a sense, represent a synthesis of everything discussed so far in the course.

Soil Constituents

What is the soil? What do we find in it? The substances found in the soil are known as the *soil constituents*. Soil consists of four basic components: air, water, organic material, and minerals. In other words, soil consists of parts of the atmosphere, hydrosphere, biosphere, and geosphere all mixed together. Soil is often portrayed graphically as the unifier of the four spheres (Fig. 26-1).

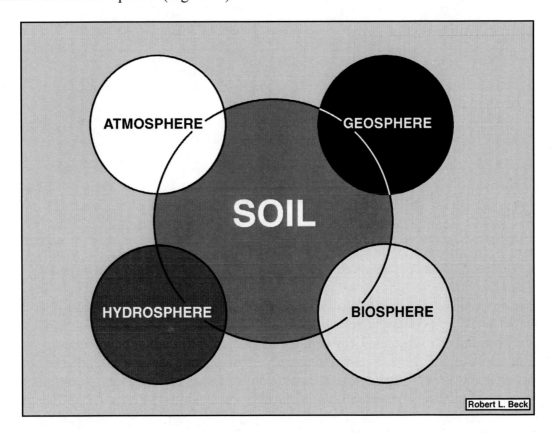

Figure 26-1. Soil and the Four Spheres of the Physical World

The air found in the soil is composed mostly of the same gases found in the atmosphere, but the soil has a much higher percentage of carbon dioxide in it than what is found in the atmosphere. Carbon dioxide makes up less than 1% of the atmosphere's volume of gases (Fig. 5-1), but it makes up about 10% of the soil's volume of gases. On the other hand there is little oxygen in the soil. Plant roots and soil organisms remove oxygen as they respire carbon dioxide.

Soil air fills the unoccupied spaces between soil particles. These unoccupied spaces are known as *pore spaces* (Fig. 26-2). When it rains water infiltrates into these pore spaces and thus displaces the air, but as the water works its way down into the ground evaporation will open up the pore spaces near the surface.

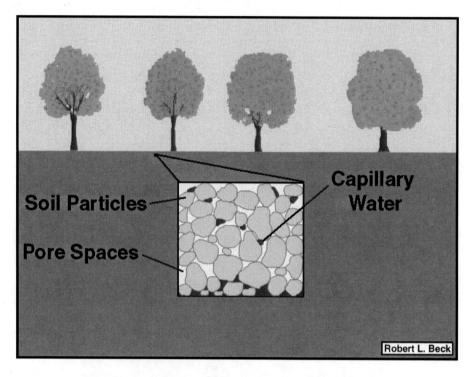

Figure 26-2. Pore Spaces and Capillary Water

There is a lot of water stored in the soil. Some of it occupies pore spaces, but much of it is held to soil particles by surface tension; such water is known as *capillary water* (Fig. 26-2). Water is also found in decaying organic matter or in soil minerals, especially clay minerals. People who work with clay soils, particularly gardeners like me, feel the water in the clay when we pick it up and squeeze it between our fingers. It is malleable because the clay minerals have absorbed water and are holding it in the clay particles themselves. When clay dries out it is quite hard to the touch and is extremely difficult to remoisten. Water is pulled into the soil by gravity after a rainfall episode or when snowmelt occurs. It can also enter via capillary action when soil particles pull up moisture from groundwater sources below the soil layer.

Animals, plants, dead organisms, and decaying matter are found in great abundance in the soil. Many worms, ants, termites, insects, spiders, and microorganisms live and die in the soil. During their lifetimes they work the soil by mixing soil particles, churning it up, digging holes, defecating, and secreting substances. All these activities generally improve soil quality—they aerate, fertilize, and improve the growing medium for plant root growth. Bacteria, fungi, molds, spores, and higher plants live in the soil. Like animals, plants generally improve soil quality. Microorganisms, both plant and animal, help decompose organic matter in the soil to produce *humus*, a substance that helps protect the soil against erosion by binding soil particles together. Microorganisms also aid living soil organisms by breaking down organic matter into usable nutrients for plant and animal growth.

As rocks weather and decompose, their mineral particles often end up in the soil and become part of the soil. Soil particles include sand, silt, and clay, which are classified by size with clay being the smallest and sand the largest. Some soil particles are a source of plant nutrients. Many of the sand particles in the soil consist of quartz grains that were originally found in granite, but were released to the soil when the granite was decomposed by weathering processes.

Genetic Factors

The substances and processes that interact to produce a soil are known as the *genetic factors*. Studying the genetic factors helps one understand how soils originate and how they are distributed over Earth's surface. Different types of soils are largely the result of different combinations of genetic factors.

The substance from which a soil originates is known as its *parent material*, the first genetic factor. Parent material, for example, might be sedimentary rock. But it could also be volcanic ash, sand, loess, glacial till, metamorphic rock, alluvial deposits, or any number of a variety of substances. My point here is that soil has to originate from something; it does not simply appear one day as a soil. Sedimentary rock is the parent material from which the soils have been derived in the unglaciated area of south-central Indiana, but in the rest of the state glacial till, loess, sand, or alluvial deposits have been the parent material.

Parent material plays a strong role in influencing soil fertility. Soils that form from volcanic deposits or limestone tend to be highly fertile, but soils that form from sand or shale tend to be highly infertile. Geographic variations in soil quality are directly linked to variations in parent material.

Time is a second genetic factor. A soil that has rock as its parent material took a long time to form. It takes thousands of years to produce a soil from native bedrock. In other substances, such as loess, soils form much more quickly, but it still takes a long time to produce the soil. In general, old soils tend to be low in fertility, for water has had a long time to leach plant nutrients out of the soil.

All soils form under some type of *climate*, the third genetic factor. Some areas of Earth are wet and other areas are dry; some areas are hot and other areas are cold; some areas have high sun rain and other areas have low sun rain; some areas have extensive cloud cover and some areas have little cloud cover. All these variations affect soil development and fertility. Soils that form in dry climates tend to have greater fertility than those that form in wet climates. The world's best soils are found in semiarid climates, and the world's worst soils are found in the tropics, where the climate is hot and wet.

Climate influences patterns of *vegetation*, the fourth genetic factor. Soils that develop in a grassland area will differ greatly from soils that develop in a needleleaf forest area, which will differ greatly from soils that develop in a desert environment. The world's best soils are found in grassland environments, and the world's worst soils are found in the forested environments of the humid tropics. Vegetation influences soil development through its root system and through contributing the remains of vegetative material such as leaves. Some vegetative material releases acids to the soil, which diminishes soil quality, but when vegetation decomposes it also releases plant nutrients that aid in soil fertility.

Slope is the fifth genetic factor. All soils form in some topographic situation, from steeply sloped land to flatland. Soils that develop on steeply sloped land tend to be of poorer quality than soils that develop on flatland. Slope contributes to rapid runoff, which reduces soil quality through erosion. Flat soils tend to be deeply developed and less susceptible to erosion, but if they form in a wetland environment they can become waterlogged, which reduces soil fertility.

Using the five genetic factors, one can make some very general statements about soil quality (Fig. 26-3). In Indiana, our best soils are found in Benton County in the northwestern part of the state. Our worst soils are found in Crawford County, which is situated on the Ohio River in the southern part of the state (Fig. 26-4).

	BEST SOILS	WORST SOILS
Parent Material	Fertile	Infertile
Climate	Dry	Wet
Vegetation	Grass	Forest
Slope	Flat	Steep
Time	Young	Old

Robert L. Beck

Figure 26-3. Genetic Factors and Soil Quality

366

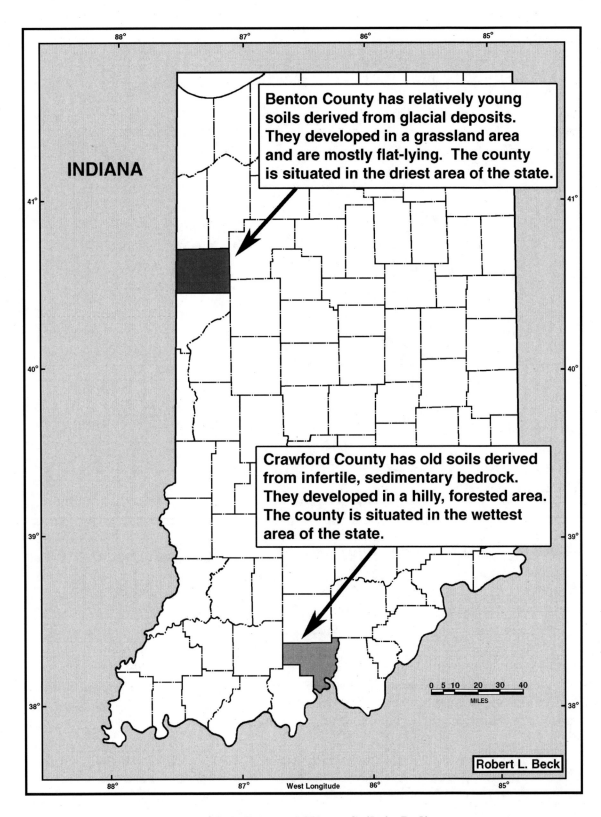

INDIANA

Benton County has relatively young soils derived from glacial deposits. They developed in a grassland area and are mostly flat-lying. The county is situated in the driest area of the state.

Crawford County has old soils derived from infertile, sedimentary bedrock. They developed in a hilly, forested area. The county is situated in the wettest area of the state.

0 5 10   20   30   40
MILES

West Longitude

Robert L. Beck

Figure 26-4. Best and Worst Soils in Indiana

Soil Texture

Soil particles mostly consist of sand-, silt-, and clay-sized particles. The Standard U.S. Classification of Soil Particle Size lists sand particles as having a diameter that ranges from 0.05 mm to 2.0 mm, silt particles have a diameter that ranges from 0.002 mm to 0.05 mm, and clay particles have a diameter less than 0.002 mm (Fig. 26-5). Soil particles are classified by size and not by composition! Some people have the mistaken notion that sand differs from silt on the basis of mineral composition instead of particle size.

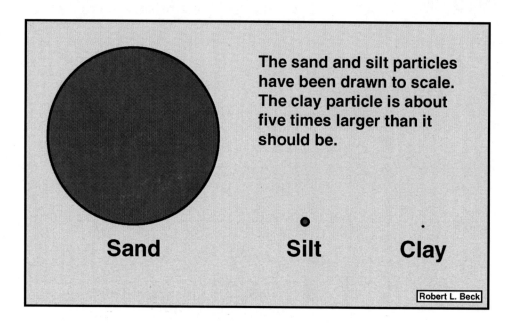

The sand and silt particles have been drawn to scale. The clay particle is about five times larger than it should be.

Sand   Silt   Clay

Robert L. Beck

Figure 26-5. Soil Particle Sizes

Farmers and gardeners know that soil texture influences crop yield. The best soils for raising food crops, most vegetables, and certain flowers are **loams**. These soils consist of an even mixture of sand-, silt-, and clay-sized particles. Loams are not too sandy, too silty, or too clayey. I add a lot of sand to the heavy clay soils of my garden in an attempt to turn them into loams. About every two years I buy a truckload of sand in the spring and have it dumped in my front yard in a relatively inconspicuous location. During the summer and fall, as I work my garden soils, I mix in a wheelbarrow load of sand every few days. Sand, however, lacks plant nutrients, so to maintain soil quality it is also necessary to fertilize it and to add organic matter, such as peat moss. Organic matter also helps the soil remain moist by absorbing water and loose by preventing clay particles from acting as a cement to bind the sand particles together.

People experienced in handling and touching soils in the field can usually tell if a soil is dominated by sand, silt, or clay. Sandy soils feel gritty when rubbed between the thumb and forefinger, silty soils have a silky feel, and clay soils have a sticky feel that has a tendency to ball up when rolled. Certain soils derived from loess have a lot of silt in them, so they feel silky to the touch. Loessial soils might also be sticky if clay is present in abundance.

Soil Profiles

A vertical cross-section of a soil is known as a *soil profile*. Soils develop vertically as the parent material from which they are derived weathers to deeper and deeper levels over long periods of time. Vertically developed soils form distinctive horizontal layers known as *soil horizons*. Different types of soils have different soil profiles and horizon development.

I show a soil profile of a typical Indiana soil formed under a forest cover (Fig. 26-6). The top layer of the soil is the *O horizon*. This layer has large amounts of leaf litter and accumulated organic debris in it, which is in various stages of decomposition. O horizons are common in forest soils, but they do not occur in grassland or desert soils—there is not enough organic accumulation in grassland environments to produce an O horizon.

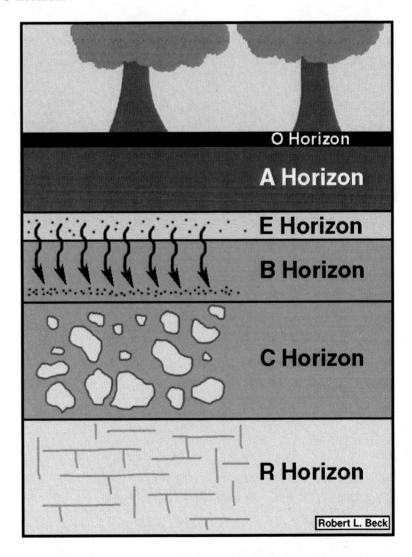

Figure 26-6. Indiana Forest Soil Profile

The *A horizon* is positioned beneath the O horizon. The A horizon is commonly known as the *topsoil,* and it is usually the most fertile horizon in a soil profile. The A horizon is typically darker in color than the underlying horizons because it has a lot of organic matter, including humus, in it. Plant roots obtain nutrients from the A horizon and seeds germinate in it. The A horizon feeds the world (Fig. 26-7).

Figure 26-7. Soil Horizons
(Robert L. Beck photo, 2002)

The *E horizon* is positioned beneath the A horizon. This horizon is known as the *zone of eluviation* because water moving through it (to lower levels under the pull of gravity) *eluviates* (removes) small mineral particles such as clays. The removal of these small particles produces a light-colored horizon relative to the horizons above and below it (Fig. 26-6).

The *B horizon* is positioned beneath the E horizon. The small particles removed from the E horizon are deposited in the B horizon in a process known as *illuviation*, so the B horizon is sometimes known as the *zone of illuviation*. The B horizon is also known as the *subsoil*. The clay particles collecting here often end up producing a *claypan*, or a hard layer in the horizon difficult for plant roots to penetrate.

The *C horizon* is positioned beneath the B horizon. This horizon is composed of partly decomposed parent material known as *regolith*. It is in this horizon that weathering is actively deepening the soil by breaking down the parent material into unconsolidated materials. The C horizon is not true soil because it lacks organic matter. Few plant roots extend all the way down to the C horizon.

The *R horizon* is positioned beneath the C horizon. In this horizon one finds the bedrock or parent material from which the soil developed. Bedrock in the R horizon is only slightly weathered . . . it is solid rock that has not begun to decompose.

Soil Orders and the Geographic Distribution of Soils

In the discipline of geography, the most common way to examine the world distribution of soils is to study the *12 soil orders* of the *Soil Taxonomy System* developed by the United States Department of Agriculture. The Soil Taxonomy System was formerly known as the *7th Approximation System*, and when it originally appeared in 1960 only 10 soil orders were recognized. A world soils map of the 12 soil orders is presented in *Goode's World Atlas*, pp. 44–45. I will be using that map to discuss the world pattern of soils. Color photographs of the profiles of the 12 soil orders, which I have included in black-and-white below, are shown on the website of the Natural Resources Conservation Service given as follows: http://www.soils.usda.gov/technical/classification/orders/.

I like to begin the study of soil orders by starting with the world's best soils for raising crops, the *mollisols*. I mentioned earlier that Benton County, in northwestern Indiana, has the best soils in the state. Those soils are mollisols, and you can see that northwestern Indiana is partially covered by them (*Goode's World Atlas*, p. 44). Mollisols develop in grassland environments, and they are especially good soils if the climate is semiarid. The soils of the central Great Plains of North America are very productive mollisols. A large mollisol belt extends from southeastern Europe, across southern Russia, and into Mongolia and northern China. A third large mollisol belt is found in South America and includes the famous Pampas region of Argentina. The low amounts of rainfall in these mollisol regions helps the soils retain much of their calcium—it is not leached out of the soil as is the case with soils in wet environments. Calcium is a plant macronutrient, so soils having an abundance of calcium tend to be very productive agriculturally. Mollisols have a soft character and they are dark colored, especially the topsoil, for it contains abundant amounts of humus derived from grasses and other herbaceous vegetation.

Mollisol   **Alfisol**   **Ultisol**   **Oxisol**
(Natural Resources Conservation Service photos)

371

The most widespread soil order in Indiana is the *alfisol*. These soils develop in humid forested environments where the temperature ranges from cool to warm. Alfisols tend to be fairly productive agriculturally, for they are relatively soft, easily workable, and generally fertile. Alfisols are not as productive as mollisols because they developed in wetter environments, so water has leached plant nutrients out of the soil to a greater degree than in the mollisols. Alfisols have subsurface clay horizons. Indiana was about 87% forested when it became a state in 1816. The soils throughout much of Indiana developed under a forest cover and became alfisols. In the northwestern corner of the state our mollisols developed under the grass cover of the Prairie Wedge.

Many subtropical and tropical areas of Earth, including the southeastern United States, have highly weathered soils with a low fertility. These soils are *ultisols* and they form in wet, warm environments where abundant precipitation has leached valuable plant nutrients from the soil. Ultisols have a reddish color due to the accumulation of iron and aluminum in the A horizon. They lack humus even though they form in forested environments. Rapid decomposition and weathering quickly remove much of the organic matter from the soil environment. Ultisols can be farmed, but to have high crop yields requires a generous application of fertilizer. Like alfisols, ultisols develop clay layers in subsurface horizons. In the humid, warm areas of Indiana near the Ohio River we find the poorest soils of the state, ultisols.

Oxisols are the most highly weathered and leached soils on Earth. Many people consider them to be the world's poorest agricultural soils. They are found in the hot, humid tropical regions such as in the Amazon Basin in Brazil and the Congo Basin in Africa (*Goode's World Atlas*, pp. 44–45). Oxisols form on ancient rocks, and they have a high degree of mineral alteration and profile development. Oxisols are thick, but they are dominated by oxides of iron and aluminum, the residual products of weathering and erosion, so they contain few plant nutrients. The oxides give the soil a deep, reddish color. It is ironic that the world's poorest soils are found in the most diverse ecosystems on Earth, the tropical rainforests. The natural vegetation does a good job of recycling the limited nutrient supply in oxisol environments, but when the flora is cleared to make way for large-scale agricultural production, the soil quickly becomes impoverished. Huge amounts of fertilizer are needed to sustain agricultural production in oxisols.

Soils that form in desert areas are known as *aridisols*. As you might suspect, these soils do not have much organic matter in them, for deserts have relatively low amounts of biomass in the ecosystem. Aridisols cover a large area of Earth. They are especially common in Africa, the Middle East, Central Asia, Australia, the western United States, and in southern South America (*Goode's World Atlas*, pp. 44–45). Aridisols have thin soil profiles, due mostly to the lack of rainfall. The lack of rainfall, however, also means aridisols have not been leached of plant nutrients; some aridisols are quite productive agriculturally if irrigated. Salt accumulation at the surface is a constant threat in aridisol ecosystems. Capillary action pulls water to the surface, and when it evaporates, salt residue is left behind. Poor irrigation practices can also result in salt buildup if the irrigation water is allowed to remain, and evaporate, on the soil surface.

Another group of tropical and subtropical soils are the *vertisols*. This is an unusual soil found in heavy clay areas where there are pronounced wet and dry seasons. India, Australia, and parts of East Africa have most of the world's vertisols (*Goode's World Atlas*, pp. 44–45). The alternating periods of wetness and dryness cause the soil clays to absorb water during the wet season and then lose it during the dry season. When the soil dries out the clays shrink producing cracks in the soil that are sometimes 1 inch wide and 36 inches deep. Substances from the surface, such as organic matter, will fall into these cracks producing a mixing effect in the soil. When the soil is exposed to the next round of rainfall, the cracks close up sealing the accumulated organic matter in the lower part of the soil. The word *vertisol* is derived from the word **invert**, which, as you know, means a turned around condition. Vertisols turn themselves over with next year's dry season. The turning effect of vertisols inhibits the formation of distinctive soil horizons.

Most of Earth's *spodosols* are found in the middle latitudes and in the subpolar latitudes. They are common around the Great Lakes in North America, but they also extend into the Canadian Shield of Quebec, Ontario, and Manitoba. In Europe, spodosols dominate much of eastern Scandinavia and the northern sections of European Russia (*Goode's World Atlas*, pp. 44–45). Spodosols form in sandy environments where coniferous trees dominate forest composition. These soils are highly acidic with the upper layers of the soil being light-colored, a product of extensive leaching. Subsurface horizons, however, are dark or reddish in color where iron, aluminum, or organic matter has accumulated through the illuviation process. O horizons commonly occur in spodosols, but the organic matter in these horizons is mostly composed of the highly acidic needles of evergreen trees such as pine, hemlock, spruce, and fir.

Aridisol **Vertisol** **Spodosol** **Histosol**
(Natural Resources Conservation Service photos)

Another group of soils found mostly in the middle to high latitudes are the *histosols*. These are soils that form in areas with a high concentration of organic matter, such as in peat bogs. They are typically waterlogged at all times and grow thicker through the continued accumulation of organic matter deposited on top of the soil. The huge amounts of organic matter in the soil gives histosols a very dark color. They are acidic and are fertile only to water-tolerant plants. When drained, histosols can become productive agriculturally, for the organic matter in the soil does help produce a loose, easily workable soil. However, if a histosol is allowed to thoroughly dry out it is likely to shrink, to become susceptible to wind erosion, and might become a fire hazard. Histosols are considered to be the least important of the 12 soil orders. They occupy only a small amount of Earth's surface, mostly in areas covered by the Pleistocene ice sheets.

Entisols are soils that have little development of profiles, so they are mostly very young, or recently formed soils. The *ent* is derived from the word *recent*. Entisols are the least developed of all soils. They have had little mineral alteration and they lack soil horizons. Entisols are widely distributed geographically. Note that entisols are found scattered throughout Africa, Australia, South America, and the Middle East. They are also found in eastern China, Spain, northern Canada, and the Nebraska Sandhills (***Goode's World Atlas***, pp. 44–45). Most of Earth's entisols are derived from parent material consisting of sand deposits. Sand does not alter easily chemically, so profile development in the soil is extremely limited. Further, if the sand is located in a dry, or semiarid, area the lack of rainfall further inhibits profile development.

To me, the ***inceptisols*** are the hardest soils to perceive mentally. They are young soils, but not as young as the entisols. They are best characterized as being immature. Inceptisols commonly occur along rivers where alluvial deposits constitute the parent material of the soil. Inceptisols, however, are also found in mountainous areas and in the high latitudes where soil profile development is lacking. Soil horizon development is present in inceptisols, but it is so faint that it is hard to observe in the field.

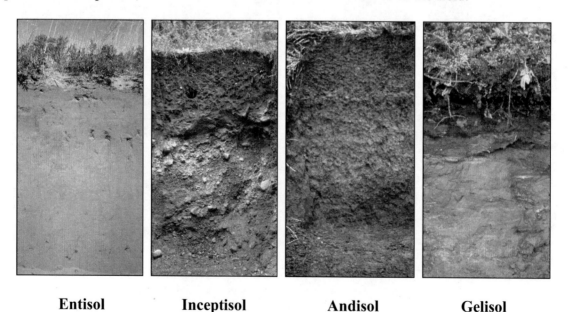

Entisol   **Inceptisol**   **Andisol**   **Gelisol**
(Natural Resources Conservation Service photos)

374

Soils derived from volcanic ash as the parent material are known as ***andisols***. This soil order was not shown on the soils map in the 21st edition of ***Goode's World Atlas***, but it is shown in the 22nd edition. Andisols are mostly found where subduction is occurring, so they form linear soil belts such as on the islands of Java and Sumatra. They are also found in Japan, Mexico, and the Pacific Northwest of the United States. These soils are fertile because there has been little downward transportation of plant nutrients within the soil and because they have not been highly weathered. Most tropical soils are not productive agriculturally, but where andisols occur in the tropics agricultural production is high and so is population density.

Soils that form in high latitude or high altitude, permafrost environments are known as ***gelisols***. This is a new soil order that was not shown on the soils map in the 21st edition of ***Goode's World Atlas***, but it is shown in the 22nd edition. Gelisols originate in cold environments, and they develop slowly due to the cold temperatures and frozen conditions. Soil-forming processes in gelisols occur in the active layer of the soil above the line of permanently frozen ground. This active layer thaws out every summer allowing water and organic matter to mix. Gelisols are the most common soils in the tundra and polar areas of Earth. They are young soils with minimal development of profiles. Before they became recognized as a soil order of their own, they were considered to be one of the ***inceptisols***.

Module 26 Objectives

You should now be able to:

- List, and briefly discuss, the four soil constituents

- Define the following phrases or words: *pore spaces, capillary water, humus, parent material, loam, regolith, zone of eluviation, zone of illuviation, 7th Approximation System*

- List the five *genetic factors* of soil formation

- Identify the best and worst soils of Indiana

- Compose some general statements about soil quality using the genetic factors

- Differentiate among *sand*, *silt*, and *clay*

- Compare and contrast a *soil profile* with a *soil horizon*

- Arrange, from top to bottom, soil horizons in an Indiana soil

- Compare and contrast the horizons found in Indiana's soils

- Compare and contrast the 12 soil orders of the *Soil Taxonomy System*

- Describe the geographic distribution of the 12 soil orders

Figure 26-8. Much of the area of Indiana north of the Wisconsin glacial boundary (p. 354) was a giant wetland at the time of European settlement. A major effort to install drainage tiles and drainage ditches to dry out Indiana's wetlands began in the 1870s. Today, a high percentage of Indiana's soils are artificially drained. In this photograph note the straightness of the drainage ditch and observe the drainage pipe poking through the left bank. Drainage tiles buried beneath the adjacent fields carry subsurface water out of the fields and discharge it into the drainage ditch via the pipe. The drainage ditch joins with a nearby stream, which, in this case, will carry it to a larger stream and thence ultimately dump it into the Gulf of Mexico.
(Robert L. Beck photo, 1986)

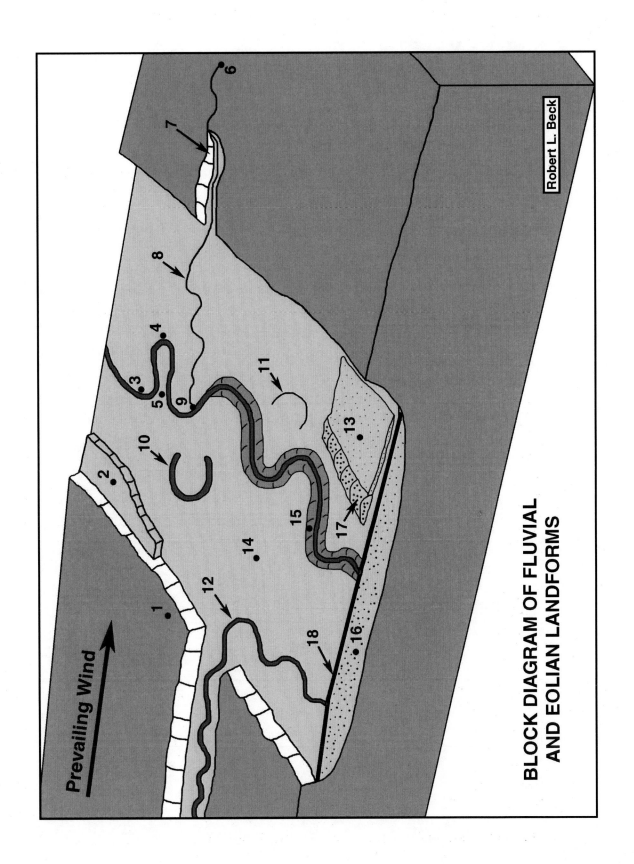

Prevailing Wind

Robert L. Beck

BLOCK DIAGRAM OF FLUVIAL AND EOLIAN LANDFORMS

GEOLOGIC TIME CHART

ERA	PERIOD	LENGTH
Cenozoic	Quaternary	2 million years
	Tertiary	63 million years
65 mya Mesozoic	Cretaceous	81 million years
	Jurassic	62 million years
	Triassic	37 million years
245 mya Paleozoic	Permian	41 million years
	Pennsylvanian	39 million years
	Mississippian	35 million years
	Devonian	50 million years
	Silurian	30 million years
	Ordovician	60 million years
	Cambrian	44 million years
544 mya Proterozoic Archaean Hadean	Precambrian	3,956 million years

Robert L. Beck

MODULE 27: COASTS

A high percentage of the world's population lives on or near a coast. Some of the world's largest cities are adjacent to the sea, for example: New York, Los Angeles, Tokyo, Osaka, Shanghai, Manila, Jakarta, Rio de Janeiro, and Bombay. Other large cities are only a few miles inland, these include London, Rome, Seoul, Sao Paulo, and Calcutta. In addition, hundreds of millions of rural people live near the sea in East Asia, South Asia, and Latin America. While coasts might not seem too important to a person like me living in central Indiana, they are of great importance to the people living on or near them, so I have included this module in the textbook for that reason.

The Rise and Fall of Coastlines

Various coasts around Earth have either emerged from the ocean or have submerged beneath it, so one should not view Earth's coastlines as holding to fixed positions. The position of the coast rises and falls in response to both natural and human processes.

COASTAL EMERGENCE

Coastal emergence is the name given to a coast that has arisen out the sea, and there are four ways in which this can happen. First, if the sea level falls, as it has done many times in Earth's history during periods of glaciation, then some of the land at the edge of the sea will arise above it as the sea falls to a new level. Second, crustal movements can uplift sections of the earth above sea level regardless of whether the sea is rising or falling. Third, the deposition of materials expelled by volcanoes or laid down by rivers can result in the formation of new land above sea level. And fourth, the growth of organisms can form a foundation upon which sediment can collect eventually causing the land to rise above sea level.

The Hudson Bay coast, especially its southern part, is one of the best examples of coastal emergence on Earth. Pleistocene ice covered the area now occupied by Hudson Bay about 20,000 years ago. The ice had been present there for such a long time, probably about 50,000 years, that the weight of it depressed the earth's crust. Hudson Bay filled with seawater when the ice melted. The removal of the ice sheet, however, has caused the earth's crust to slowly rebound because the weight of the ice has been removed. This adjustment process by which the earth's crust slowly rises in response to weight removal is known as *isostatic rebound*. The rebounding crust underneath modern Hudson Bay has drained off water from the edges of it to make the area of Hudson Bay smaller while contributing to seafloor emergence along its coast.

The same situation is occurring in the Gulf of Bothnia and the Baltic Sea in northern Europe. The Scandinavian ice sheet was positioned there 20,000 years ago, so when it melted the Baltic Sea filled with seawater. The Baltic Sea, however, is isostatically rebounding just as is Hudson Bay. The Baltic Sea is getting smaller in area as rebounding continues to occur, which causes coastal emergence along its shores—the old city center of Gdańsk, which is Poland's principal seaport on the Baltic Sea, is not as close to the sea today as it was when it was founded over 1,000 years ago.

Magma extruded as lava from volcanoes situated near coastlines contributes to the expansion of coastal areas if the lava solidifies above sea level. For example, the coastlines of Iceland and Hawaii continue to change as lava adds new land to these islands. The deposition of sediment by rivers works largely the same way, for new islands continue to form from deltaic sediments dropped by rivers. The mouths of the Ganges River in South Asia (*Goode's World Atlas*, p. 235) have produced dozens of small islands, in a swamp region known as the *Sundarbans*, at the head of the Bay of Bengal. In addition, the growth of coral reefs near the edges of landmasses sometimes results in the formation of low islands, as in the Bahamas.

COASTAL SUBMERGENCE

Coastal submergence occurs when the sea level rises or when the crust sinks. Global warming has caused glaciers to shrink worldwide. I am not aware of a single glacier that has grown larger in the past 60 years—they have all been melting away, but glaciologists use the term *ablation* to refer to a combination of melting + evaporation. The water in ablating glaciers has to go somewhere, so most of it eventually ends up in the ocean as it is drained off landmasses by streams. The sea level has been rising as a direct result of glacial ablation; coasts all over Earth are now being submerged under seawater.

The coast of Louisiana is the most affected area in North America by sea level rise (*Goode's World Atlas*, p. 91). The sea has flooded large areas of southern Louisiana not only because the sea is rising, but also because southern Louisiana is sinking (subsiding) due, in part, to lack of deposition of sediments formerly dropped by the Mississippi River when in flood. The confining of the Mississippi River to a fixed channel diverts the deposition of sediment to its delta instead of spreading it out over the coastal plain as it did during earlier times.

Rising sea levels cause the area of the oceans to expand and the area of the landmasses (continents and islands) to contract. Many of the world's islands that are now just a few feet above sea level will, in the near future, be underwater. People living near sea level should be worried about this, and many are. Some island countries, such as the Maldives off the southwestern coast of India (*Goode's World Atlas*, p. 236), are threatened with extinction unless the sea level stabilizes. The average elevation of the Maldives is only about five feet above sea level, which makes it the lowest country on Earth. The highest natural elevation in the Maldives is about eight feet above sea level, but construction activity by humans has raised certain areas of the Maldives several feet above that.

The depressing of the earth's crust underneath a glacier can cause the earth's crust beyond the edge of the glacier to rise in response. This process is similar to one in which a person pushes down in the center of a malleable substance only to see it rise up beyond the edges of his or her hands. As the weight of a Pleistocene glacier pressed down on the earth's crust beneath it, certain areas of the earth's crust nearby were uplifted as a result. One such area is in the vicinity of the Frisian Islands off the northern coast of the Netherlands (*Goode's World Atlas*, p. 191). Some of the land now occupied by these islands was raised due to the weight of the Scandinavian ice sheet pressing down nearby. With the melting of the last Ice Age glacier, seawater filled the depression left by the ice sheet forming the Baltic Sea. The removal of the weight of the glacier, however, has caused not only the crust underneath it to rebound, but also the subsidence of the lands marginal to the glacier that were pushed up when the ice was in place. The Frisian Islands became islands with the rising sea level produced my glacial melt, but they have also been subjected to periodic subsidence as the land beneath them sinks.

Types of Coasts

A coast is not simply a *coast*, for there are different types of coasts depending on the underlying rock structure, the action of erosion agents, the effects of biological organisms, the deposition of sediment, and the presence of faults. A cartographer who does a good job portraying coastlines on maps will show the type of coast through the use of appropriate linework.

One of the most common coast types is the ***ria coast***. The name of this coast is derived from the Spanish word for river, *rio*. A ria coast has been shaped by the erosional activities of rivers, which have cut through the coastline producing numerous indentations in it. Peninsulas jutting out into the ocean and rounded offshore islands are two other characteristic features of ria coasts. The Chesapeake Bay coast is a fine example of a ria coast (*Goode's World Atlas*, p. 117). The rivers presently emptying into Chesapeake Bay are now doing so while the sea is at a high level, but during the Pleistocene Ice Age, when the sea level was considerably lower, these same rivers were eroding the land surface now currently underneath Chesapeake Bay. These Ice Age rivers shaped the land by downcutting valleys and eroding hilltops. With the release of water locked up in the Ice Age glaciers, the sea level rose and in the process drowned the valley now occupied by Chesapeake Bay. The coastline of the modern Chesapeake Bay was thus shaped by the eroding actions of rivers, which were flooded as sea level rose with the ablation of the Wisconsin Glacier. The coastline of Chesapeake Bay is thus a submerged coast, for the old coastline of this area of North America is now underwater and out in the Atlantic Ocean.

Downfaulted or subducting blocks of the earth's crust along the coastal margin of a continent produce a ***fault coast***. This type of coast tends to be straight with few indentations, which reflects the subsurface fault line. The coast of northern Chile is a nice example of a fault coast, for the Nazca Plate is subducting beneath the South America Plate producing a coastline with few indentations (*Goode's World Atlas*, p. 168).

A coast carved by the action of glacial ice lobes is known as a ***fjord coast***. The ice lobes deepen and widen the valleys through which they move. When the glacier melts these steep-walled glacial troughs, fjords, fill with seawater. The western coast of Norway is often cited as the world's best example of a fjord coast (***Goode's World Atlas***, p. 184); for it is penetrated by long, narrow, and deep bodies of water separated from each other by peninsulas and islands. The capital of Norway, Oslo, is situated on a fjord. Other excellent examples of fjord coasts include the southwestern coast of New Zealand's South Island (***Goode's World Atlas***, p. 278) and the southeastern coast of Alaska (***Goode's World Atlas***, p. 126). Haines, Alaska, for example, is situated on a fjord (Fig. 27-1). The word *fjord* is of Norwegian origin; in Old Norwegian the word was spelled *fiord*. In Norway and Denmark the word is applied to almost any sea inlet, but in the discipline of geography the word *fjord* has a much more restricted usage referring only to a coast with steeply pitched, parallel, high walls smoothed by the action of ice. The seafloor of the fjord is often deeper than the seafloor offshore, for the weight and moving mass of the glacier gouged out its bottom. A submerged rock platform separates the deep water of the fjord from the shallower water of the ocean immediately offshore.

Figure 27-1. Fjorded Coast Near Haines, Alaska
(Robert L. Beck photo, 1975)

The coast of Texas and certain sections of the Atlantic coastal plain of the southeastern United States are outstanding examples of a ***barrier-island coast***. No one explanation is suitable to describe the origin of this type of coast. The typical barrier-island coast is composed of gently dipping sedimentary rock formations of low relief with long, linear islands positioned just offshore with the crests of the islands running roughly parallel to the coastline of the continent. Please observe the long islands positioned just offshore the Texas coast in ***Goode's World Atlas***, p. 123. The islands are named, and the major ones include: Galveston Island, Matagorda Island, San Jose Island, Mustang Island, and Padre Island. Barrier islands along the coast of North Carolina include Hatteras Island and Ocracoke Island, with Pamlico Sound situated between those two islands and the mainland to the west (**Goode's World Atlas**, p. 125). The Texas and Atlantic coastal plains are underlain with relatively young sedimentary deposits laid down on North America's continental shelf. Repeated crustal uplifts have raised these sedimentary deposits above sea level, so the Texas and Atlantic coastal plains are of young age geologically and are of low relief. The barrier islands offshore were built by waves and wind. Gaps between the barrier islands are known as **tidal inlets**; strong currents flow through these gaps either landward or seaward depending on whether the tide is rising or falling. Storms of great intensity can create new inlets in the barrier island, and such storms might also rework the sand deposits of the beach by pushing some of it over the barrier island from the seaward side to the landward side.

A type of coast confined to warm, tropical and subtropical waters from about 30° N. Lat. to 25° S. Lat. is the **reef coast**. A water temperature above 68°F (20°C) is necessary for dense coral growth, which produces the reef. To produce a reef, the seawater in which the coral live must be well aerated and free of suspended sediment. Coral thrive in areas subjected to wave attack from the open ocean, but muddy water prevents coral growth, so coral reefs are not found near the mouths of silt-filled streams. Coral reefs have flat tops; they are often covered with seawater at high tide and are exposed at low tide. There are three types of coral reefs—fringing reefs, barrier reefs, and atolls. **Fringing reefs** are attached to the shore of a landmass, which might be an island, and develop as a platform extending seaward from the landmass; they are widest where wave action is strongest. **Barrier reefs** are positioned out and away from the shore and are separated from the landmass by a lagoon; barrier reefs have gaps in them allowing water from breaking waves to exit the lagoon and thus return to the open ocean. **Atolls** are mostly circular coral reefs enclosing a lagoon but without any land inside. The coral forming the atoll most typically develops around a volcano, so the foundations of most atolls are resting on the undersea remnants of volcanoes. Weathering and erosion eventually removes the volcanic core by planing it off, which leaves behind the atoll with the lagoon occupying the position of the erased volcano.

A coast formed when a volcano erupts and ejects lava into the sea is known as a **volcano coast**. Because it is dense, non-explosive, and molten, basaltic lava makes a good volcano coast. Native Hawaiian Islanders developed cultural traditions based on the interplay between two powerful forces: erupting volcanoes that add land to the islands and the relentless ocean that wears it away. The two forces clash directly when the lava hisses as it flows into the sea.

Sediment dropped in the sea by large rivers near their mouths sometimes accumulates to produce a **delta coast**. Not all large rivers, however, have deltas. For example, there is no delta at the mouth of the Congo River, in Africa. The word **delta** as the name of these landforms was first applied by the Greeks to the triangular shaped deposit dropped by the Nile River at its mouth, which has roughly the same shape as the Greek capital letter delta (Δ). Delta shapes vary, for they are not all triangular. The Mississippi River delta, in the Gulf of Mexico, is of the **birdsfoot** type.

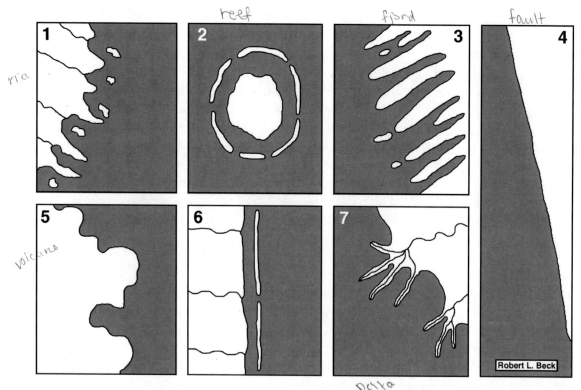

ria *reef* *fjord* *fault*

volcano *Delta*

Figure 27-2. Based on my written descriptions in the preceding paragraphs, and also by studying *Goode's World Atlas*, you should now be able to identify these seven types of coasts. The dark areas show ocean water and the light areas are land.

Figure 27-3. These small icebergs (foreground) have broken off a glacier (background) along the coast of Alaska. What type of coast is forming here?
(Robert L. Beck photo, 1975)

384

Waves

The rise and fall of the forward movement in the surface area of a body of water is known as a **wave**. Each water particle rises up in the crest of the wave and falls to its original position in the trough as the wave moves forward. The size of the wave depends largely on the speed of the wind, the direction of the wind, and the **fetch** of the wind, which is the distance over open water the wind blows. The height of a wave is the distance between its crest and its trough; the length of a wave is the distance between two successive wave crests. Waves experience little loss of energy as they travel across the deep ocean, but when they reach shallow water (as along a coast) the drag of the seafloor steepens the wave causing it to leap forward as a **breaker**.

Breaking waves hit coasts with enormous force. Particles large and small are carried in the wave and are thrust against the coast causing erosion, and sometimes producing distinctive landforms in sea cliffs such as caves, notches, and rock arches. Waves usually hit coasts obliquely, and not head on (Fig. 27-4). The rush of wave water up onto a coast is known as its **swash**, and the return of wave water back to the sea following the slope of the coast is known as its **backwash**. Please observe in Figure 27-4 that the swash (represented by the dashed arrow) is the landward extension of the wave hitting the coast obliquely. The black dot in the drawing shows a beach particle at various positions on the coast numbered sequentially. The swash picks up the particle at position 1 and carries it inland to position 2, but the backwash, which follows the slope of the coast, carries the particle to position 3 instead of returning it to its original location at position 1. The swash of the next wave will pick up the particle at position 3, carry it inland, and ultimately drop it at position 4 with the returning backwash. The beach particle (black dot) thus moves down the beach sideways due to the unceasing effects of swash and backwash. The sideways movement of beach particles is known as **beach drift**.

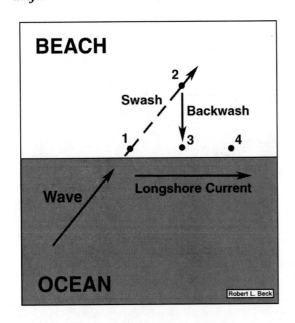

Figure 27-4. Littoral Drift

When strong winds push waves onshore the water level near the shore is slightly raised, and as it flows back to the sea a **longshore current** (Fig. 27-4) is generated that carries water parallel to the shore in a direction away from the wind. This current might be capable of carrying sand along the sea bottom near the coast in a direction parallel to the coastline. When this happens the process is known as **longshore drift**. Beach drift and longshore drift both move particles in the same sideways direction. When operating collectively the process is then known as **littoral drift**.

Coastal Landforms

As is the case with glaciers, streams, and volcanoes, distinctive landforms are associated with coasts all over Earth. Some of the coastal landforms are produced by erosional processes, but others are produced by depositional processes.

The term *coastal plain* refers to land of low elevation bordering a sea or ocean with a gentle gradient sloping seaward. Coastal plains can be produced by the deposition of sediment carried down from the land by streams, but they can also be formed through the action of waves eroding the coastline. In addition, coastal emergence of the continental shelf exposed by falling sea levels also produces a coastal plain.

Coastal plains are some of the most densely settled areas on Earth. The coastal plains of eastern China, for instance, supply the Chinese population with huge quantities of food needed for their sustenance. The United States has one of the world's largest coastal plains, and the southwestern tip of Indiana is not too far from it (Fig. 27-5). Evansville, Indiana, is situated at about 387 feet above sea level, but it is positioned 573 miles north of New Orleans, so the fall in elevation from Evansville to New Orleans is only about 8 inches per mile, which is almost flat. Rising sea levels, produced by the

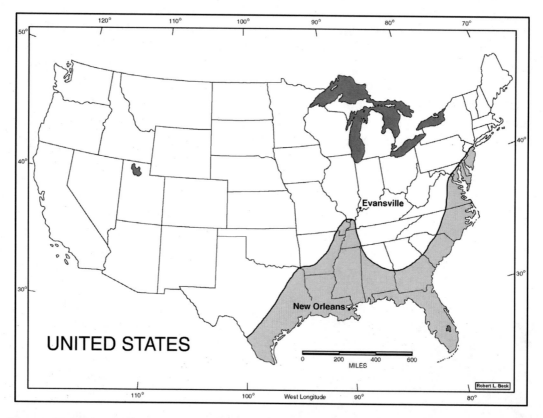

Figure 27-5. The Atlantic-Gulf Coastal Plain of the United States begins in the north at about New York City. It thence widens as it extends along the southeastern coast of the United States to wrap around the Appalachian Mountains in Georgia and Alabama. It thence extends north into the middle Mississippi River valley reaching all the way to southern Illinois. From there it curves back to the southwest to include Missouri's Bootheel, eastern and southern Arkansas, all of Louisiana, and coastal Texas.

melting of glaciers caused by global warming, is considered by many conservationists to be the greatest environmental threat facing humans today. If the glaciers melt away entirely, the sea level will rise dozens of feet inundating vast areas of the coastal plains devastating agricultural production and forcing hundreds of millions of people to migrate inland.

A *marine terrace* is another type of landform associated with coasts. In some ways they are similar to alluvial terraces found along certain streams, for they both often have a stair-stepped appearance when viewed as a cross-section (Fig. 27-6). The origin of marine terraces, however, is different than the origin of alluvial terraces. Marine terraces are formed when a sudden rise of the coast exposes a former section of the seafloor adjacent to a landmass. The exposed seafloor is now above sea level and it typically has either a flat surface or one with a slight dip seaward. Marine terraces are useful along mountainous coasts because they offer flat strips of land positioned between the coastline and the mountainous interior. Transportation lines are often built on them for that reason. They are also useful for building sites and can be productive agriculturally if the soil conditions are suitable.

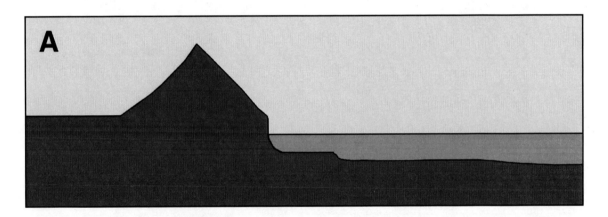

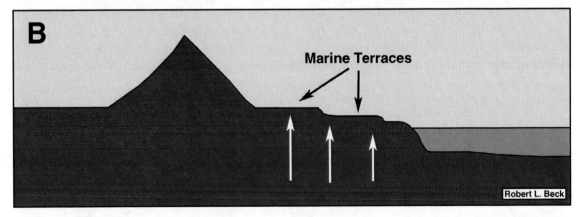

Figure 27-6. In diagram A the sea is hitting a cliff that is part of a mountain. Crustal uplift (represented by the white lines with arrows) raises the former seafloor above sea level in diagram B, which produces *marine terraces* between the mountain and the new coastline.

A coastal landform everyone is familiar with is a **beach**, which is composed of loose material that has accumulated along a seacoast or lakecoast near the limits of wave action (Fig. 27-7). The loose material making up the beach can consist of a variety of substances—sand, mud, pebbles, and volcanic debris are just a few examples. Beach material is classified by particle size, so while most people probably have a mental image of a beach composed only of sand, there are also gravel beaches, pebble beaches, cobblestone beaches, and many others.

Figure 27-7. This beach, along the coast of Maine, is confined to the head of a cove, so it is known as either a *pocket beach* or a *bay head beach*.
(Robert L. Beck photo, 1988)

I mentioned in Module 23 that waves can produce a landform known as a **spit**, which is also known as a **sandspit**. Littoral drift moves sand sideways along a beach. If a bay is present, littoral drift will carry the sand into the open ocean as a long finger of land to produce the spit (Fig. 27-8). Spits are attached to the seashore, but they can extend seaward many miles. Homer Spit, in Alaska, is one of North America's classic spits and it is nearly five miles long (p. 310).

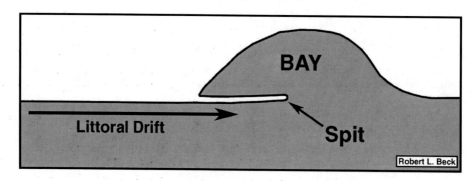

Figure 27-8. Littoral drift produces a *spit* if a bay is present.

Islands

An island is a landmass surrounded on all sides by water. So why is Australia designated a continent and not a large island, like Greenland? Well, it is a matter of opinion, for although Australia is surrounded on all sides by water and is therefore an island, it is so large that geographers and others refer to it as a continent based on its size. Further, by tradition Australia is one of the seven continents, so that also makes it a continent even though it is a big island.

Geographers use the phrase *archipelago* to refer to a group of islands. For example, the Canadian islands in the Arctic Ocean off the north shore of mainland Canada are sometimes referred to as the *Canadian Archipelago*, for they are a group of islands belonging to Canada (*Goode's World Atlas*, p. 85). Today, any group of islands might be termed an *archipelago*, but when the phrase was initially coined it referred specifically to the islands of the Aegean Sea (*Goode's World Atlas*, p. 201). One of the least known archipelagos of the United States is the Alexander Archipelago of southeastern Alaska (*Goode's World Atlas*, p. 126).

The terms *high islands* and *low islands* have been used to describe the various islands in the Pacific Ocean, but the terms can also be used appropriately in other areas of Earth. High islands have a mountainous core, which, in the Pacific Ocean, is usually either an active or inactive volcano. The island of Bora Bora, in French Polynesia, is a good example of a *high island*. High islands in the Pacific are ringed with coral (a living organism) that has attached itself underwater to the volcano. The growth of the coral produces a reef that might encircle the high island, but if weathering and erosion remove the mountainous core leaving only the reef behind, but with portions of it above sea level, it is then known as a *low island*. By definition, atolls are low islands, for they do not have a highland core. The island of Tarawa, which is part of the Gilbert Islands in the country of Kiribati, is a good example of a low island.

Another type of island is known as a *continental island*, which is a piece of a continent spatially separated from a nearby continent by seawater. The island of Trinidad, on the edge of the Caribbean Sea, is an excellent example of a continental island (*Goode's World Atlas*, p. 165). Geologically, Trinidad is related to the continent of South America, but it is an island because it is separated from South America by a strait. The geologic origin of Trinidad is therefore different that the geologic origin of the nearby volcanic and coral islands of the Lesser Antilles. Another good example of a continental island is Borneo, in the East Indies (*Goode's World Atlas*, p. 282). This island is very much different than the two neighboring islands of Java and Sumatra, which are volcanic islands associated with a subduction zone (*Goode's World Atlas*, p. 22). Borneo is positioned near the center of the Southeast Asia subplate attached to the Eurasian plate.

The bodies of wild animals, especially mammals, confined to islands are often much smaller than their relatives on continents. This concept is known as *island dwarfism*. The pygmy elephants still living on Borneo are one such example. There were many dwarf elephants confined to islands throughout the world, including in the

Mediterranean Sea, during the Pleistocene Ice Age. Fossil remains of these dwarf elephants, which were only about one-tenth the size of a modern elephant, have been found all over Earth. No one really knows why island dwarfism occurs, but it is probably related to the limited availability of resources on islands producing smaller animal bodies as a result.

Animals confined to islands move as passengers on the islands when plate movement occurs. The complex of islands in the southeastern Asian countries of Indonesia and the Philippines has a mix of animals related to the nearby landmasses of Asia and Australia. Alfred Russel Wallace, a 19th century biogeographer, was the first person to define the boundary line between Asiatic animals and Australian animals on the islands of the East Indies. His boundary line is today known as *Wallace's Line* (Fig. 27-9). Wallace was about 14 years younger than Charles Darwin, but Wallace's work in Southeast Asia led him to develop a theory of evolution independent of Darwin. The work of Wallace stimulated Darwin to publish his theory of evolution before Wallace could beat him to the press. It is interesting to note that both Wallace and Darwin developed a theory of evolution while studying animals on islands.

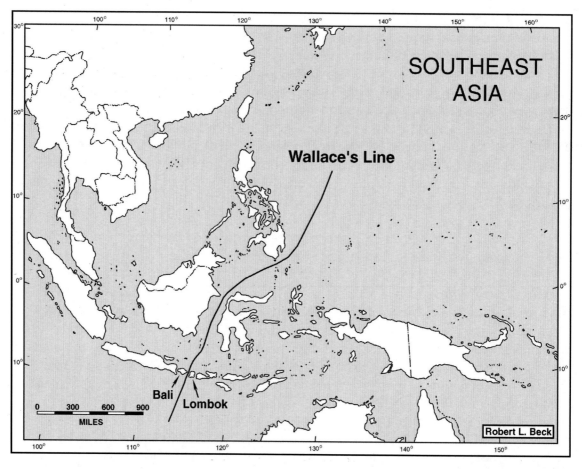

Figure 27-9. The line separating Asiatic animals from Australian animals on the islands of the East Indies was defined by biogeographer Alfred Russel Wallace in the late 19th century. Wallace developed a theory of evolution at about the same time as Charles Darwin.

Figure 27-10. These islands, along the coast of Maine, used to be hilltops on land attached to the mainland. Rising sea levels have turned them into islands. What type of coast is this? *(Robert L. Beck photo, 1988)*

Module 27 Objectives

You should now be able to:

- Contrast *coastal emergence* with *coastal submergence*

- Explain the processes by which coastal emergence and coastal submergence occur

- Identify seven different types of coastlines and explain the differences among them

- Define or identify: *coastal plain, marine terrace, archipelago, atoll, high islands, low islands, continental island, tidal inlet, island dwarfism*

- Explain why rising sea levels are such a major threat to the human population

- Describe why particles move sideways down a beach

- Discuss the similarities and dissimilarities of *beach drift* and *longshore drift*

- Define or identify: *fetch, swash, backwash, littoral drift, breaker, longshore current, Wallace's Line*

- Contrast *swash* with *backwash*

- Explain the differences among a *fringing reef*, a *barrier reef*, and an *atoll*

- Describe the formation process of a *marine terrace*

- Discuss why marine terraces are viewed as useful by humans in areas of mountainous topography

- Describe how *spits* are formed

- Describe how a *pocket beach* is different than a *barrier-island beach*

Figure 27-11. In this photograph, waves are seen breaking on the shore of Lake Michigan at the Indiana Dunes State Park. The silhouette of downtown Chicago can be faintly seen on the horizon. A lake boat, probably returning to Minnesota to pick up a load of iron ore, has just left the Gary, Indiana, lakeshore after having dropped its load near a steel mill. Indiana is one of the leading steel producing states in the United States, and virtually all the iron ore used to make steel in Indiana is carried into the state via the Great Lakes waterways.
(Robert L. Beck photo, 2007)

MODULE 28: DESERTS

Deserts cover about 20 percent of Earth's land surface, yet they hold few people, so in the subdiscipline of human geography they are said to be one of the five types of ***empty areas***; the other four are mountains, glaciers, swamps, and tropical rainforests. Few people, relative to all people on Earth, have much firsthand knowledge and experience working with desert environments. I think the popular notion of deserts is they are not too complex, for does not the lack of water prevent a diverse arrangement of physical features while also bringing a sameness to deserts? This short module is meant to dispel some erroneous beliefs concerning deserts and to introduce a few of the major landforms and other features common to desert areas.

A desert is defined on the basis of climatology, not geology. More specifically, in a ***desert*** the amount of water that can be evaporated away in a year by the solar radiation available (potential evaporation) is considerably greater than the amount of precipitation that actually falls from the sky. Some people define a desert simply on the basis of annual rainfall, with an average total of less than 10 inches being the defining criterion. Climatologists insist, however, that such a simple definition is inadequate; for one really must compare the amount of rainfall with potential evaporation to assess the amount of water available for use by plants and animals.

People have different opinions as to what constitutes a desert, but both cold deserts (BWk) and hot deserts (BWh) are found on Earth, and in Module 16 the different types of deserts were classified with respect to latitude, topography, interior location, prevailing winds, and ocean currents. What one person views as a desert another person might not, and it is difficult to precisely draw a line on a map separating semiarid and arid areas. The perception of a desert is often a matter of the experience of an observer. For example, when people from the humid east first encountered the Great Plains of North America they viewed it as a desert, and so they labeled it as the *Great American Desert* on some nineteenth century maps. Today, of course, it is realized the Great Plains is not a true desert—it is semiarid grassland with a BSk climate.

Landforms in deserts are easily seen because they are not masked with vegetation. People who study geomorphology and geology often perceive vegetation to be a barrier between the viewer and the substances that are really important—the landforms and rocks beneath the vegetation. To these people, vegetation is bothersome and unimportant. I have never met either a geomorphologist or a geologist who knew much about vegetation when compared to a competent biogeographer.

The distinctive desert landforms on Earth are a product of many factors. Yet when people think of deserts they often immediately think of cacti and sand dunes. Some deserts, however, have almost no vegetation, and sand dunes are also found in humid areas such as the sand dunes of northern Indiana. When thinking about deserts it is important to separate our perception of deserts from the reality of deserts—not all deserts are sandy, not all deserts are devoid of vegetation, not all deserts have thorny vegetation, not all deserts are constantly dry: some deserts have a lot of vegetation, some deserts have water features, some deserts are linked with specific landforms, and some deserts have diverse landforms while not being linked to any specific landform. To understand deserts it is important to rid one's mind of any preconceived ideas about them.

Sand Deposits

As mentioned in Module 23, a **sand dune** is a type of eolian (wind-blown) deposit. Sand dunes might therefore be found wherever a source of sand is available and wherever windy conditions prevail allowing a dune to form. These conditions, while often present in desert environments, are not restricted to desert environments, so sand dunes are also found in humid areas and in semiarid areas. For instance, individual sand dunes, now covered with vegetation, are one of the distinctive features of the Kankakee Outwash Plain of northern Indiana (Dfa climate); and in the Sand Hills of Nebraska, which cover an area of about 18,000 square miles (one-half the area of Indiana), thousands of sand dunes have been stabilized with a grass cover in a semiarid area (BSk climate). You should now purge any thoughts in your head that sand dunes are found only in deserts, for that is simply not the case. Just because sand dunes are common to deserts does not mean they are found only in deserts.

TYPES OF SAND DUNES

Different types of sand dunes have been named and are recognized as such in the geographic literature (Fig. 28-1). One of the most visually striking sand dunes is the **barchan**, which is in the shape of a crescent, almost like a crescent moon. The two horns of the barchan point downwind. The windward side of a barchan has a gentle slope, but the leeward side (inside the two horns) has a steep slope. This steep, leeward side is known as the **slip face**, and as sand is blown over the top of the dune and deposited in the slip face it comes to rest at an angle of about 35 degrees, which is known as the **angle of repose**. Some people prefer the name **crescent dune** to describe this type; the name **parabolic dune** is also used, but technically there is a difference between a parabolic dune and a barchan, for not all parabolic dunes have steep slip faces. Barchans are found all over Earth, so they are not restricted to Africa and Asia as some people erroneously believe.

Little barchans move faster than big barchans, so sometimes little barchans run into the backsides of big barchans, which gives the appearance the dunes are merging. Barchans occur individually or in groups. The arms of barchans can be separate or they can be touching the arms of adjacent barchans. Photographs of individual barchans are commonly presented in introductory physical geography textbooks.

Barchans originate when sand collects on the leeward side of some object, which might be a rock, a small hill, or a clump of brushy vegetation. The dune begins to migrate when a sufficient amount of sand has collected. Pebble-covered ground surfaces typically surround barchan dunes, so when the dune moves away from its place of origin a new dune might begin to form in the same spot if the producing object still exists. Barchans are often arranged linearly (as in a chain) downwind from the sand source and producing object. The word *barchan*, of Turkish descent, was originally applied to the sand hills of the Kirghiz (Kirgiz) Steppe of Central Asia, which is located in Kazakhstan between the Aral Sea and Lake Balkhash (*Goode's World Atlas*, p. 218). The Kirghiz Steppe was labeled in the 21st edition of *Goode's World Atlas*, but it is not labeled in the 22nd edition. Russians adopted the word to describe this type of dune, which is also known as a *barchane, barkan, barkhan,* and *balqan.*

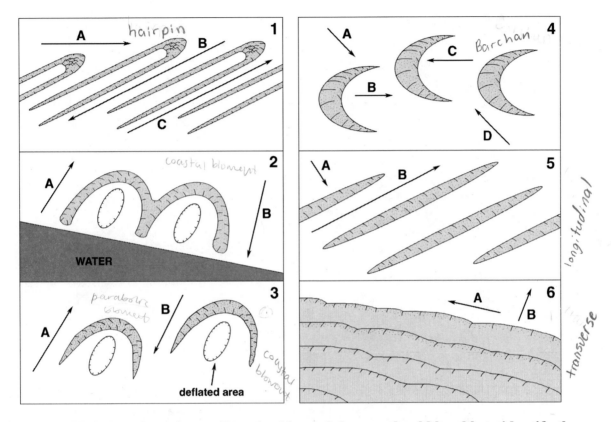

Figure 28-1. Based on the readings in this module, you should be able to identify the six *types of sand dunes* shown in this drawing. The numbers on the drawing do not necessarily match the numbered list of dunes presented in the readings.
(Robert L. Beck drawing, 2011)

A second type of sand dune is the ***coastal blowout dune***. Like barchans, coastal blowout dunes have a crescent shape, which is probably better expressed as a horseshoe shape. Unlike barchans, where the dune crest is bowed upwind, the dune crest of coastal blowout dunes is bowed downwind. In this regard the shape of coastal blowout dunes is the exact opposite of barchans. Certain sections of the eastern and southern shores of Lake Michigan are lined with coastal blowout dunes, some of which are protected for public access at the Indiana Dunes State Park and at Wilderness State Park in Michigan.

Coastal blowout dunes are found adjacent to sandy beaches (Fig. 28-2). As strong winds blow from water to land over these beaches they sometimes pick up sand grains and blow them inland. The winds often deflate a saucer-shaped area inside the arms of the dune, so the dune itself is positioned marginal to this deflated area on three sides. An abundance of sand must be present to produce coastal blowout dunes; many beaches do not have them due to lack of sand or because the prevailing wind is not in the proper location to produce such dunes.

Fig. 28-2. This *coastal blowout dune* was produced by strong winds blowing over Lake Michigan. It is located in the southwestern corner of Michigan's Wilderness State Park. The deflated area of the dune is positioned near the center of the photograph. The arms of the dune curve inland from the sides of the photograph.
(Robert L. Beck photo, 2011)

Transverse dunes form in areas with a superabundance of sand. There is so much sand that the ground is completely covered with it, which prevents the formation of barchans and longitudinal dunes. Transverse dunes take the form of wavelike ridges, which are separated from each other by broad, sandy swales with deep depressions. From above, transverse dunes resemble ocean waves, for the crests of the dunes (just like ocean waves) trend at 90 degree angles to the wind direction. Unlike ocean waves, which are highly mobile, transverse dunes give the appearance of ocean waves frozen to immobility. Transverse dunes typically form in sandstone areas subjected to a high degree of weathering; they also might lie adjacent to sandy beaches where strong winds blow from sea to land.

A fourth type of sand dune is the *longitudinal dune*. This type consists of a lengthy ridge of sand with its long axis running parallel to the direction of the wind. Longitudinal dunes often occur in dune fields and are positioned parallel to each other with flat surfaces separating the individual dunes. A single longitudinal dune can extend well over 100 miles. The Simpson Desert, which is part of Australia's Great Artesian Basin (*Goode's World Atlas*, p. 272), is noted for the abundance and length of its longitudinal dunes. Another area of Earth famous for its longitudinal dunes is the Rub'al-Khali (Empty Quarter) of the Arabian Peninsula (*Goode's World Atlas*, p. 220). In the Simpson Desert the axes of the dunes run north–south, but in the Rub'al-Khali they run northeast–southwest, which is reflective of the northeast trade winds.

Parabolic blowout dunes, the fifth type, develop on plains where the wind is strong and the vegetation sparse. These dunes form on the downwind sides of deflation hollows. The dunes have roughly the same shape as barchans, but the dune crest bows downwind like the coastal blowout dune. Parabolic blowout dunes do not have steep slip faces and might be stabilized with a grass cover in semiarid areas; however, if the dune does migrate downwind it might develop into a *hairpin dune*, which has two extremely long arms connected to each other by a tightly curved sand ridge. If the bow end of a hairpin dune is removed by deflation, the two remaining arms will no longer be connected to each other, so they will then turn into longitudinal dunes.

SAND SEAS

Areas of Earth covered with extensive sand deposits are sometimes known as *sand seas*, but in North Africa and Arabia they are known as *ergs*, and in Central Asia they are known as *kum* or *qum*. Two big sand seas in the Sahara Desert are the *Grand Erg Occidental* (western sand sea) and the *Grand Erg Oriental* (eastern sand sea). The locations of these two sand seas are shown in *Goode's World Atlas* on pp. 258–259. A third sand sea of the Sahara is the *Grand Erg de Bilma*, which is located in eastern Niger. In Turkmenistan one finds the *Kara Kum*, and in Uzbekistan a prominent sand sea is the *Qizilqum* (*Goode's World Atlas*, p. 226).

The Sand Hill region of northern Nebraska is a sand sea, but I have never heard anyone refer to it using that name. This sand sea is the largest sand deposit in the Western Hemisphere. The sand dunes in the Sand Hills have been stabilized with a grass cover, so they are not migrating (Fig. 28-3). Various types of dunes are found in the Sand Hills including parabolic blowout dunes, transverse dunes, and longitudinal dunes. The Sand Hill region is labeled on a map in *Goode's World Atlas* (p. 114). Many of the least populated counties in the United States are located in the Sand Hills. For example, Arthur County, Nebraska, has less than 500 people living in it, but its area of more than 700 square miles is about twice the size of many Indiana counties.

Figure 28-3. Grass-stabilized sand dunes in the Nebraska Sand Hills are seen on the horizon in this photograph. *(Robert L. Beck photo, 1990)*

Rocky Features of Deserts

Some deserts are known for their rocky features and not for sand deposits. In many cases the sand has simply been blown out of these rocky deserts and deposited downwind. In North Africa a desert plain covered with pebbles, rocks, and gravel is known as a *reg*, and if such conditions are present on a plateau surface it is then known as a *hamada*. In both instances deflation has removed the sand particles leaving only pebbles or heavy rocks behind. One such area is the *Hamada de Tinrhert*, which is positioned just south of the *Grand Erg Oriental* in eastern Algeria (***Goode's World Atlas***, p. 259).

Particles of various shapes remain behind in desert environments when wind removes sand and other lightweight materials. Over time, pebbles and heavy particles might become closely fitted together due to jostling in the wind, earth movements, the pull of gravity, and through the action of water. Salts in solution drawn to the surface by capillary action might cement the particles together with the evaporation of capillary water. A surface composed of closely fitted materials is known as ***desert pavement***, which is a characteristic feature of many rock-dominated deserts (Fig. 28-4). Desert pavement might also consist of bedrock polished smooth by blown sand. Desert pavement helps protect the land from further deflation.

A thin, dark-colored, skin on rock surfaces in hot deserts is known as either ***desert varnish*** or ***desert patina*** (Fig. 28-5). The dark color is produced principally by either manganese or iron oxides. Desert varnish is thought to form through the action of microorganisms, dew, and clay particles, which react chemically with the iron and manganese under the hot sun. Iron oxides give the varnish a reddish color, and manganese oxides give the varnish a blackish color. Desert varnish only forms on stable rock surfaces, so it is relatively common to see it on desert pavement or on large rocks that have had little exposure to precipitation and wind abrasion.

Figure 28-4. The flat surface in the foreground is *desert pavement* in Arizona.
(Robert L. Beck photo, 1987)

Sedimentary rocks formed from minerals precipitated from a solution due to evaporation are known as *evaporites*. They often form in small basins in desert environments with limited water inputs. Gypsum is a common evaporite mineral, so is halite (rock salt).

Figure 28-5. The black coating covering the center rock in this photograph is *desert varnish*. The artistic scratchings in the rock are *petroglyphs* drawn by American Indians many centuries ago. *(Robert L. Beck photo, 1987)*

Hydrologic Features of Deserts

A stream cannot originate in a desert (BW climate region), for potential evaporation is greater than precipitation. Streams, however, do flow through deserts, and such a stream, as mentioned in Module 24, is known as an *exotic stream*. Old stream channels are found in a few deserts on Earth. These channels were carved under past climatic conditions when rainfall was plentiful.

The Arab word *wadi* denotes a stream channel or valley in a hot desert or semiarid steppe. The use of this term is especially common in the Sahara Desert of North Africa and in the Arabian Peninsula. Wadis are typically dry, but they might also carry water after a heavy rain. The water table might be positioned just a few feet below the surface of a wadi. The Arab word *wadi* became the Spanish word *guadi* in river names when Spain was ruled by the Moors of North Africa in the Middle Ages.

In the Intermontane region of the western United States and Mexico, the word *bolson* is used to describe a drainage area not connected to the ocean by a stream (Fig. 28-6). Precipitation falling in a bolson typically evaporates, but if enough of it falls then some of it might run off and flow to the center of the bolson where it collects to form a shallow lake known as a *playa*. Hot conditions give the playa a short life, for the water in it quickly evaporates with exposure to the sun. Salts accumulate in the playa with repeated collection and evaporation of rainwater. Playas, then, are salt lakes often set in the midst of *salt flats* and areas of alkaline mud.

Figure 28-6. This *bolson*, in Arizona, is rimmed with low mountains. No streams flow out of it, but rainwater drains to the center of it sometimes producing a *playa*, which evaporates leaving the *salt flats* shown as a white strip just above the dark xerophytic vegetation positioned near the center of the photograph.
(Robert L. Beck photo, 1987)

The most famous salt flat in the United States is the *Bonneville Salt Flats* located in Utah (Fig. 28-7). This salt flat is part of the lake bottom of old Lake Bonneville, which existed about 15,000 years ago during the Pleistocene Ice Age. The climate was wetter in Utah then than it is now. Many lakes formed during this wet period. These lakes are known as ***pluvial lakes*** because they formed during a wet period in a normally dry area. The word *pluvial* means "relating to or characterized by rain." The Intermontane region

Figure 28-7. The Bonneville Salt Flats, shown in this photograph, were covered by a *pluvial lake* during the Pleistocene Ice Age. *(Randy Folker photo, 1999)*

400

of Utah is typically dry, but during the Ice Age it was wet due to the alteration of the world's rainfall pattern by the glacial ice. The Intermontane area returned to its dry condition after the glaciers retreated, so the lakes dried up. For thousands of years, during the period of glacial ablation, the winter season brought water containing salts to the pluvial lakes. During the summer the lakes would dry up leaving the salt behind. As the modern climate emerged the pluvial lakes finally dried up entirely. Lake Bonneville was about the size of modern Lake Michigan, so it covered about one-quarter the area of Utah. Its shoreline fell to increasingly lower levels as the warming climate evaporated the lake. Old shoreline levels around Lake Bonneville have been identified. Remnants of American Indian settlements have been found on the old shorelines, which are many feet above the modern salt flats.

The lack of vegetation in desert environments contributes to the formation of **mudflows**, which is one of the mass wasting processes identified in Module 23. After a heavy precipitation event, water draining out of mountains lacking dense vegetation is quickly channeled into gullies and streams. The water carries with it a variety of solid materials including liquefied mud. Upon emerging from the narrow confines of the canyon or channel in which it flowed, the stream water spreads out over the earth's surface as a fanlike sheet of water thus dropping most of its solid load as a result. Repeated deposition of solid material where a stream disgorges from a mountain range eventually produces a landform known as an **alluvial fan** (Fig. 28-8).

Figure 28-8. Two *alluvial fans* are seen at the base of the mountain range in this photograph. They have a fanlike shape with gentle slopes, which contrasts with the steep slopes of the mountains. The whitish flat surface in the foreground is the dried up salt encrusted bed of a *playa*. Note the mountains lack dense vegetation, so rainwater falling on them rapidly runs off. The photograph was taken in California's Anza-Borrego Desert State Park, which is situated between San Diego and the Salton Sea.
(Tim Brothers photo, 1992)

An area in a hot desert with water present to sustain plant growth is known as an *oasis*. The water might emerge from a natural spring, be part of a wadi, or be tied in some way to an exotic stream. The popular perception of an oasis is one of smallness, for do they not consist of a group of palm trees surrounding a waterhole with desert all around (Fig. 28-9)? Some oases are small, especially those in the Sahara Desert, but an oasis can also cover hundreds of square miles supporting a large population as along the Nile River in Africa or along the Euphrates River in Iraq.

Fig. 28-9. *Date palms* **are common oases plants in the Middle East and North Africa. This photograph shows date palms growing in the Coachella Valley just north of the Salton Sea in California. The Coachella Valley is the leading area of date production in the United States. Water is diverted from the Colorado River, via a canal system, to irrigate farmland adjacent to the Salton Sea.**
(Randy Folker photo, 1999)

Desert Vegetation

To survive, vegetation in desert environments must be able to live with minimal inputs of water, and such vegetation, as mentioned in Module 16, is known as *xerophytic vegetation*. Differences in temperature, however, also play a role in the distribution of xerophytic vegetation. This concept is demonstrated nicely in the two major deserts of the southwestern United States—the Mojave Desert and the Sonoran Desert.

The Mojave Desert and the Sonoran Desert border each other in both California and Arizona (Fig. 28-10). The Mojave Desert, however, is of high elevation when

402

compared to the low elevation of the Sonoran Desert. The elevation of the Mojave Desert varies from about 3,000 to 6,000 feet above sea level, so it has a cooler annual temperature than the hot Sonoran Desert, which has an elevation ranging from sea level to about 3,000 feet. This variation of temperature is expressed in the plants inhabiting the two deserts. The *Joshua tree* is a marker plant of the Mojave Desert, so it can tolerate

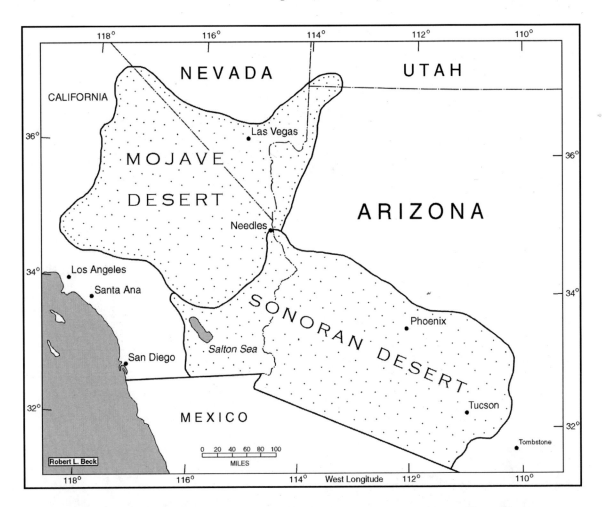

Figure 28-10. Southwestern Deserts. The approximate boundaries of the two major deserts of the southwestern United States are shown in this map.

relatively cool temperatures (Fig. 28-11). This is in stark contrast to the *saguaro cactus*, which, in the United States, is found only in the Sonoran Desert. Neither the Joshua tree nor the saguaro cactus is distributed throughout the whole range of its respective desert. For example, the saguaro cactus lives only in Arizona (and also Mexico) even though the Sonoran Desert extends into southern California (Fig. 28-10). The saguaro cactus is a symbol of Arizona and not California, so Arizonans use graphic images of it to promote their state as evidenced by including it on license plates of passenger vehicles.

The *creosote bush* is another common xerophytic plant found in the southwestern deserts of the United States. However, unlike the *Joshua tree* and the *saguaro cactus*, the *creosote bush* is found in both the Mojave Desert and the Sonoran Desert, so it is not a marker plant as are the other two. The *creosote bush* is one of the most successful of all desert plants, and its extensive geographical range is indicative of such. It has a deep tap root, wax-coated leaves, and is both bitter-smelling and bitter-tasting, so most animals do not bother messing with it. In addition, other plants typically do not grow near it, which reduces competition for water (Fig. 28-14).

Figure 28-11. Marker Plants of the Mojave and Sonoran Deserts. The *Joshua tree* (left) is a marker plant of the Mojave Desert, which has a cooler climate than the Sonoran Desert marked by the *saguaro cactus* (right).
(Robert L. Beck photos, 1987)

Figure 28-12. *Fan palms* indicate the presence of an oasis in the Sonoran Desert. These photographs were taken at California's Anza-Borrego Desert State Park.
(Tim Brothers photos, 1992)

Punas

Some people use the word *puna* to refer to a high, bleak, desert plateau covered with either extensive salt deposits or grasses (Fig. 28-13). It is a Spanish word derived from the Quechua Indian language. The *Puna de Atacama* refers specifically to a large plateau at a high elevation in northeastern Chile, northwestern Argentina, and southern Bolivia (***Goode's World Atlas***, p. 168). That salt encrusted plateau covers an area of about 69,000 square miles, which is slightly less than two times the area of Indiana.

Figure 28-13. This *puna*, in Peru, is situated at about 12,000 feet above sea level. Herd animals—llamas, alpacas, and sheep—are seen grazing the widely spaced grasses covering the puna's surface in the bottom photograph.
(Tim Brothers photos, 1997)

Module 28 Objectives

You should now be able to:

- Identify six types of sand dunes on a drawing and indicate their direction of movement with respect to the prevailing wind

- Define or identify the following phrases or terms: *angle of repose, slip face, empty area, barchan, deflation, erg, kum*

- Explain the difference between a *reg* and a *hamada*

- Describe the formation of *desert pavement* and distinguish between two types of desert pavement

- Contrast the formation of *desert varnish* with the formation of *evaporites*

- Explain the difference between an *exotic stream* and a *wadi*

- Define or identify the following terms: *bolson, playa, salt flat, oasis, puna*

- Describe how a *pluvial lake* is different than a *nonpluvial lake*

- Explain how the distribution of the *Joshua tree* is different than the *saguaro cactus* even though both plants are desert dwellers in the southwestern United States

- Compare and contrast the Mojave Desert with the Sonoran Desert

Figure 28-14. These creosote bushes, in the Sonoran Desert, are ringed with barren land, for other plants do not want to grow near them. *(Robert L. Beck photo, 1987)*

406

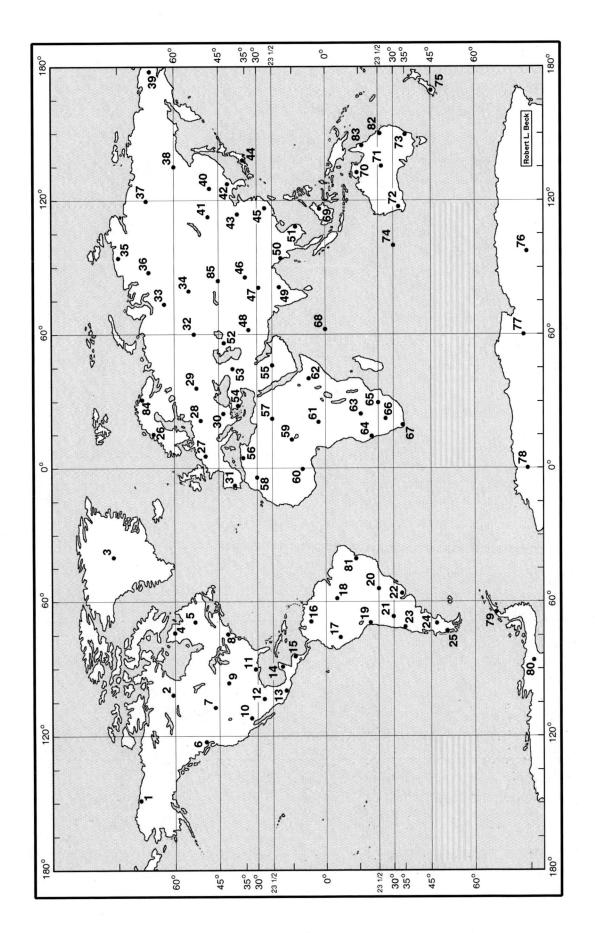

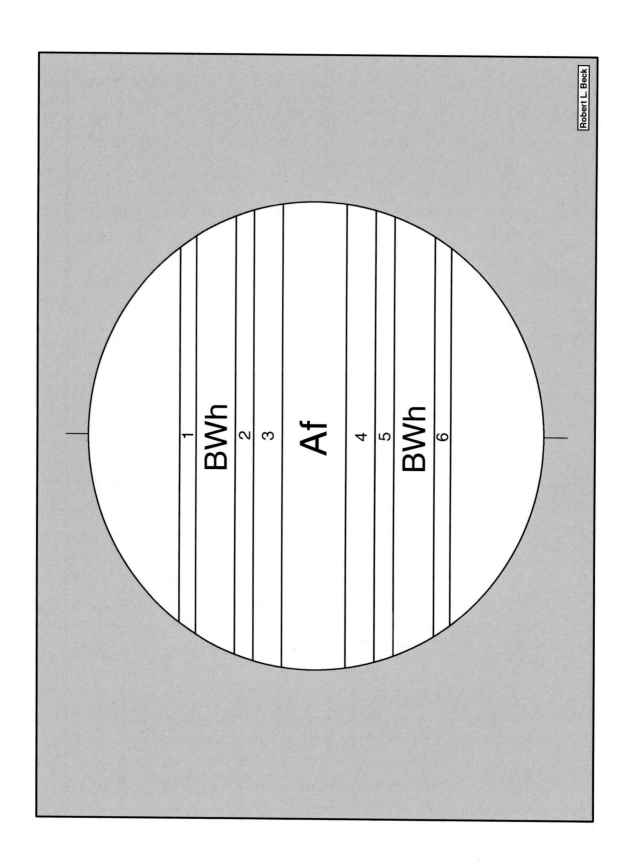

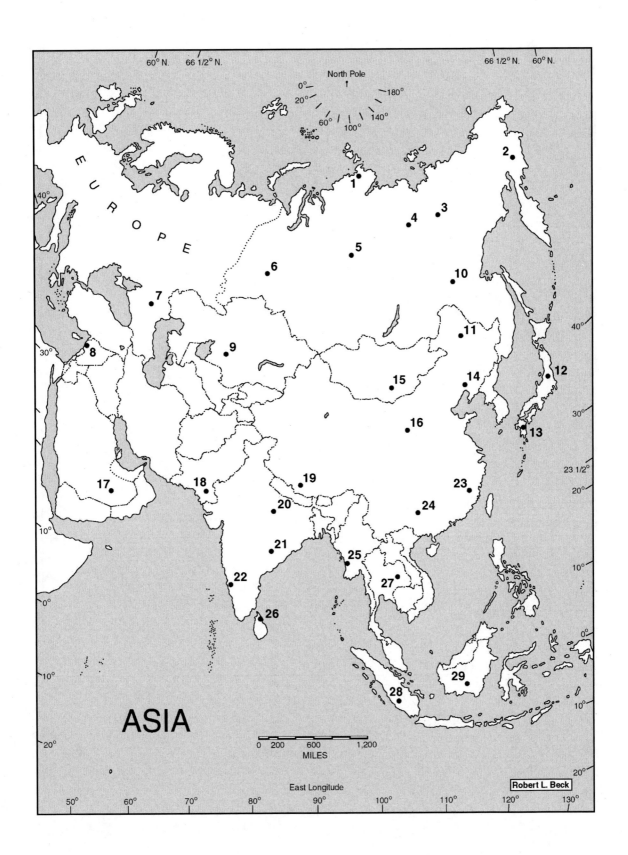

ASIA

0 200   600   1,200
MILES

East Longitude

Robert L. Beck

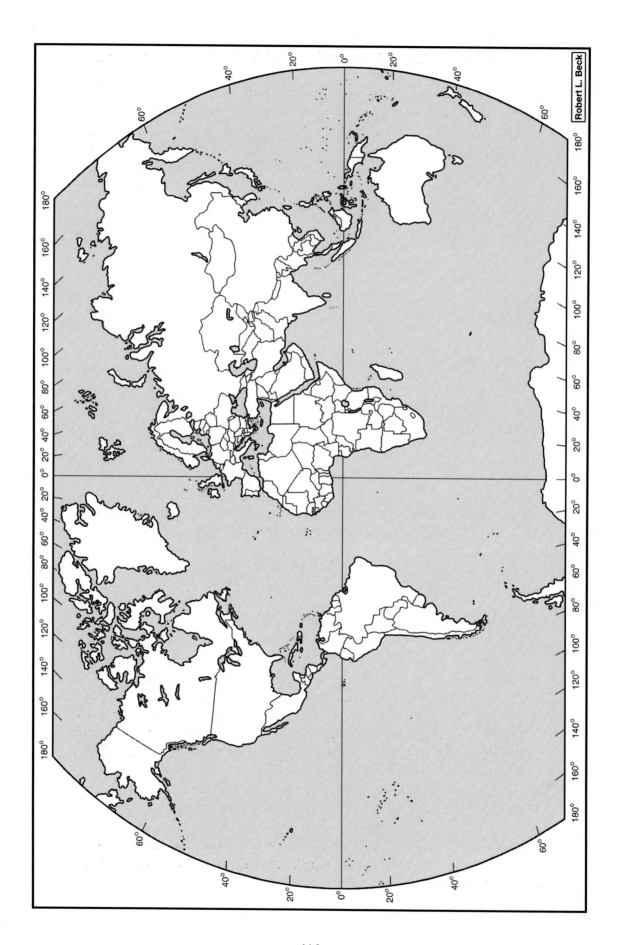

Robert L. Beck

410

SELECTED BIBLIOGRAPHY WITH ANNOTATIONS

The references included in this bibliography are those that have greatly influenced my thoughts about Earth and the geographic patterns found on it. Most of these works are rather old, but they are still worth reading for the ideas they contain. I have included references pertaining to physical geography, human geography, historical geography, regional geography, and cartography. Also included are works by historians, biologists, novelists, nonfiction writers, demographers, economists, and environmentalists that have a geographic, philosophic, scientific, or educational perspective. I consider this bibliography to be the strongest element of my book. I started it in the early 1970s, and it slowly continues to grow. I have given copies of it to many students over the years. If you like to read, and are interested in geography, these works will give you years of enjoyment and countless learning opportunities.

Abbey, Edward. *Desert Solitaire: A Season in the Wilderness*. New York: Touchstone, 1968.

An account of living, and working, at Arches National Monument in southeastern Utah. Beautifully written passages. Enjoyable.

Abbot, E. C. ("Teddy Blue") and Smith, Helena Huntington. *We Pointed Them North: Recollections of a Cowpuncher*. New Edition. Norman: University of Oklahoma Press, 1955. First published in 1939.

True stories of one of the first cowboys who drove cattle from Texas to Montana over the open range. Worth reading for anyone who has an interest in the Great Plains, cowboy life, and the movement of animals.

Adkins, Howard G. "The Imported Fire Ant in the Southern United States." *Annals of the Association of American Geographers* 60 (September 1970): 578–592.

This article caught my eye when I first read its title, in the 1970s, for I had never seen a publication in the geographic literature devoted to an insect. I first heard about fire ants in about 1958 from an uncle who was in the Navy and was stationed in Pensacola, Florida. Fire ants were accidentally introduced into the United States in the early 1900s, probably through the port of Mobile, Alabama. This article discusses their spread throughout the southern United States, why they are viewed as an insect pest, and attempts to eradicate them. An usual work of interest to biogeographers and regional geographers who study North America.

Anderson, Edgar. *Plants, Man, & Life*. Berkeley: University of California Press, 1952.

A book focused on the interaction of humans and plants, especially crops and the origins of agriculture. Many interesting discussions and stories. Dated, but still worth reading.

Attenborough, David. *The Living Planet*. Boston: Little, Brown and Company, 1984.

Well written and filled with examples of animals and plants adjusting to changes in nature. Biome and ecosystem organization.

Baldwin, William O. *Historical Geography of the Brewing Industry: Focus on Wisconsin*. Ph.D. dissertation. Urbana: University of Illinois, Department of Geography, 1966.

An interesting work on the historical geography of the beer industry. Highly recommended for both its cultural and economic considerations.

Barrows, H. H. "Geography as Human Ecology." *Annals of the Association of American Geographers* 13 (March 1923): 1–14.

An early article defining geography as the study of human ecology. Easy to read and worth reading for those interested in the history of geographic thought.

Bates, Marston. "Man as an Agent in the Spread of Organisms." In: *Man's Role in Changing the Face of the Earth*, Volume II, pp. 788–804. Edited by William L. Thomas, Jr. Chicago: University of Chicago Press, 1956.

A discussion of how and why humans have helped spread plants and animals around Earth. Rather difficult to read. Numerous examples of plant and animal introductions.

Beck, Robert L. *North American House Types*. Indianapolis: IUPUI University Library, 2010.

An exceptionally thorough and well documented work detailing about 180 house types found in the United States and Canada. Anyone interested in house types must read this book. Replete with photographs and drawings. The book is held in IUPUI's Digital Collections, so it is available online. Highly recommended.

Bennett, Merrill K. "Aspects of the Pig." *Agricultural History* 44 (April 1970): 223–235.

An article focusing on the domestication and world dispersal of the pig. Interesting and entertaining, but no maps or graphics.

Bergquist, James M. "Tracing the Origins of a Midwestern Culture: The Case of Central Indiana." *Indiana Magazine of History* 77 (March 1981): 1–32.

An excellent article that traces how the culture of central Indiana originated. Certainly worth reading for anyone interested in the geography of Indiana. The article is published in a history journal, but I would classify it as being as much geographic as it is historic.

Berry, B. J. L. *Sampling, Coding and Storing Flood Plain Data.* **USDA Agricultural Handbook No. 237. Washington, D.C., 1962.**

An important article defining the stratified systematic unaligned sampling technique. I used this sampling technique in my Ph.D. dissertation.

Berry, Brian J. L. and Baker, Alan M. "Geographic Sampling." In: *Spatial Analysis: A Reader in Statistical Geography*, **pp. 91–100. Edited by Brian J. L. Berry and Duane F. Marble. Englewood Cliffs, NJ: Prentice-Hall, 1968.**

A useful work that compares and contrasts various sampling techniques used in the discipline of geography. Anyone who needs to collect spatially sampled data must read this article.

Berry, Wendell. *The Gift of Good Land: Further Essays Cultural and Agricultural.* **San Francisco: North Point Press, 1981.**

An elaboration of his earlier book. Wendell Berry's books are definitely worth reading.

———. *The Unsettling of America: Culture and Agriculture.* **New York: Avon Books, 1977.**

Difficult to read, but one of the best books ever written about the linkages between agriculture and education in American culture and on the dangers of specialization. Berry is one of the leading "farmer-philosopher" writers in the United States. Everyone should read this book. I highly recommend it, for it stresses how important agriculture, and generalization, is to the social and economic health of the United States.

Beston, Henry. *The Outermost House.* **1st Owl book edition. New York: H. Holt, 1992. Originally published: New York: Doubleday, 1928.**

A pleasant bit of writing about observing nature while living alone for a year in a small house on Cape Cod. Easy to read.

Bloom, Benjamin S., ed. *Taxonomy of Educational Objectives: The Classification of Educational Goals.* **New York: David McKay Company, Inc., 1956.**

The classic book that defines Bloom's pedagogical hierarchy. If you intend to teach, you need to be aware of this book. This book guides my teaching philosophy and the way I structure my courses. The hierarchy puts *knowledge* as the foundation of education, not *creativity*.

Brown, Lloyd A. *The Story of Maps*. New York: Bonanza Books, 1949.

Title is descriptive of the book's contents. An excellent book for those interested in the history of mapmaking. Interesting stories. Includes discussions about the use of early mapping tools. Mercator's 1538 map naming North America and South America for the first time is shown.

Brown, Ralph H. *Historical Geography of the United States*. New York: Harcourt, Brace & World, 1948.

Probably the best book ever written on the historical geography of the United States. Brown was an American geographer with a great career ahead of him when he died unexpectedly at a young age.

Brown, Tom Jr. and Watkins, William Jon. *The Tracker*. New York: Berkley Books, 1978.

Full of really interesting true stories about the life of Tom Brown, Jr. who is perhaps the world's best animal tracker. The wild (feral) dogs story is fantastic.

Carrier, Jim. "The Colorado: A River Drained Dry." *National Geographic* 179 (June 1991): 4–35.

A descriptive account of the depletion of the water in the Colorado River for human uses in the southwestern United States.

Carson, Rachel. *Silent Spring*. Boston: Houghton Mifflin, 1962.

The classic book on the dangers of the biological magnification of DDT. One of the first books that raised environmental awareness in the United States that led to the passage of the National Environmental Policy Act, signed by President Nixon. The NEPA created the Environmental Protection Agency (EPA).

Carter, Jimmy. *An Hour Before Daylight: Memories of a Rural Boyhood*. New York: A Touchstone Book, 2001.

A delightful account of growing up in the rural South in the 1930s. Written by former President Jimmy Carter. Many interesting stories and observations.

Castaneda, Carlos. *The Teachings of Don Juan*. Berkeley: University of California Press, 1968.

This book, when it was first published, was promoted as being a nonfictional account of an anthropologist researching the drug-induced powers of an American Indian sorcerer living in Mexico. It made the cover of *Time* magazine. The book was later proven to be a fraud, but it is still an interesting read. Scary.

Cather, Willa. *Death Comes for the Archbishop.* **New York: Alfred A. Knopf, 1927.**

An enjoyable novel set in Acoma, New Mexico. Acoma is one of the oldest continuously inhabited settlements in the United States. It is an American Indian community built on a defensible site on top of a mesa. I visited the site in 1986. Highly recommended.

Catt, Neal A. and Webb, George W. **"Watermelon Production in Southwestern Indiana."** *Professional Paper No. 10*, **pp. 11–27. Terre Haute: Indiana State University, Department of Geography, 1978.**

A short paper that discusses why Indiana is one of the leading producers of watermelons for the late-summer market. Useful for those who have an interest in the geography of Indiana, economic geography, or the geography of agriculture. Webb was the chairman of my master's thesis committee in graduate school.

Caudill, Harry M. *The Watches of the Night.* **Boston: Little, Brown and Company, 1976.**

A continuation of his earlier book. Read this book only after reading *Night Comes to the Cumberlands*.

———. *Night Comes to the Cumberlands.* **Boston: Little, Brown and Company, 1963.**

Written by a nongeographer, this book is really a historical geography of Kentucky's Cumberland Plateau. Particular emphasis is placed on the environmental ravages of strip coal mining. Many interesting stories. You must certainly read this book if you have an interest in Kentucky or the Appalachian Mountains. Highly recommended.

Childs, Herbert. *El Jimmy: Outlaw of Patagonia.* **Philadelphia: J. B. Lippincott Company, 1936.**

The true story of James Radburne, who migrated from England to Tierra del Fuego in 1892 to work on a large sheep ranch. Radburne's experiences living in Tierra del Fuego and southern Patagonia are described. One learns a lot about the culture of the Tehuelche Indians and how it was vastly different from the culture of the Fuegian Indians. The reader certainly begins to understand how economic and political forces changed the physical and human landscape of southern Patagonia in the late 1800s and early 1900s.

Chisholm, Michael. *Human Geography: Evolution or Revolution*? **Harmondsworth, England: Penguin Books, Ltd., 1975.**

An excellent book especially useful for differentiating the types of theories used in human geography—normative theories vs. positive theories.

———. *Rural Settlement and Land Use.* London: Hutchinson University Library, 1962.

An outstanding book that clearly explains Von Thünen's theory and the location rent concept. Anyone who studies economic geography or the geography of agriculture must read this book. Highly recommended.

Christaller, Walter. *Central Places in Southern Germany.* Translated by Carlisle W. Baskin. Englewood Cliffs, NJ: Prentice Hall, 1966.

The classic work on central place theory. Those interested in economic geography and urban geography must read this book.

Clark, Alan. *Barbarossa: The Russian-German Conflict, 1941–45.* Reprint edition. New York: Perennial, 2002. Originally published: New York: Morrow, 1965.

A book to be read by those interested in the history of the fighting along the Russian front during World War II. Maps detail the movement of ground forces. The conflicts between Hitler and his generals and the conflicts between generals are described. Well written and easy to read.

Clark, Audrey N. *Longman Dictionary of Geography: Human and Physical.* Harlow, United Kingdom: Longman Group Limited, 1985.

A useful, specialized dictionary for finding the meanings of words, both common and obscure, related to the discipline of geography.

Clavell, James. *Shogun.* New York: Dell Publishing Co., 1975.

A novel set in feudal Japan that weaves political intrigue with the acquisition of power. It is hard to put this book down, for you just want to keep reading it. It is perhaps my favorite novel. One learns a lot about Japan by reading it. Clavell lived in East Asia for many years. He was a Japanese POW during World War II. Clavell wrote several books set in East Asia, but this was his most successful one.

Cochran, Thomas C. "Carnegie: The Man and His Times." In: *Problems in American History, Volume II, Since Reconstruction,* 3rd ed., pp. 2–9. Edited by Richard W. Leopold, Arthur S. Link, and Stanley Coben. Englewood Cliffs, NJ: Prentice Hall, 1966.

Carnegie's "Gospel of Wealth" is detailed here. Interesting views on how wealth should be used and disposed of.

Commoner, Barry. "How Poverty Breeds Overpopulation (and not the other way around)." *Ramparts* 13 (August-September 1975): 21–25, 58–59.

The demographic transition theory is discussed in this article. As the title indicates, Commoner argues that overpopulation is the result of poverty, so to eliminate overpopulation we need to eliminate poverty. An important contribution. Widely debated.

Cottler, Joseph and Jaffe, Haym. *Map Makers*. Boston: Little, Brown, and Company, 1937.

A book written for young readers about famous explorers, adventurers, and expeditions. Older students of geography will also find it worth reading.

Coyne, Jerry A. *Why Evolution Is True.* New York: Viking, 2009.

Title is descriptive of the book's contents. Clearly written and easy to understand. Recommended reading for anyone who must learn about biological evolution.

Croker, Thomas C., Jr. "Longleaf Pine: The Longleaf Pine Story." *Journal of Forest History* 23 (January 1979): 32–43.

A well-written article describing the geographic extent of the southern longleaf pine forest and the history of its exploitation. Forest conservation practices, including the role of prescribed burning, are discussed.

Croner, Stan and Lopez, Gary. *Evidence for the Ice Age.* VHS Video Tape. Chicago: Encyclopaedia Britannica Educational Corporation; American Geological Institute, 1988 (remake of 1965 original).

Excellent teaching video using time lapse photography to show the glacial movement of ice.

Cronon, William. *Changes in the Land: Indians, Colonists, and the Ecology of New England.* New York: Hill and Wang, 1983.

An explanation of the changing New England landscape of the colonial period. Interesting and detailed with a thorough bibliography, but not a map, drawing, photograph, chart, or visual aid of any kind included in the book.

Crosby, Alfred W., Jr. *The Columbian Exchange: Biological and Cultural Consequences of 1492.* Westport, CT: Greenwood Press, 1972.

A historical account of the consequences of the Old World and New World plant and animal exchanges initiated by Christopher Columbus. Definitely worth reading for anyone interested in biogeography and in the transfer of plants and animals to new environments.

Craughwell, Thomas J. *How the Barbarian Invasions Shaped the Modern World.* Beverly, Massachusetts: Fair Winds Press, 2008.

A well-written and easily readable book highlighting the invasions of the Goths, Huns, Vandals, Saxons, Franks, Vikings, and Mongols.

Darby, H. C. "The Problem of Geographical Description." *Transactions and Papers of the Institute of British Geographers* No. 30, (1962): 1–14.

An outstanding article that discusses the difficulty of writing good regional geography. Highly recommended.

Darkoh, M. B. K. "Growth Poles and Growth Centres with Special Reference to Developing Countries—A Critique." *Journal of Tropical Geography* 44 (June 1977): 12–22.

The growth pole theory is discussed in this article. Worth reading for anyone interested in economic development. Well written, for the tone of the article inspires me to want to study growth poles.

de Saint Exupéry, Antoine. *Wind, Sand and Stars.* New York: Harcourt, Brace & World, 1940.

An unusual book, written by a French aviator, which details some of the experiences of various air mail pilots. Descriptions of weather events and airplane crashes. Philosophical views of the meaning of human life. Book is at times difficult to read, for clear passages are separated from each other by obscure observations and musings. Interesting remarks concerning Islam and Muslim attitudes. Discussion of the Spanish Civil War. Some people believe this is the best adventure book ever written. I do not agree with those people, but it is a book that should be read by anyone seeking fulfillment in their life and those who are interested in flying.

Dewey, John. *The Living Thoughts of Thomas Jefferson.* New York: Longmans, Green and Co., 1940.

A book that covers Thomas Jefferson's views on a variety of subjects. The lack of an index hurts its usefulness, but it is well worth reading.

Diamond, Jared. *Guns, Germs, and Steel: The Fates of Human Societies.* New York: W. W. Norton & Company, 1999.

Another fine example of a geography book written by a nongeographer. The book discusses the role of plant and animal domestications and the rise of civilizations. Excellent reading and quite thought-provoking.

Dicken, Peter and Lloyd, Peter E. *Location in Space: Theoretical Perspectives in Economic Geography*. 3rd ed. New York: Harper & Row Publishers, 1990.

A textbook on economic geography. The chapters on Christaller's central place theory, Von Thünen's theory, and the role of transportation in the organization of economic activities are especially useful.

Durant, Will. *The Story of Philosophy*. New York: Simon and Schuster, 1926.

An outstanding book that clearly differentiates the thoughts of several famous philosophers. Required reading for anyone who wants a basic knowledge of philosophy.

Ehrlich, Paul R. *The Population Bomb*. New York: Ballantine, 1968.

The classic book on the exploding human population. This book made a big splash when it first appeared on the scene. Population control, to achieve zero population growth (ZPG), is necessary and urgently needed to prevent world catastrophe. Doom and gloom, but a must read for people who study economic development, demography, natural resources, and environmental conservation.

Elton, Charles S. "The Invaders." In: *Man's Impact on Environment*, pp. 447–458. Edited by Thomas R. Detwyler. New York: McGraw-Hill Book Company, 1971. Originally published in *The Ecology of Invasions by Animals and Plants*. London: Methuen & Co., Ltd., 1958.

Seven case histories of human introductions of plants and animals are discussed in this article. Maps showing the spread of the introduced organisms greatly contribute to the overall presentation. Worthwhile to read if you have an interest in environmental conservation or biogeography.

Emerson, Ralph Waldo. "Nature." In: *The American Tradition in Literature*, 3rd ed., Volume I, pp. 1064–1098. Edited by Sculley Bradley, Richmond Croom Beatty, and E. Hudson Long. New York: W. W. Norton & Company, 1967.

Argued to be the first article written in America having an environmental theme.

Epstein, H. "Domestication Features in Animals as Functions of Human Society." In: *Readings in Cultural Geography*, pp. 290–301. Edited by Philip L. Wagner and Marvin W. Mikesell. Chicago: University of Chicago Press, 1962.

A discussion of animal domestications for economic reasons. Human wants have altered the bodies of domesticated animals.

Estall, R. C. and Buchanan, R. O. *Industrial Activity and Economic Geography.* **3rd (revised) ed. London: Hutchinson University Library, 1973.**

An outstanding book that discusses the factors influencing the location of manufacturing and industrial activity. Required reading for anyone interested in economic geography, manufacturing, and location theory.

Fenneman, Nevin. "The Circumference of Geography." *Annals of the Association of American Geographers* **9 (1919): 3–11.**

Geography needs to be more than the study of distributions because other disciplines also study distributions. If geography were to be eliminated as an academic discipline the study of distributions would therefore continue. The core of geography should be the study of areas and regions, not distributions. No other discipline synthesizes the physical and human features of defined areas of Earth. This is what sets geography apart from all other disciplines, so it is the core around which the discipline should be built. Entertaining comment concerning the word "mere." An interesting article for those concerned with the history of geographic thought.

Francaviglia, Richard V. "Iota: Four Vignettes in the Life of a Prairie Town." *Places* **2 (July 1975): 16–18.**

A short, but delightful, description of the changes that occur in a small, fictitious prairie town as economic and technological changes occur in the larger nation outside of the town. Reads like a poem.

———. "The Cemetery as an Evolving Cultural Landscape." *Annals of the Association of American Geographers* **61 (September 1971): 501–509.**

A stimulating article on the geography of cemeteries. Full of good observations concerning the spatial patterns observable in cemeteries. Tombstone types are discussed. Highly recommended for anyone interested in cultural geography and landscape analysis.

Gates, Paul W. "Hoosier Cattle Kings." *Indiana Magazine of History* **44 (March 1948): 1–24.**

A relatively small number of people purchased most of the prairie lands of northwestern Indiana at the time of early settlement. Some of these landowners sought to establish themselves as landed gentry, but others developed their lands as large cattle feeding operations. Tenant farmers working the land for absentee landlords became a characteristic element of this part of the state due to the initial settlement pattern. One landowner, Moses Fowler, amassed twenty-five thousand acres. Landed estates of four thousand acres or more were common. This article is worthwhile to read if you have an interest in the settlement and economic development of northwestern Indiana.

———. "Land Policy and Tenancy in the Prairie Counties of Indiana." *Indiana Magazine of History* 35 (March 1939): 1–26.

An article that must be read if one is to truly understand the settlement pattern of Indiana. The prairie region of the state had a vastly different settlement history than the forested region of the state. I contend this variation in settlement history can still be seen on Indiana's cultural landscape if one possesses the necessary knowledge and skills to observe it.

Glassie, Henry. *Pattern in the Material Folk Culture of the Eastern United States.* Philadelphia: University of Pennsylvania Press, 1968.

An outstanding book on the diffusion of folk culture in the eastern United States. Well researched with an abundance of detailed references. A must read for anyone interested in the geography of house types and in the diffusion of culture.

Gould, Peter and White, Rodney. *Mental Maps.* New York: Penguin Books, 1974.

An interesting book on the geography of perception. People have mental images of places formed by the selective channeling of information to the brain. Mental maps carried by people greatly influence the decisions they make and their perception of Earth space. Different groups of people have different mental maps based on their varying life experiences.

Griswold, Alfred Whitney. "The Jeffersonian Ideal." In: *Farming and Democracy*, Chapter 2, pp. 18–46. New Haven and London: Yale University Press, 1948.

An excellent summary of Thomas Jefferson's views concerning the relationships between agriculture and democracy. Good references.

Haggett, Peter. *Locational Analysis in Human Geography.* New York: St. Martin's Press, 1966.

A book full of ideas about how to use various techniques in the discipline of geography. Well worth knowing about.

Hardeman, Nicholas Perkins. *Shucks, Shocks, and Hominy Blocks: Corn as a Way of Life in Pioneer America.* Baton Rouge: Louisiana State University Press, 1981.

A fascinating presentation on the social history of corn. Numerous drawings greatly add to the book's appeal and effectiveness, but only one map, and the boundaries of the Corn Belt shown on it are inaccurate—something unforgiveable in a book such as this. Cultural geographers, economic geographers, and people who study the geography of agriculture will find this work to be of great interest.

Hardin, Garrett. "Living on a Lifeboat." *Bioscience* **24 (1974): 561–568.**

The lifeboat theory is presented here. A must read for students of environmental conservation and population geography. Thought-provoking and well argued by Hardin, a biologist.

———. "The Tragedy of the Commons." *Science* **162 (December 1968): 1243–1248.**

This is it, the article that set in motion a wide-ranging discussion concerning the use of natural resources by the rapidly growing human population. Everyone should read this article, but especially those who have any interest at all in environmental conservation, population growth, and the use of resources. Highly recommended.

Haring, L. Lloyd and Lounsbury, John F. *Introduction to Scientific Geography Research.* **2nd ed. Dubuque, IA: Wm. C. Brown Company Publishers, 1975.**

Title is descriptive of this thin book written for beginning graduate students on how to conduct research and write a master's thesis in geography.

Harlan, Jack R. *Crops and Man.* **Madison, WI: American Society of Agronomy, 1975.**

The origin of agriculture and the domestication of crop plants are examined. Interesting discussion on the differences between weeds and crops. Detailed.

Hart, John Fraser. *The Rural Landscape.* **Baltimore & London: The Johns Hopkins University Press, 1998.**

America's rural landscape is examined by one of its leading rural geographers. Well written and quite readable. The section on the geographic distribution of barns in the eastern United States is especially enlightening and educational.

———. "The Highest Form of the Geographer's Art." *Annals of the Association of American Geographers* **72 (March 1982): 1–29.**

Perhaps the best article ever written defending the regional approach in the study of geography. All graduate students who are studying geography should be required to read this article, for it is outstanding. You absolutely must read this article if you have an interest in regional geography.

———. *The Look of the Land.* **Englewood Cliffs, NJ: Prentice Hall, 1975.**

A delightful examination of the rural landscapes of the United States. Recommended reading for anyone interested in rural geography. Good set of useful references is included.

———. *Regions of the United States*. New York: Harper & Row, 1972.

Title is descriptive of the book. Anyone who is interested in the geography of the United States must read this book.

———. *The Southeastern United States*. Princeton, NJ: Van Nostrand, 1967.

An interesting regional geography written by a prominent American geographer noted for his writing abilities.

Heilbroner, Robert L. *The Worldly Philosophers*. 5th ed. New York: A Touchstone Book, 1980.

The basic ideas of economic philosophers are presented in this book. Well worth reading if you have an interest in economics or economic geography.

Heller, Herbert L., ed. *Sourdough Sagas*. Cleveland and New York: The World Publishing Company, 1967.

An account of the people who participated in the Alaska Gold Rush of the late 1890s and early 1900s. Interesting stories of living, working, and surviving in Alaska. Easily readable. I found out about this book from Heller's widow. She was living in Greencastle, Indiana when I moved there in 1990.

Hilliard, Sam B. "Pork in the Ante-Bellum South: The Geography of Self-Sufficiency." *Annals of the Association of American Geographers* 59 (September 1969): 461–480.

Southern pork production and consumption in the 20 years preceding the Civil War is examined in this article. Louisiana and South Carolina were the two southern states where pork consumption far exceeded pork production. Live hogs and cured pork moved from the Upland Southern states to the Lowland Southern states before the Civil War. Pork also moved, via the Mississippi River, from the Corn Belt states to New Orleans.

———. "Hog Meat and Cornpone: Food Habits in the Ante-Bellum South." *Proceedings of the American Philosophical Society* 113 (February 1969): 1–13.

An excellent article on the consumption of pork and corn in the southern states before the Civil War. Must be read by anyone who studies the geography of diet and by those who are interested in the cultural and historical geography of the United States.

Hollister, C. Warren. *Medieval Europe: A Short History*. 2nd ed. New York: John Wiley & Sons, 1968.

A concise and well-written book on the history of medieval Europe. One of the few history books I have read that actually uses maps, and quite effectively, too. I enjoyed reading this book and in the process learned a lot about how the geography of modern Europe has been shaped by its medieval past.

Hopkins, Charles D. *Describing Data Statistically.* **Columbus, Ohio: Charles E. Merrill Publishing Company, 1974.**

An excellent little book that does an effective job of communicating the basics of introductory descriptive statistics. Hopkins was my first statistics professor in college and he was an outstanding teacher, one of the best.

Hudson, John C. *Across This Land: A Regional Geography of the United States and Canada.* **Baltimore and London: The Johns Hopkins University Press, 2002.**

Perhaps the best textbook ever written on the regional geography of the United States and Canada. It reads like a novel, so it does not have the burdensome and heavy feel of a textbook. Loaded with information, but some important geographical aspects of North America have either been omitted or intentionally excluded. Useful maps. Few, but appropriate, photographs. Highly recommended.

Hughes, J. Donald. "The Hunters of Euboea: Mountain Folk in the Classical Mediterranean." *Mountain Research and Development* **16 (May 1996): 91–100.**

An analysis of Dio Chrysostom's *Seventh Discourse*, which describes an event that probably occurred between 85 A.D. and 90 A.D. in Greece when it was part of the Roman Empire. The event concerns the extension of the social and economic power of cities into the rural and wilderness areas surrounding them, and the attempt by people living in the wilderness areas to resist assimilation into the cities. This article is easy to read and it has useful information concerning land use and rural life around ancient Greco-Roman cities. Visually confusing map in Figure 1.

———. *Ecology in Ancient Civilizations.* **Albuquerque: University of New Mexico Press, 1975.**

A readable account of the environmental degradation that occurred in the ancient Mediterranean and Middle Eastern civilizations, with the principal focus being on Greece and Rome. The human attitudes toward nature and the impact of civilizations on the natural environment are the two main themes of the book. Chapter 2 includes a nice essay on the Mediterranean climate and its vegetation. Included in the book are discussions of the religious attitudes certain ancient civilizations had about nature. History provides numerous examples of ancient people who failed to live in harmony with their natural environments, which helped cause the collapse of their civilizations. Our modern ecological crisis has ancient roots, for, like many people of long ago, humans today too often view the natural features of Earth only in terms of economic utility without considering that humans are part of nature and not separate from it. A couple of maps at the beginning of the book, but that is it. The lack of maps is not unexpected given that the author is an historian. An interesting and pleasant book to read, but with disturbing information and conclusions. The book should be read by students of environmental conservation and by those interested in the history and use of resources, for it reinforces the idea that humans should be stewards of the earth and not exploiters or abusers of it.

Hyde, H. Montgomery. *Stalin: The History of a Dictator*. **New York: Popular Library, 1971.**

An outstanding biography of Joseph Stalin, communist dictator of the Soviet Union. After reading the book one begins to understand why some people believe Stalin was the most ruthless man who ever lived, even more ruthless than Adolf Hitler. Highly recommended for those interested in the history of Russia during the first half of the twentieth century.

Isaac, Erich. *Geography of Domestication*. **Englewood Cliffs, NJ: Prentice Hall, 1970.**

A useful book for studying the major theories of plant and animal domestications. Interesting discussion on the early tools used by agriculturalists. Major and secondary agricultural hearths are identified, as are the routes of diffusion of important grain crops, fruits, fiber crops, and animals. *Cultivation* is contrasted with *domestication*. The wild ancestors of important domesticated plants and animals are listed, so are some of the characteristics of wild plants. The difficulties researchers face when researching agricultural origins is discussed throughout the book. Somewhat difficult to read, but an interesting book if one takes time to study it thoroughly.

Jackson, Wes. *Altars of Unhewn Stone: Science and the Earth*. **San Francisco: North Point Press, 1987.**

A book of essays concerned with the need to develop a system of self-sustaining agriculture based on solar power. An enlightening discussion comparing and contrasting *biological information* with *cultural information* in the study and use of ecosystems. Title appropriate for the book's contents.

———. *New Roots for Agriculture*. **New edition. Lincoln: University of Nebraska Press, 1985.**

A discussion of Wes Jackson's long-term goals and work efforts at the Land Institute in rural Kansas to change American agriculture from a system based on annual monoculture to one based on perennial polyculture. Futuristic.

James, Preston E. *All Possible Worlds: A History of Geographical Ideas*. **Indianapolis and New York: Odyssey Press, 1972.**

An excellent book on the history of geographic thought. All people who intend to make *geography* a career need to read and study this book. Several photographs of famous American and European geographers.

Johnson, Martin. *Over African Jungles.* **New York: Harcourt, Brace and Company, 1935.**

A delightful account of flying over Africa at low elevations and photographing wildlife. Entertaining stories of true adventures.

Johnson, Vance. *Heaven's Tableland.* **New York: Farrar, Straus and Company, 1947.**

The story of the agricultural development of the southern Great Plains of Kansas, Oklahoma, and Texas is described in this wonderful book. The waves of settlers who occupied the area, their reasons for doing so, and the problems they encountered are discussed. The human actions that led to the Dust Bowl problems of the 1930s are identified. Excellent descriptions of dust storms are included. Students who are interested in the historical geography of the United States should read this book, especially those who study the Great Plains. Settlement geographers concerned with how people use and abuse semiarid lands should also read it. Students of environmental conservation will find it fascinating and educational. The book reinforces the idea that some environmental problems, such as the stabilization of dust, require a concerted, long-term effort on the part of thousands of people. Magnificent title.

Jordan, Terry G. and Kaups, Matti. *The American Backwoods Frontier: An Ethnic and Ecological Interpretation.* **Baltimore and London: Johns Hopkins University Press, 1989.**

Jordan and Kaups present an exceptionally strong case for arguing that Finnish settlers introduced cultural elements into the Mid-Atlantic region of the American colonies well suited for use in settling the wooded frontier of the United States. Finns, and other Europeans, adopted certain cultural traits of the American Indians, and interbred with them, to produce a backwoods society that helped clear the way for a second wave of settlers that both pushed and followed them. The book presents a new thesis concerning the settlement of the United States and must be read by anyone interested in settlement geography and specifically as it relates to the historical geography of the United States. An outstanding contribution to the geographic literature.

Jordan, Terry G. "Early Northeast Texas and the Evolution of Western Ranching." *Annals of the Association of American Geographers* **67 (March 1977): 66–87.**

An article in which Jordan retracts some opinions concerning the origins of cattle ranching in Texas he made in an earlier article. Upland Southerners brought open range cattle ranching to northeastern Texas mostly after 1820. A distinctly Anglo herding system existed in this area, which contrasted with the Hispanic influenced cattle ranching system of southern and coastal Texas.

————. "The Texan Appalachia." *Annals of the Association of American Geographers* 60 (September 1970): 409–427.

A well-written and convincing article documenting the existence of a transplanted mountaineer culture from the Southern Appalachians and Ozarks to the hill lands of central Texas. An excellent example of thematic, regional geography. One learns how to use both the physical and cultural elements of an area to support a research thesis.

————. "The Origin of Anglo-American Cattle Ranching in Texas: A Documentation of Diffusion from the Lower South." *Economic Geography* 45 (January 1969): 63–87.

An article presenting substantial evidence that cattle ranching in Texas originated in the coastal prairie lands of southeastern Texas and not in the semiarid lands of southern Texas. Lowland Southerners (from the Carolinas, Georgia, Alabama, Mississippi, and Louisiana) brought cattle ranching into the coastal prairie lands of Texas. Cattle ranching in Texas is thus a product of Lowland Southern Anglo-American culture and not one of Mexican or Spanish culture. An enjoyable article, and easy to read, with a well-defined thesis—a mark of Terry Jordan.

————. "The Imprint of the Upper and Lower South on Mid-Nineteenth Century Texas." *Annals of the Association of American Geographers* 57 (December 1967): 667–690.

The American South is divided culturally into two sections—the Lowland South and the Upland South. The names of these two sections are derived from the topographic differences found in that area of the country. The Lowland South lies almost entirely on the low elevation coastal plains adjacent to the Gulf of Mexico and the Atlantic Ocean. The Upland South is found in the hilly and mountainous areas of the South well inland from the sea. Jordan argues both culture regions are found in Texas. Eastern and southeastern Texas is an extension of the Lowland South; it developed a plantation system based on slave labor, an emphasis on cotton production, a lack of self-sufficiency in food production, a reliance on mules as work animals, and strong support for the Confederacy. The hill country and the Blackland Prairie of interior Texas is an extension of the Upland South; wheat was emphasized as a cash crop, cotton was of minor importance in the economy, slaves were scarce, the horse was the main work animal, food surpluses were produced, and there was limited support for the Confederacy. A well-written article that should be read by those interested in the historical geography of the United States. Another excellent example of Jordan defending a well-defined thesis using a persuasive writing style.

Kaatz, Martin R. "The Black Swamp: A Study in Historical Geography." *Annals of the Association of American Geographers* 45 (March 1955): 1–35.

A historical geography of the poorly drained wetland area in northwestern Ohio that was known as the Black Swamp. Well worth reading if you have an   interest in the settlement geography of the Midwest. People who study the geography of North America must read this superb article.

Klimm, Lester E. "The Empty Areas of the Northeastern United States." In: *Cultural Geography: Selected Readings*, pp. 166-178. Edited by Fred E. Dohrs and Lawrence M. Sommers. New York: Thomas Y. Crowell Company, 1967. Originally published in *Geographical Review* 44 (July 1954): 325–345.

An examination of the least populated areas of the northeastern United States.

Kniffen, Fred. "Folk Housing: Key to Diffusion." *Annals of the Association of American Geographers* 55 (December 1965): 549–577.

An outstanding article that examines how the migrations of people can be seen by studying the house types constructed by them. Many scholars have been strongly influenced by this classic article. Must be read by students who are interested in in the study of house types and the settlement geography of the United States.

———. "The American Covered Bridge." *Geographical Review* 41 (Januay 1951): 114–123.

The origins, diffusion, and distribution of covered bridges in the United States is examined in this interesting article. Nice map does an effective job in its communication intent.

———. "Louisiana House Types." *Annals of the Association of American Geographers* 26 (December 1936): 179–193.

An early article on the geography of house types. This is the article in which the I-house was named.

Kollmorgen, Walter M. "The Woodsman's Assault on the Domain of the Cattlemen." *Annals of the Association of American Geographers* 59 (June 1969): 215–239.

An outstanding work on the settlement of the treeless Great Plains by people who migrated to it from the tree abundant eastern United States. Settlers of the Great Plains grew up in a culture based on cheap, and readily available, supplies of wood. Cultural and technologic change was necessary to settle the treeless interior of the United States. Highly recommended.

Krejcie, Robert V. and Morgan, Daryle W. "Determining Sample Size for Research Activities." *Educational and Psychological Measurement* **30 (Autumn 1970): 607–610.**

A useful article for quickly determining the appropriate sample size when the size of a population is known. I used this article to determine the sample size of the data set I collected for my Ph.D. dissertation. I also had a couple of students use it in research projects involving sampling. It is a good article to know about, especially if you are interested in statistical applications.

Kunstler, James Howard. "Home from Nowhere." *Atlantic Monthly* **278 (September 1996): 43–66.**

Zoning controls and the broad similarities in the education of planners throughout the various educational institutions of the United States is leading to a landscape of sameness across the country. Regional geographic differences that might lead to interesting variations in the built landscape are often ignored for legal or aesthetic reasons. An interesting article.

Leighly, John, ed. *Land and Life.* **Berkeley and Los Angeles: University of California Press, 1969.**

A collection of the writings of Carl O. Sauer, one of America's most influential geographers. Tim Brothers, another geography instructor at IUPUI, studied under Jonathan Sauer, son of Carl O. Sauer, at UCLA.

Leopold, Aldo. *A Sand County Almanac.* **New York: Oxford University Press, 1949.**

Many environmentalists consider this to be the most important book ever written in the United States. It has a delightful manner about it, which I like immensely. It records the true stories of Leopold's actions and observations while spending his weekends on a worn-out farm he purchased in Wisconsin. It also records some of Leopold's adventures and observations while traveling in North America. Highly, highly recommended. Lots of big words, so use your dictionary. One of the few conservation books with a positive tone, and not one of doom and gloom.

Lewis, Peirce F. "Common Houses, Cultural Spoor." *Landscape* **19 (January 1975): 1–22.**

The migration of people can be seen by examining their house types. My thoughts concerning the distribution of house types in the United States were strongly shaped by this article. Anyone who is interested in house types must read it. Fabulous title.

Lindsey, Alton A., ed. *Natural Features of Indiana*. Indianapolis: Indiana Academy of Science, 1966.

A good, solid book for understanding the physical geography of Indiana. I used this book to develop my course on the geography of Indiana.

Lowdermilk, W. C. *Conquest of the Land Through Seven Thousand Years*. Reprint edition. U.S. Department of Agriculture, Agriculture Information Bulletin No. 99. Washington, D.C.: Government Printing Office, 1986.

The classic work on the human impacts on the soil, especially with regard to soil erosion.

Lovelock, James. *The Ages of Gaia: A Biography of Our Living Earth*. New York: W. W. Norton & Company, 1988.

The Gaia theory proposes that Earth is a living organism. This book is loaded with ideas, but most scientists dismiss the Gaia theory. The daisy world theory is discussed.

Lutgens, Frederick K. and Tarbuck, Edward J. *The Atmosphere: An Introduction to Meteorology*. 2nd ed. Englewood Cliffs, NJ: Prentice Hall, 1982.

An excellent book to read to begin the study of meteorology.

Mackinder, H. J. "The Geographical Pivot of History." In: *Systematic Political Geography*, pp. 107–129. Edited by Harm J. de Blij. New York: John Wiley & Sons, 1967.

The Heartland theory. A must read for anyone interested in world politics and political geography. Classic.

Maclean, Fitzroy. *Eastern Approaches*. New York: Little, Brown and Company, 1950.

An exceptionally interesting account of Maclean's involvement in World War II and his travels in Central Asia and North Africa. He parachuted into Yugoslavia during World War II to contact Marshal Tito.

Malmström, Vincent H. *Geography of Europe: A Regional Analysis*. Englewood Cliffs, NJ: Prentice Hall, 1975.

Now clearly dated, but still an excellent little book on the regional geography of Europe. Especially useful for its historical geography, physical geography, and regional geography within European countries. Nice maps.

Markham, Beryl. *West with the Night.* **San Francisco: North Point Press, 1983. First published in 1942.**

An adventure book written by the first person to fly solo across the Atlantic Ocean from east to west—England to Nova Scotia. The book mostly focuses on Markham's life growing up in East Africa in the 1920s and 1930s. She was raised by her father on his farm in Kenya, where she learned to work with horses. Markham later became a professional race horse trainer. Around 1930 she became one of the first female pilots in East Africa to carry mail and supplies between cities, mining camps, and safari camps. Stories include spotting elephant herds for hunters, flying over the Sudd, working with animals, hunting wild boar, and interacting with different racial and ethnic groups in Africa. A wonderful book that should be read by anyone with an interest in Africa or in flying airplanes. It is probable the book was not actually written by Markham, but by her third husband.

Marsh, George Perkins. *Man and Nature: Or, Physical Geography as Modified by Human Action.* **Edited by David Lowenthal. Cambridge, Massachusetts: The Belknap Press of Harvard University Press, 1965. Originally published in 1864.**

Difficult to read because of its age, but the book is filled with interesting observations. Marsh helped stimulate environmental awareness in the United States at a time when concern for nature was practically nonexistent.

Maslow, Abraham H. *Motivation and Personality.* **3rd ed. New York: Harper & Row, 1987.**

All students who are interested in the environment should know something about Maslow's "hierarchy of needs" concept. Maslow was a psychologist, but his concept is interesting and worth studying for its environmental implications.

Mather, Eugene and Hart, John Fraser. "The Geography of Manure." In: *Cultural Geography: Selected Readings,* **pp. 333–347. Edited by Fred E. Dohrs and Lawrence M. Sommers. New York: Thomas Y. Crowell Company, 1967. Originally published in** *Land Economics* **32 (February 1956): 25–28.**

Commonly referred to as "that bullshit article" by many geographers, the article discusses the uses of manure for soil enrichment around Earth. Different animals will, of course, produce different types of manure. Cow manure has quite different characteristics than chicken manure, so spatial variations in animal production lead to spatial variations in soil enrichment. Worth reading for anyone interested in agriculture, manure, or rural geography.

Matthiessen, Peter. *The Snow Leopard.* **New York: Penguin Books, 1978.**

An account of a journey through the Himalayan Mountains to the Plateau of Tibet. Matthiessen accompanied George Schaller, a famous field biologist, in search of Himalayan blue sheep with hopes of seeing the world's rarest big cat, the snow leopard. One learns a fair amount about Buddhism and the culture of Nepal by reading the book, but it is a difficult read.

McCullough, David. *John Adams.* **New York: A Touchstone Book, Simon & Schuster, 2001.**

The life of John Adams, second President of the United States, is described, especially his political philosophy. A heavy read, but one learns a lot about the early development of the United States.

McKnight, Tom and Hess, Darrel. *Physical Geography: A Landscape Appreciation.* **9th ed. Upper Saddle River, NJ: Pearson Prentice Hall, 2008.**

An introductory physical geography textbook that is both readable and understandable. Standard geography textbook widely used in the United States.

McKnight, Tom L. *Oceania: The Geography of Australia, New Zealand, and the Pacific Islands.* **Englewood Cliffs, NJ: Prentice Hall, 1995.**

A regional geography of Australia, New Zealand, and the Pacific Islands. Concise and well written by an American geographer who possessed considerable knowledge of Australia.

————. **"Australia's Buffalo Dilemma."** *Annals of the Association of American Geographers* **61 (December 1971): 759–773.**

An interesting article focusing on the introduction, distribution, and human uses of water buffalo in Australia. Water buffalo have considerable advantages over cattle in Australia's northern tropics, but cattle ranchers want the water buffalo to be eradicated, or at least considerably reduced in numbers, and confined to a small area of the country.

————. **"Barrier Fencing for Vermin Control in Australia."** *Geographical Review* **59 (July 1969): 330–347.**

The introduction of exotic animals into Australia by various groups of people has greatly affected the geography of the continent. Efforts to reduce the damage caused by some of these animals led to the building of fences in an attempt to control the spread of rabbits (introduced by Europeans) and dingos (introduced by Aborigines). Some of these fences are thousands of miles long. Maps in the article show the locations of the principal rabbit-proof and dingo-proof fences. An engaging article by McKnight, a good writer of geography.

McNee, Robert B. "The Changing Relationships of Economics and Economic Geography." *Economic Geography* **(July 1959): 189–198.**

A useful review of the differences between economics and economic geography. Economists have historically stressed the study of consumption as a means for analyzing market forces while assuming a spaceless world. Economic geographers have historically stressed the study of production and movement of goods with little concern for market forces. Students of economic geography must read this article.

McNeill, William H. "American Food Crops in the Old World." In: *Seeds of Change*, **pp. 43–59. Edited by Herman J. Viola and Carolyn Margolis. Washington, D.C.: Smithsonian Institution Press, 1991.**

A book published to recognize the 500th anniversary of the discovery of America by Christopher Columbus. American Indians were growing crops that had never been seen by Europeans when Columbus arrived in the New World. Columbus and other Europeans carried many of these crops back to Europe, where some are now widely grown.

———. *Plagues and Peoples*. **Garden City, New York: Anchor Press, 1976.**

An outstanding book, written by a historian, which chronicles the plagues that have affected Earth's human population and how they have shaped its history. The diffusion of diseases is discussed. A must read for anyone interested in the field of medical geography. The lack of supporting visual materials is a serious flaw, for there is only one map in the book (spread of the Black Death in Europe).

McPhee, John. *The Control of Nature*. **New York: Noonday Press, 1989.**

A book that describes three human efforts to control the natural environment. Readable.

———. *The Pine Barrens*. **New York: Ballantine Books, 1968.**

A book focusing on the Pine Barrens region of southern New Jersey. Many entertaining stories about the people who live and work in this distinctive area. Natural features of the environment such as groundwater, native plants, birds, and trees are also discussed. I am an admirer of John McPhee's writings, but the problem I have with him is he seems to be ignorant that he is writing *geography*, and if he does know it he either refuses to recognize it or intentionally dismisses it. The absence of a map of any kind greatly hurts this book. McPhee is constantly referring to various Pine Barrens settlements, past and present, without providing a general reference map. The burden is left entirely up to the reader to find out where these places are located. McPhee does not even provide a map showing the areal extent of the Pine Barrens! Well worth reading if you have an interest in regional geography.

———. *Encounters with the Archdruid*. New York: Noonday Press, 1971.

An account of McPhee's three excursions with David Brower, former president of the Sierra Club. Interesting discussions concerning the difference between conservation and preservation. Well written and easy to read. Students really like this book. I had dinner with David Brower, in Greencastle, when he came to speak at DePauw University in the early 1990s.

———. *Oranges*. New York: Farrar, Straus and Giroux, 1967.

Another *geography* book authored by McPhee, but not indicated as such by him. This time his topic focuses on the distribution of oranges, a fruit originally domesticated in China or Southeast Asia. Here again, I suspect many people who read this book have absolutely no idea that what they are reading is a literary work composed of a combination of topical, historical, and regional geography. McPhee is a master of taking an earth feature, finding some interesting and obscure characteristics of it, personally observing and experiencing it in the field, talking with local experts about it, and building a storyline around it in a spatial framework—classic geography research and writing, but you would not know it by reading his words, for he seldom uses the word *geography*, and then only to refer to different areas of the country. This is a superb book—entertaining, easy to read, and full of information about oranges.

Meine, Curt. *Aldo Leopold: His Life and Work*. Madison: The University of Wisconsin Press, 1988.

A biography of Aldo Leopold, perhaps the most famous naturalist and conservationist in American history.

Meinig, D. W. *Southwest: Three Peoples in Geographical Change, 1600–1970*. New York: Oxford University Press, 1971.

A historical geography of the Southwestern United States with particular emphasis on the interplay among Anglo, Hispanic, and American Indian cultures in Arizona and New Mexico. Quite interesting.

———. *Imperial Texas*. Austin: University of Texas Press, 1969.

An important work concerning the historical geography of Texas. Reading this book enables one to understand the forces that shaped Texas and how those forces have influenced the Texan view of the world. Highly recommended.

—————. "The Mormon Culture Region: Strategies and Patterns in the Geography of the American West, 1847–1964." *Annals of the Association of American Geographers* 55 (June 1965): 191–220.

An important work in regional geography. This is the article in which Meinig used his *core-domain-sphere* model to analyze and define the Mormon culture region of the western United States. The Meinig model can be used to analyze, and portray graphically on a map, any formal region.

Michener, James A. *The World Is My Home: A Memoir*. New York: Random House, 1992.

The autobiography of James A. Michener. An outstanding book and one full of literary works that Michener recommends. Definitely worth reading.

—————. *The Covenant*. New York: Random House, 1980.

My favorite novel written by James A. Michener. A fictional account of the historical development of South Africa. Hard to put down.

Miller, Victor C. and Westerback, Mary E. *Interpretation of Topographic Maps*. Columbus, OH: Merrill Publishing Company, 1989.

An outstanding, but technical, book on interpreting landforms and geologic structures through the study of topographic maps by the preeminent authority on the subject—V. C. Miller, one of my teachers in graduate school. V. C. Miller was a student of Armin K. Lobeck.

Moise, Edwin E. *Modern China: A History*. London and New York: Longman, 1986.

A brief examination of the main points of Chinese history. Worthwhile to read.

Monmonier, Mark. *How to Lie with Maps*. 2nd ed. Chicago: University of Chicago Press, 1996.

An excellent book that discusses the uses and abuses of maps. Maps used for political propaganda, maps that advertise, and map blunders are all shown. An important book that should be read by cartography students and anyone who needs to analyze and design maps.

Moorehead, Alan. *The March to Tunis*. New York: Dell Publishing Co., 1965.

A superb account of the war in North Africa during World War II. Excellent book.

———. *The Blue Nile*. New York: Dell Publishing Co., 1962.

A companion to his earlier book, but the books should be read separately. A masterful job of describing the 19th-century events that helped shape Egypt and the Blue Nile region of Sudan and Ethiopia.

———. *The White Nile*. New York: Dell Publishing Co., 1960.

A compelling book about the search for the head of the Nile River and the historical events that occurred in the Nile region from 1856 through 1900. Outstanding description of the world's most formidable swamp, the Sudd. Certainly worth reading. I enjoyed it immensely.

Mumford, Lewis. *The City in History*. New York: Harcourt Brace Jovanovich, 1961.

The classic book on the historical development of cities. A lengthy book, but full of good ideas about the origin of cities and how they were transformed by technological innovations.

Nabhan, Gary Paul. *Enduring Seeds: Native American Agriculture and Wild Plant Conservation*. Berkeley, CA: North Point Press, 1989.

An exceptional book dedicated to the idea that not only do the seeds of the wild ancestors of our grain crops need to be preserved but so do the native agricultural systems that cultivate those wild ancestors. Native peoples have intimate knowledge of the processes that sustain many genetically important, but economically unimportant, plant communities. It is not enough to just preserve seeds for the sake of genetic diversity, for to rebuild an agricultural complex using preserved seeds might require a complex arrangement of other factors known only by the native growers. In addition, some wild plants survive only around human settlements, so if those settlements are wiped out the wild plants will be, too. A further point about this book concerns the importance of preserving plants in dry, tropical environments. Many of our important food crops have come from these environments, but little effort has been made to preserve them—attention has been focused on preserving the remaining tropical rainforests, which diverts attention from other environments that also require preservation. An outstanding work full of nontraditional ideas about conservation and preservation. Highly recommended.

Parsons, James J. "Starlings for Seville." *Landscape* 10 (Winter 1960–1961): 28–31.

An interesting account of the capture and uses of starlings (the bird) in Seville, Spain.

Pielou, E. C. *After the Ice Age: The Return of Life to Glaciated North America.* **Chicago: University of Chicago Press, 1991.**

Title is descriptive. Overkill hypothesis is discussed. Drawings of extinct animals. Students of glaciation, and postglacial landscapes in particular, will find this to be a good book to read. Unattractive maps, many poorly drawn.

Pirkle, E. C., Yoho, W. H., and Henry, J. A. *Natural Landscapes of the United States.* **4th ed. Dubuque, IA: Kendall/Hunt Publishing Company, 1985.**

An informative book that examines the landscapes of the United States by breaking them down into physiographic regions. Anyone who teaches a course on the geography of the United States will find this book useful.

Ponting, Clive. *A Green History of the World: The Environment and Collapse of Great Civilizations.* **New York: Penguin Books, 1991.**

An outstanding book that traces the historical record of human actions in modifying Earth's natural environment. Filled with useful information, but sources are not footnoted. Must be read by anyone who has an interest in environmental conservation or environmental history. Highly recommended. I have read it at least five times.

Quam, L. O. "The Use of Maps in Propaganda." *Journal of Geography* 42 **(January–December 1943): 21–32.**

The classic article, often cited, about how maps have been used to manipulate the thoughts of people with the intent to shape their beliefs and mold public opinion. Cartographic designers must read this article. Anyone who likes maps will find it quite interesting. Highly recommended.

Raban, Jonathan. *Old Glory: An American Voyage.* **New York: Simon and Schuster, 1981.**

An Englishman's description of a boat trip taken down the Mississippi River in the late 1970s. Enjoyable.

Rapoport, Amos. *House Form and Culture.* **Englewood Cliffs, NJ: Prentice Hall, 1969.**

Anyone who is interested in house types and in the factors that influence the form of houses must read this book. One of the classic books written on the geography of house types.

Reischauer, Edwin O. *The Japanese*. Cambridge, MA: Harvard University Press, 1978.

A dated, but historically interesting, book on the culture of Japan. Required reading for anyone interested in understanding the Japanese people.

Reisner, Marc. *Cadillac Desert: The American West and Its Disappearing Water*. New York: Viking Penguin, 1986.

A highly exaggerated and sensationalized account of the misuse of water in the western United States; but nonetheless, it is still an important book to read for anyone interested in environmental politics and water resources. Written by a journalist.

Richason, Benjamin F. "Wetland Transformation in the Wisconsin Drift Area of Indiana." *Proceedings of the Indiana Academy of Science for 1959* 69 (1960): 290–299.

Most of Indiana covered by Wisconsin ice (the last of the Pleistocene Ice Age glaciers) has been artificially drained by humans. These artificially drained areas are shown on maps in this article, which graphically portray the area of the state covered with swamps and wetlands during the settlement period. It is surprising how much of the state was poorly drained. One begins to understand why swamps and wetlands delayed settlement of large areas of central and northern Indiana until drainage ditching equipment was invented.

Roberts, Neil. *The Holocene: An Environmental History*. Second Edition. Malden, MA: Blackwell Publishers, 1998.

A detailed presentation on the history of the Holocene, which is the postglacial period of time, beginning about 12,000 years ago, in which we are currently living. The environmental history of this epoch is coupled with the growth of the human population and its cultural developments. A study of Holocene natural environments is therefore intimately connected with the study of human cultural evolution and dispersals. An outstanding book that weaves together how the natural environment influenced human development and how the actions of humans have influenced the natural environment. The book is filled with specific examples used to support general observations. The excellent photographs, charts, and graphs add to the book's character and greatly strengthen the finished product. Relatively few maps are included in the book; some of them are quite well done, but others are difficult to interpret. This book should be read not only by geographers (especially biogeographers and cultural geographers), but also by students of anthropology and anyone interested in climate change.

Robinson, Arthur H. *Early Thematic Mapping in the History of Cartography.* Chicago and London: The University of Chicago Press, 1982.

Title is descriptive of the book. A good book to read about the history of data portrayal on maps. Discusses the origins of dot maps, proportional symbol maps, choropleth maps, flow maps, and isarithmic maps. Anyone interested in the history of cartography must read this book.

Rooney, John F., Jr. and Butt, Paul L. "Beer, Bourbon and Boone's Farm: A Geographical Examination of Alcoholic Drink in the United States." *Journal of Popular Culture* 11 (Spring 1978): 832–856.

A basic examination of the geographical patterns of beer, distilled spirits, and wine consumption in the United States. Informative maps. Easy to read.

Rooney, John F. Jr. "Up from the Mines and Out from the Prairies: Some Geographical Implications of Football in the United States." *Geographical Review* 59 (October 1969): 471–492.

Relatively little has been published in academic journals in the United States on the geography of sports. The areas of the United States noted for producing football players are identified and mapped. Worthwhile to read if you have an interest in football. The article also reinforces the concept that geographers study distributions of all kinds.

Sacks, Oliver W. *The Island of the Colorblind and Cycad Island.* New York: Alfred A. Knopf, 1996.

A report of a medical doctor's trip to Micronesia. He observes firsthand how people who are colorblind fare in life, and he discusses the possible origins and effects of a degenerative neurological disease on Guam. One learns a lot about cycads, the importance of islands in studying biogeography, the difficulty of isolating the causes of a disease, and about Micronesian life and culture in general. Well written and easy to read, but the medical terms are cumbersome for those not accustomed to them. Be sure to read the end notes as you are going through the book, for they add a lot to the story.

Sauer, Carl O. "The Education of a Geographer." In: *Land and Life*, pp. 389–404. Edited by John Leighly. Berkeley and Los Angeles: University of California Press, 1969.

All who aspire to be geographers must read this article. Sauer, one of the giants of the discipline, offers good advice for novice geographers and for geography teachers. His views on regional geography and on field work are especially noteworthy.

—————. *Agricultural Origins and Dispersals*. New York: American Geographical Society, 1952.

Sauer's classic work on the origin and diffusion of agriculture. Many people who study agricultural origins feel obliged to cite this book. Outstanding for its contributions, but now somewhat dated.

Schaefer, Fred K. "Exceptionalism in Geography—A Methodological Examination." *Annals of the Association of American Geographers* (September 1953): 226–249.

Exceptionally hard to read, but an important contribution concerning the role of quantitative methods and scientific inquiry in the discipline of geography.

Schumacher, E. F. *Small is Beautiful*. New York: Harper & Row, 1973.

The subtitle, *Economics as if People Mattered*, is descriptive of the book. The book presents an alternative view of economics. Unusual and interesting. Full of ideas. Students of economic geography, economics, and community development must read this book.

Sears, Paul B. *Deserts on the March*. Norman: University of Oklahoma Press, 1935.

A readable account of the Dust Bowl era. Those interested in desertification, environmental conservation, or the Great Plains will find this book worth reading.

Shelton, John S., advisor. *Rocks That Form on the Earth's Surface*. VHS Video Tape. Chicago: Encyclopaedia Britannica Educational Corporation; American Geological Institute, c. 1990 (remake of 1964 original).

A most useful teaching video to show the formation of sedimentary rocks. Time lapse photography simulates the cementation of minerals, which helps students understand that both sediment and cement are necessary ingredients to produce sedimentary rocks.

Silverberg, Robert. *Lost Cities and Vanished Civilizations*. New York: Bantam Books, 1962.

An introductory book about the fall and rediscovery of six lost cities—Pompeii, Troy, Knossos, Babylon, Chichén Itzá, and Angkor. This was one of the first books that stimulated my interest in geography, history, and archaeology. No maps or graphics are included in the book, so that is a weakness, but it is well written and it helps one begin to understand the depths of history.

Sjoreen, Andrea and Powell, Richard L. "An Analysis of the Irregularity of Surveyed Sections in Indiana." *Proceedings of the Indiana Academy of Science for 1980* **(90) (1981): 313–322.**

An interesting article showing the locations of the irregularly surveyed sections of the township and range system in Indiana. This system, established by Congress as part of the Ordinance of 1785, is used to subdivide land throughout most of the state. Surveyors had to adjust for the curvature of the earth as they laid out certain north-south survey lines, which resulted in the irregularity of some surveyed sections.

Skinner, B. F. *Walden Two.* **New York: Macmillan, 1976. First published in 1948.**

A fictional account of a modern utopian community named *Walden Two*. The community, unlike the dirty and disheveled communes of the 1960s hippies, embraces cleanliness and modern technology. The goal is to produce a society where everyone works at both mental and physical activities for a minimal number of hours during the day, which allows the pursuit of individual interests and creative activities during the remainder of the day. Members of the community are given lifetime employment, health benefits, use of facilities, transportation services, food and lodging, and old age security. All money earned through individual creative efforts is given back to the community. The book certainly causes one to think about the failures of modern urban living, methods of education, the role of work, and the wasteful use of resources in capitalistic economies. Highly recommended. Please also read Skinner's 1976 new introduction, *Walden Two Revisited.*

Sobel, Dava. *Longitude.* **New York: Penguin Books, 1995.**

The story of the process by which longitude was finally defined. The book details the development of Harrison's chronometer. Interesting.

Sokolov, Raymond A. *Fading Feast: A Compendium of Disappearing American Regional Foods.* **New York: Farrar, Straus and Giroux, 1981.**

A book that must be read by people who are interested in the geography of food. The author, a noted authority on cuisine, travels the United States seeking traditional regional foods to sample. Recipes are included in the book. A delightful book that is easy to read. It made me hungry many times before I finished reading it. Interesting observations and stories. Indiana persimmons are discussed.

Spurr, Stephen H. "Silviculture." *Scientific American* **240 (February 1979): 76–82, 87-91.**

An important article, written by a famous American forester, which discusses forest management principles. A good article to read for those interested in trees and environmental conservation.

Stamp, Sir L. Dudley and Morgan, W. T. W. *Africa: A Study in Tropical Development.* 3rd ed. New York: John Wiley and Sons, 1972.

The classic work on the geography of Africa written by one of the leading authorities of the continent. Dated, but still of great use especially with regard to the physical and historical geography of Africa.

Stegner, Wallace. *Beyond the Hundredth Meridian.* Boston: Houghton Mifflin, 1953.

Hard to read, but an outstanding book on the geography of the dry lands of the western United States. Lucid portrayal of the difficulties of land use planning on the federal level. John Wesley Powell's famous expedition down the Colorado River is described. Highly recommended.

Steinbeck, John. *The Grapes of Wrath.* Reprint edition. New York: Penguin Books, 1977. First published in 1939.

The American masterpiece about the migration of poor farmers from Oklahoma to California during the Great Depression in the Dust Bowl days of the 1930s. Outstanding novel that should be read by everyone.

Stewart, George R. *Names on the Land.* New York: Random House, 1945.

A must read for anyone interested in the study of the American placenames. One can begin to understand the patterns of names found on maps after reading this enjoyable book. Highly recommended.

Stewart, Omer C. "Fire as the First Great Force Employed by Man." In: *Man's Role in Changing the Face of the Earth*, Volume I, pp. 115–133. Edited by William L. Thomas, Jr. Chicago: University of Chicago Press, 1956.

Humans have been modifying the environment for thousands of years. Fire was the first major tool humans used to alter Earth's surface. This article is certainly worth reading for those interested in environmental conservation and in the human use of fire to produce desired changes in the environment.

Strunk, William Jr. and White, E. B. *The Elements of Style.* 3rd ed. New York: Macmillan Publishing Co., Inc., 1979.

The classic, timeless book filled with examples on how to write effectively. A thin little book, but big in ideas, which can be quickly read, but will take a lifetime to master. All who write must read this book and have a copy of it accessible at all times.

Taylor, Peter J. *Quantitative Methods in Geography: An Introduction to Spatial Analysis.* **Boston: Houghton Mifflin, 1977.**

A useful book for selecting quantitative methods to be used in geographic research.

Thoreau, Henry David. *Walden.* **New York: The New American Library, Inc., 1960.**

The classic book detailing the attempt by Thoreau to live a simple life at Walden Pond. I did not see the point of this book when I was forced to read it in high school. I think you have to reach a certain level of maturity to truly understand what Thoreau is saying. I did not have that level of maturity in high school, and I do not think many people do, so it probably should not be read for the first time until much later in life. I now understand it and I highly recommend it.

Thornbury, William. *Regional Geomorphology of the United States.* **New York: John Wiley, 1965.**

A thorough, but quite interesting, book that discusses the physiographic regions of the United States. Dated, but well worth reading.

————. **"Glacial Sluiceways and Lacustrine Plains of Southern Indiana."** *Indiana Geological Survey Bulletin No. B4.* **Bloomington: Indiana Geological Survey, 1950.**

A publication one must read to understand the landforms of southern, and especially southwestern, Indiana. The locations of the major Illinoian glacial lakes and drainageways are shown on well-drawn maps. The location of Lake Eminence, of Wisconsin age, is also shown. Valley train deposits, the relation of loess to glaciofluvial sluiceways, the character of the lacustrine plains, and the partially buried bedrock hills known as "island hills" are discussed. An informative and interesting work.

Toffler, Alvin. *The Third Wave.* **New York: Morrow, 1980.**

The wave theory of human population growth is discussed in this book. Worth reading for a different view of the human population explosion.

Transeau, Edgar Nelson. "The Prairie Peninsula." *Ecology* **16 (July 1935): 423–437.**

The great contribution of this article is the map showing the location of prairie grasslands in the Midwest. Northwestern Indiana is clearly part of the "Prairie Peninsula" extending into the eastern Midwest from the central Great Plains.

Trewartha, Glenn T. *An Introduction to Climate*. 4th ed. New York: McGraw-Hill Book Company, 1968.

An old classic. Title is descriptive. This was the book through which I was introduced to both meteorology and climatology.

Tuan, Yi-Fu. *Space and Place*. Minneapolis: University of Minnesota Press, 1977.

An interesting book that documents how people feel about space and place.

Turnbull, Colin M. *The Mountain People*. New York: Touchstone Books, 1972.

An anthropologist details the lives of people who are starving to death in East Africa because they were forced, by their government, to abandon their lifestyle and live in a tract of land unsuitable for them. Heartbreaking, but still interesting.

Turner, Frederick Jackson. *The Frontier in American History*. New York: Henry Holt and Company, 1947.

The famous "Turner thesis" is presented here. This thesis is widely debated in the discipline of history. All geographers should be exposed to it, especially those who are interested in the geography of the United States and those who are interested in settlement geography.

Tzu, Sun. *The Art of War*. Translated by Thomas Cleary. Boston: Shambhala Publications, 1988.

A translation of one of the greatest Chinese classical texts. The book was compiled more than two thousand years ago. It is considered by many people to be the best strategy book ever written. Students of military history and geography must read this book.

Veregin, Howard, ed. *Goode's World Atlas*. 21st ed. Chicago: Rand McNally & Company, 2005.

The standard atlas used in college geography courses taught in the United States.

Vermeer, Donald E. and Frate, Dennis A. "Geophagy in a Mississippi County." *Annals of the Association of American Geographers* 65 (September 1975): 414–424.

Interesting article on the subject of geophagy—earth eating. Well worth reading if you have an interest in food, medical geography, and the cultural geography of the United States. Unusual.

Viola, Herman J. and Margolis, Carolyn, eds. *Seeds of Change*. Washington and London: Smithsonian Institution Press, 1991.

An outstanding book that discusses plant and animal exchanges, including diseases, between the Old World and the New World initiated by Christopher Columbus. Beautifully illustrated.

Watts, May Theilgaard. *Reading the Landscape of America*. New York: Collier Books, 1975. Originally published as *Reading the Landscape: An Adventure in Ecology*. New York: Macmillan, 1957.

A fascinating work, by one of America's leading naturalists, on learning to read the landscape by studying plants. Anyone who is interested in plants must read this book. I learned a lot about the geographic distribution of plants by reading it. Delightful drawings add to the book's appeal. Highly recommended.

Webb, Walter P. *The Great Plains*. New York: Ginn, 1931.

The classic book on the historical geography of the Great Plains, but written by a historian. Dated, but quite enjoyable to read. Highly recommended. Interesting.

Werth, Alexander. *Russia at War 1941–1945*. New York: Avon Books, 1964.

This is the book you should read if you read only one book on the war between Germany and the Soviet Union during World War II. A fascinating and well-written book.

White, Lynn Jr. "The Historical Roots of Our Ecologic Crisis." In: *Man's Impact on Environment*, pp. 27–35. Edited by Thomas R. Detwyler. New York: McGraw-Hill Book Company, 1971.

This article presents the idea that our modern environmental problems are largely based on religious attitudes toward the land. In particular, the Judeo-Christian view that humans have mastery over the land and all its organisms, both plant and animal.

————. *Medieval Technology and Social Change*. London, Oxford, and New York: Oxford University Press, 1962.

An outstanding book on technological changes, and their effects on society, that occurred in the medieval period, especially in Europe. Difficult to read, but thoroughly referenced and filled with ideas. The lack of maps and paucity of graphics greatly detracts from its usefulness. Fairly typical of the writing of many historians—highly detailed, interesting, but virtually no visuals to support the words.

Whitney, Gordon. *From Coastal Wilderness to Fruited Plain.* **Cambridge and New York: Cambridge University Press, 1994.**

A highly detailed, and thoroughly researched, book on the plants and settlement of the United States. Difficult to read because of the detail, but absolutely loaded with useful information for those who are interested in plants and the geography of the United States.

Wilson, Edward O. *The Diversity of Life.* **New York: W. W. Norton & Company, 1992.**

A modern classic on the diversity of life on Earth. Quite interesting, but difficult to read.

Winchester, Simon. *The Map That Changed the World.* **New York: HarperCollins Publishers, 2001.**

The story of William Smith and the origins of the discipline of geology. Smith drew the world's first geological map of an entire country—England. The book is well written, and it is easy to understand how Smith's background and work experiences led him to conceive and eventually compile the map. The book also provides a background on how geological ideas conflict with certain religious ideas. Must be read by anyone who is interested in geology and by those who are concerned with the clash between science and religion.

Winberry, John J. and Jones, David M. **"Rise and Decline of the 'Miracle Vine': Kudzu in the Southern Landscape."** *Southeastern Geographer* **13 (November 1973): 61–70.**

An article that documents the introduction, diffusion, and problems of kudzu's introduction into the United States as an erosion control plant. An interesting article for biogeography students and anyone who wants to learn more about this aggressive plant.

Young, Louise B. **"Easter Island: Scary Parable."** *World Monitor* **4 (August 1991): 40–45.**

An interesting article that compares a small island in the Pacific Ocean, surrounded by a vast body of water, with Earth, a small planet surrounded by a vast outer space. Environmental degradation nearly destroyed the human population of Easter Island, so will such a situation occur on Earth?

Zelinsky, Wilbur. *The Cultural Geography of the United States: A Revised Edition.* **Englewood Cliffs, NJ: Prentice Hall, 1992.**

This book is filled to the brim with potential research ideas concerning the cultural geography of the United States. Hard to read, with lots of big words and a flowery writing style, which cause many novice geography students to find the book unappealing and confusing. I think it is an outstanding work, so I highly recommend it for anyone concerned with understanding the cultural patterns found in the United States.

————. "Classical Town Names in the United States: The Historical Geography of an American Idea." *Geographical Review* 57 (October 1967): 463–495.

A detailed work on the use of classical town names such as Rome, Athens, Troy, and many others as placenames for American towns. Anyone who studies placenames has to read this article.

————. "Generic Terms in the Place Names of the Northeastern United States." In: *Readings in Cultural Geography*, pp. 129–156. Edited by Philip L. Wagner and Marvin W. Mikesell. Chicago: The University of Chicago Press, 1962.

A thorough work on the geography of placenames in the northeastern United States. Recommended for anyone interested in studying cultural patterns by examining the names found on maps.

————. "Where the South Begins: The Northern Limit of the Cis-Appalachian South in Terms of Settlement Landscape." *Social Forces* 30 (December 1951): 172–178.

An article in which Zelinsky attempts to define a regional boundary using visible evidence and statistical data. His lists of landscape features that characterize Southern towns and Southern country sides are quite interesting. A good article to read, but somewhat brief.

Zencey, Eric. "The Rootless Professors." In: *Rooted in the Land*, pp. 15–19. Edited by William Vitek and Wes Jackson. New Haven and London: Yale University Press, 1996.

A short, interesting essay discussing the bias against hiring professors who grew up in an area in which a university is situated. To bring new ideas into a university, professors are typically hired from afar. This results in a lack of local knowledge by those who are teaching in the university, which gives the impression to students that local issues, environments, and features are unimportant. Local concerns should be of paramount importance to professors, but they are ill equipped to deal with them because they did not grow up in the area. Many professors tend to think of education as an assault against the local, or parochial, point of view in an attempt to produce a cosmopolitan student view of the world. Such action serves to disconnect students from the local area and helps separate people from their local natural environments.

INDEX

ABOUT THE AUTHOR

Robert L. Beck, born and raised in Nebraska, is a Senior Lecturer in the Department of Geography at Indiana University Purdue University Indianapolis (IUPUI). He started teaching at IUPUI in 1982, the year he received his Ph.D. degree from Indiana State University. His M.A. degree is also from Indiana State University and his B.A. degree is from Hastings College. He taught at DePauw University, mostly on a part-time basis, from 1988 to 2000. In the late 1970s and early 1980s he worked as a research scientist at Argonne National Laboratory, near Chicago, on energy and environmental projects.

Dr. Beck, the recipient of four IUPUI teaching awards, has published two other geography books. *North American House Types* is the first digital textbook written by an IUPUI faculty member placed in the Digital Collections of IUPUI's University Library. It was also published by Van-Griner Publishing in 2010. *Seven Continents and More* is a student mapbook for use in various introductory geography courses; it was published by the Kendall-Hunt Publishing Company in 2008.

Dr. Beck lives with his wife, Cheryl L. Beck, in a delightful Cape Cod Revival, built in 1967, in a beautiful rural area of Putnam County, Indiana. He enjoys reading, playing games, bird watching, traveling, matchcover collecting, and viewing old movies. Further, he enjoys visiting art galleries, museums, historic sites, farms, nature preserves, and areas of physiographic interest. He raises bantam chickens and is a pet lover of both cats and dogs. He likes to work in his shop on woodworking projects; work in his greenhouse raising young plants; work in his office writing books; work in his garden raising flowers and vegetables; and work in his yard tending his lawn, shrubs, and trees. His wife is a private piano teacher and is the music director, organist, and pianist at the Presbyterian Church in Greencastle, Indiana.

****